McGraw-Hill Mathematics

Assessment Guide

- ▶ Chapter Pretests and Posttests (Forms A and B)
- ▶ Cumulative Tests
- ▶ Scoring Charts and Prescription Tables
- ▶ Teacher Interview
- ▶ Portfolio and Performance Assessment
- ▶ Self-Assessment
- ▶ Journal Writing
- ▶ Final Test
- ▶ Questionnaire, Form, and Checklist

Mc Graw Hill McGraw-Hill
School Division
New York   Farmingto

D1511774

GRADE 2
CONTENTS

How to Use the Assessment Guide

This *Assessment Guide* is intended to assist you in developing, organizing, and managing multiple assessment strategies. **McGraw-Hill Mathematics** includes opportunities to assess students' knowledge on both a formal and an informal basis.

It is the philosophy of this series that the primary purpose of assessment is to improve students' learning, not just to grade their work. Assessment should provide an occasion for students to learn and to evaluate their own work. It should be an integral part of instruction, not simply an end point. Therefore, strategies for monitoring progress as well as summative measures, such as chapter tests, are all included in this guide.

The following is a brief description of the six assessment strategies provided in this program.

Teacher Interview

The Teacher Interview is an informal assessment strategy designed to help you measure your students' understanding of mathematics concepts. This guide includes a **Teacher Interview Questionnaire** that you can use to document your interviews with students. It also provides information on questioning strategies and help with interviewing techniques.

Journal Writing

Journal Writing is another informal assessment strategy. Here students are given the opportunity to write down how they think about mathematical concepts in their journals. The program provides numerous opportunities for journal writing.

Paper-and-Pencil Tests

Chapter tests and cumulative and final tests in this *Assessment Guide* provide a snapshot of the content that the student has mastered. Chapter tests are available in free-response and multiple-choice formats. These tests are easy to grade, and they measure student understanding, skill level, and problem-solving ability.

How to Use the Assessment Guide *(continued)*

Performance Assessment

In Performance Assessment, students are asked to perform mathematics procedures and make problem-solving decisions that require an understanding of mathematical concepts. The emphasis is on problems set in realistic situations outside of school.

Portfolio Assessment

Portfolios give you a means of evaluating students' understanding of concepts and abilities to reason and communicate mathematically. Blackline Masters are provided for both student and teacher to help with selecting and documenting student portfolios.

Self-Assessment

Self-assessment gives the students opportunity to look at their work and assess how well they are doing. This guide provides a checklist for students to use as they review their work.

Teacher Interview

The **Teacher Interview** is an informal technique designed to be part of the process of monitoring student progress. Interviews can help you assess your students' knowledge of mathematics concepts. The purpose of the interview is to try to discern a student's thinking well enough to determine what to do next. By using questioning strategies, you can learn how each of your students is understanding the concepts you are teaching.

Where to Begin

A generic **Teacher Interview Questionnaire** is included in this *Assessment Guide* (see page 13). You may customize this questionnaire to suit your needs. In addition, later in this guide you will find a Teacher Interview section for each chapter. These interview questions focus on the major ideas of each chapter. Another possibility is the **Sum it Up!** question in each Pupil Edition lesson as a starting point for the interview.

Classroom Management

Select a time when groups of students are engaged in different activities. As students work, you can either interview small groups or individuals at your desk or move around the room to talk to students. Conduct the interviews in whatever manner best suits your own teaching style. Target a few students each day. Over the course of two weeks, you should be able to interview all the students in your class.

Recordkeeping. Probably the most important thing to remember is to date the notes you take. In this way a student's progress can be monitored. If you are using the **Teacher Interview Questionnaire** (see page 13), you can write student responses on this form. Another technique would be to keep a class roster with enough space under each student's name for you to take notes about the student's answers to questions.

Some Hints for Questioning Strategies

- Try to ask open-ended questions.

- The question could be a follow-up to work the student has done or to a response the student has made.

- Clarifying Questions: "What do you mean by...?" Or "How did you do that?"

- Probing Questions: "Do you think that will always be the case?" or "How can you prove that your answer is right?"

- Challenging Questions: "What if the problem was changed in the following way?"

- Try not to pose questions that lead the students to the correct answer.

Interviewing Techniques

- Try to keep a relaxed atmosphere. Get students off to a positive start with a question you are sure that they can handle.

- Tell the students what you are doing. Explain that you are questioning them so that you can learn how they think when they solve math questions. Emphasize the thinking process as opposed to getting a correct answer.

- Rephrase your question if the student doesn't understand it.

- The interview session is not a time for you to teach or correct a student's errors. Concentrate on learning more about the student's thought processes. You may want to take notes on problems you need to help the student with at another time.

- Observe your student's behavior during the interview. You can often gain insight into a student's thinking through his or her actions.

- After you've asked a question, give the student some time to answer. Your focus should be on observing. Allowing the students to do most of the talking will supply you with a wealth of information on the way they think about mathematics.

*See page 13 in this Assessment Guide for the **Teacher Interview Questionnaire**.*

Journal Writing

Journal Writing is the second component of the process of monitoring student progress. Journals provide an opportunity for students to use writing and drawing to show their understanding of mathematics concepts. Mathematics journals can provide you with valuable information about how and what your students are thinking about math.

The Value of Journal Writing

Writing helps students develop thinking skills. Expressing understanding of a concept in writing is also a means of discovering that understanding. Journal writing gives the student the opportunity to clarify, reflect, and summarize on mathematics lessons. Students can pose a question, explore a train of thought, support an argument, or come to a conclusion. Writing can itself be a form of problem solving.

Journal Writing can:

- ◎ Help students become comfortable with reflecting on their own learning.
- ◎ Promote self-assessment of the student's mathematical thinking.
- ◎ Give students the opportunity to restate information they just learned.
- ◎ Provide you with information on how a student is thinking about concepts taught.

Where to Begin

McGraw-Hill Mathematics provides several opportunities for students to write in their journals. In the chapter by chapter section of this guide you will find a feature on journal writing for each chapter. In addition, journal prompts can be found in the **Problem Solving, Check Your Progress,** and **Performance Assessment** sections of the Pupil Edition. All prompts are specific to the material covered in the chapter.

Journal Writing *(continued)*

Talking to Your Students About Journal Writing

Emphasize clarity and focus, rather than fluency, in math journals. Tell your students that the idea is to explain a mathematical idea, using illustrations when appropriate, in a way that is to the point.

Discuss the prompts and notify the students if any of their journal entries will be seen by their peers.

Classroom Management

Students can use folders, spiral notebooks, or sections of binders in which to keep their journals. Just be sure that they keep their writing together so that you can easily keep up a dialog with the student.

Assessment and Feedback

It would be best to read and respond to the journals at least once each chapter. You may want to write directly in the journal. Encourage students to respond to your entries. Try to provide constructive feedback that will help students further their understanding of a particular topic.

Paper-and-Pencil Tests

McGraw-Hill Mathematics includes three levels of paper and pencil tests. On the chapter level, there are pre- and posttests available in two formats. Cumulative tests measure student progress at approximately three chapter intervals. The final test is designed to assess student understanding of the content of the entire year.

Chapter Tests

The **Chapter Tests** measure student progress on individual chapter objectives. These tests are available as Form A and Form B, both with pretest and posttests. Both forms test the same objectives and have the same number of items. Form A tests are multiple-choice and are parallel in length and content. Form B tests are free-response formats with content identical to Form A. Occasionally items on the Form B tests require students to select the best answer.

By using both the multiple-choice and the free-response formats, you may help ensure that students get practice taking standardized tests and also have an opportunity to demonstrate higher level thinking skills.

Each **Chapter Test** is designed to be scored by objective and by total test.

Cumulative Tests

The **Cumulative Tests** follow the conclusion of Chapters 3, 6, and 10. They are multiple choice tests that measure the student's progress through a group of chapters. The **Cumulative Test** after Chapter 3 measures all or most of the content from the first three chapters. The **Cumulative Tests** after Chapters 6 and 10 measure some of the content from previous chapters, but with a greater emphasis on content from the most recently taught chapters. Each **Cumulative Test** contains 20 items.

Final Test

The **Final Test** is a comprehensive multiple-choice test that measures student progress on skills covered from the beginning of the year. The **Cumulative Tests** and the **Final Test** are designed to be scored as a total test.

Paper-and-Pencil Tests *(continued)*

Administering the Tests

The tests are not timed. In most cases they may be administered in one sitting. For the multiple choice tests, students may mark their answers on the generic **Student Answer Sheet** found on the next page, on the test page, or on a separate sheet of paper. Responses to the free-response Form B **Chapter Tests** should be marked directly on the test or on a separate piece of paper.

It is most important that your students understand exactly what they are supposed to do. Review the directions and the test items before giving the test. During the test, monitor the students to make sure that they are following directions, working on the appropriate task, and indicating their responses correctly.

Try to make the environment as comfortable as possible. Make an effort to minimize distracting noises or activities that might draw the students' attention away from the test.

Evaluating Test Scores

The **Chapter Tests, Cumulative Tests,** and **Final Test** provide an indication of each student's general mathematical achievement. Achievement on the **Chapter Test** is reported by objective, while the **Cumulative** and **Final Tests** are reported as a total test. Scores on these tests may indicate if a student has mastered one or more of the mathematical areas tested. The test scores, therefore, can be used to plan further activities, whether for reteaching or enrichment.

*See page 15 in this Assessment Guide for the **Student Answer Sheet**.*

*See page 16 in this Assessment Guide for the **Monitoring Student Progress form**.*

*See pages 17–19 in this Assessment Guide for the **Monitoring Class Progress form**.*

Performance Assessment

In mathematics, performance assessment emphasizes what the student *does* and *thinks* with problems that involve realistic situations outside of school. Students are asked to perform mathematics procedures and make problem-solving decisions that require an understanding of mathematical concepts.

The Goals of Performance Assessment

The **Performance Assessment** tasks at the end of each chapter:

- Assess the "big ideas" in the chapter
- Balance concept and process, knowing and doing
- Elicit reasoning
- Provide opportunities for varied learning styles and intelligences
- Set a "real-world" context as often as possible
- May involve teamwork

Where to Begin

At the end of each chapter of the Pupil Edition, there is a **Performance Assessment** task. This task is designed to allow students to apply their knowledge of the chapter in a practical situation. The problem-solving, activity-based assignments in each chapter also offer important assessment opportunities with more extended time frames and greater potential for students to explore mathematics in engaging situations.

Evaluating Student Performance

Responses in this type of assessment are not simply right or wrong, but rather show a continuum of the degree of understanding. To evaluate students in a fair and consistent way, **McGraw-Hill Mathematics** provides you with scoring rubrics. At the end of each chapter in the Teacher Edition you will find a scoring rubric specifically designed for that chapter's **Performance Assessment** task. These rubrics are 3-point scales that provide you with specific criteria on which to evaluate students' work. You might want to distribute these rubrics to your students so that they understand how they will be assessed. Students should receive feedback about their performance with respect to the criteria. In this way, assessment will serve to improve student performance, not just monitor it.

Portfolio Assessment

A portfolio is a collection of students' work that can be used as an important assessment tool. Portfolio assessment:

- ⑥ Focuses attention on performance criteria

- ⑥ Documents the improvement of students' work over time

- ⑥ Fosters students' self-assessment and reflection

- ⑥ Develops students' ownership in learning

- ⑥ Communicates with students, parents, and other teachers

- ⑥ Evaluates the instructional program

What Goes in a Portfolio?

The portfolio is a place for student work that highlights their understanding of concepts, problem solving, reasoning, communication, and connection making. Any task that provides evidence of these abilities is a candidate for inclusion in the portfolio. In particular, **McGraw-Hill Mathematics** provides the following features for use in the portfolio:

- ⑥ Performance Assessment

- ⑥ Journal Writing

- ⑥ Sum it Up!

- ⑥ Math and Science: Problem Solving

- ⑥ Chapter Project

- ⑥ Chapter Enrichment

One important goal of the portfolio is to foster student ownership of his or her work. Therefore, material to go in the portfolio should always be selected with the student. You may prefer to keep a "working" portfolio where all student work is held. Then every three or four weeks, you and the student can determine which pieces will go in the "showcase" portfolio, which is shared with external audiences, such as parents and next year's teacher.

Selecting the Showcase Portfolio

Selecting the showcase portfolio is very important. It is an significant part of a student's self-assessment. Have your students use **My Portfolio** (blackline master) to write about the selections they've made. In addition, each piece may be annotated by the student or teacher indicating where it demonstrates specific portfolio criteria, such as using appropriate problem-solving criteria. Since portfolios collect student work over time, be sure to include work that shows improvement. Remember to write the date on all work.

You may also want to consider a multimedia portfolio. Here students who are not strong in writing can demonstrate their mathematics proficiency through photographs, audio or video tapes, and computer software.

Classroom Management

Working portfolios need to be used in ongoing instruction and therefore must be accessible to students. Cardboard boxes or milk crates can be used to house working portfolios. As students complete performance tasks and other appropriate exercises, they will need to store drafts of their work. When students revise their work they will need access to their portfolios again. If possible, allow students to move about the room to access their portfolio material. Learning to take responsibility for one's own work can be a fruitful by-product of using a portfolio.

As selections are made for the showcase portfolio, those materials not selected can be sent home to parents or discarded. Showcase portfolios need not be accessible on a daily basis and may be stored in a file cabinet or closet.

Small-Group Strategies

Teachers who use portfolios often find that by using flexible grouping strategies they are able to work intensively with small groups of students on particular topics while other students work independently. Since students generally finish performance-oriented tasks at different rates, this approach works well with portfolio work. It can also free you up to confer with individuals or groups concerning portfolio work.

Reviewing Portfolios

A good strategy for reviewing portfolios is to look at just a few each day. Even if each portfolio is reviewed every two weeks, this schedule can provide you with enough information to meet with students to discuss their portfolios.

*See page 20 in this Assessment Guide for the student's **My Portfolio** form.*
*See page 21 in this Assessment Guide for the teacher's **Portfolio Assessment** form.*

Self-Assessment

Self-assessment empowers the students and gives them the sense that they are in control of an important aspect of their school work. Students should be able to look at their work and assess how well they are doing. Self-assessment is an important aspect of the process of selecting a showcase portfolio as well.

Checklist

McGraw-Hill Mathematics provides a checklist for students to use in the self-assessment process. The **Self-Assessment Checklist** uses simplified language to provide students with a means of comparing their work against established criteria. This list correlates to the teacher's blackline master **Portfolio Assessment Form** (see page 22). It is particularly suitable for extended tasks, such as performance assessment tasks. To promote and guide student self-assessment, you might want to attach checklists to the work in the student's portfolio. Then use this information in conferences to improve your student's understanding of classroom standards.

*See page 22 in this Assessment Guide for the student's **Self-Assessment Checklist.***

Teacher Interview Questionnaire

Student Name _____ Date _____

Chapter _____ Cluster _____ Lesson _____

For Individual Students

Can you tell me how you got your result? (Can you tell me more?)

_____

_____

What were some of the things you were thinking when you solved
the problem?

_____

_____

Can you show me how you prove that your answer is right?

_____

_____

What would happen if (you changed)...

_____

_____

Can you think of anything we learned in class that helped you solve this problem?

_____

_____

For Students in a Group

Is there anything different about the way you would solve this problem than the
other students suggested?

_____

_____

Can you tell me more about how you would solve this problem?

_____

_____

Student Name _____ Date _____

McGraw-Hill Mathematics
GRADE 2

☐ **Chapter** _____   ☐ **Cumulative** _____   ☐ **Final** _____

Choose One

1. Ⓐ Ⓑ Ⓒ Ⓓ   11. Ⓐ Ⓑ Ⓒ Ⓓ

2. Ⓕ Ⓖ Ⓗ Ⓙ   12. Ⓕ Ⓖ Ⓗ Ⓙ

3. Ⓐ Ⓑ Ⓒ Ⓓ   13. Ⓐ Ⓑ Ⓒ Ⓓ

4. Ⓕ Ⓖ Ⓗ Ⓙ   14. Ⓕ Ⓖ Ⓗ Ⓙ

5. Ⓐ Ⓑ Ⓒ Ⓓ   15. Ⓐ Ⓑ Ⓒ Ⓓ

6. Ⓕ Ⓖ Ⓗ Ⓙ   16. Ⓕ Ⓖ Ⓗ Ⓙ

7. Ⓐ Ⓑ Ⓒ Ⓓ   17. Ⓐ Ⓑ Ⓒ Ⓓ

8. Ⓕ Ⓖ Ⓗ Ⓙ   18. Ⓕ Ⓖ Ⓗ Ⓙ

9. Ⓐ Ⓑ Ⓒ Ⓓ   19. Ⓐ Ⓑ Ⓒ Ⓓ

10. Ⓕ Ⓖ Ⓗ Ⓙ   20. Ⓕ Ⓖ Ⓗ Ⓙ

Monitoring Student Progress

Student Name _____

Chapter	Form A		Form B		Performance Task	Comments
	Score	%	Score	%	Score	
1	/20		/20			
2	/20		/20			
3	/20		/20			
4	/20		/20			
5	/20		/20			
6	/20		/20			
7	/20		/20			
8	/20		/20			
9	/20		/20			
10	/20		/20			
11	/20		/20			
12	/20		/20			
13	/20		/20			
14	/20		/20			

	Score	%
Cumulative Test 1	/20	
Cumulative Test 2	/20	
Cumulative Test 3	/20	
Final Test	/20	

Student	Chapter 1			Chapter 2			Chapter 3			Cumulative 1	Chapter 4			Chapter 5			Chapter 6			Cumulative 2
	A	B	PA	A	B	PA	A	B	PA		A	B	PA	A	B	PA	A	B	PA	

A = Form A **B = Form B** **PA = Performance Assessment**

Student	Chapter 7			Chapter 8			Chapter 9			Chapter 10			Cumulative 3
	A	B	PA	A	B	PA	A	B	PA	A	B	PA	

A = Form A   **B = Form B**   **PA = Performance Assessment**

Student	Chapter 11			Chapter 12			Chapter 13			Chapter 14			Final
	A	B	PA	A	B	PA	A	B	PA	A	B	PA	

A = Form A   B = Form B   PA = Performance Assessment

My Portfolio

Name _____

Name of Work	Why this is in my portfolio.
1. _____	_____
	_____
2. _____	_____
	_____
3. _____	_____
	_____
4. _____	_____
	_____
5. _____	_____
	_____
6. _____	_____
	_____
7. _____	_____
	_____
8. _____	_____
	_____
9. _____	

Portfolio Assessment Form

Student Name _____ Grade _____

Teacher _____ Date _____

This portfolio shows evidence that the student:	Little Evidence	Partial Evidence	Adequate Evidence	Substantial Evidence
Understands concepts				
Selects appropriate strategies to solve problems				
Provides quality explanations				
Expresses concepts, ideas, and thinking in an organized and clear way				
Uses mathematical representations (models, graphs, charts, pictures, diagrams, numerals, symbols, mathematical vocabulary) appropriately and accurately				
Makes connections to real-world situations, other mathematical ideas, or other subject areas				

I would characterize the quality of the work in this portfolio as —

_____

_____

This student shows growth in —

_____

_____

This student would benefit from instruction in —

_____

_____

Self-Assessment Checklist

Name _____

Look over your math work. Check ✔ the things you did.

Understanding

☐ My work shows that I know about the big math "idea."

Problem Solving

☐ I answered the whole question.

☐ I showed how I got my answer.

Reasoning

☐ I explained why I did my work the way I did.

☐ I explained why my answer is a good one.

Communicating

☐ My writing was clear.

☐ I used models, pictures, or charts with my work.

Now complete these sentences.

The math strategy I used to solve this problem was —

_____

From this problem I learned —

_____

Chapter-1 Teacher Interview

Core Concept: *Addition and Subtraction Strategies and Facts to 12*

Student Activity: The student demonstrates an understanding of adding and subtracting facts to 12. Have 12 small objects, such as coins, buttons, or markers, and a number line available for the student. Ask the student such questions as, "If you add 3 buttons to 5 buttons, how many will you have?"

Teacher Question 1:

◎ Here are 5 buttons. If you add 3 buttons to the group, how many will there be?

Understanding Student Response	Practice and Improvement
Student gives an incorrect response, such as '7' or '9'.	Review lesson 1 to help the student count on from 5 to 8 on a number line. Practice with similar questions.
Student gives a response that indicates they have subtracted instead of added.	Review lesson 1 to remind the student that adding means increasing the total, not decreasing it. Ask the student to use the number line to practice adding and have them make up other examples.

Teacher Question 2:

◎ What happens to the sum if you turn around the addends?

Understanding Student Response	Practice and Improvement
Student says that the sum increases or decreases.	Review lesson 2 to show that the sum will not change. Have the student use the number line to add, starting with one addend the first time and then the other addend the next time. Compare the results.
Student says that addition must always start with the larger addend.	Review "turnaround facts" in lesson 2 and have the student do examples like those in the **Practice** section in lesson 2.

Teacher Question 3:

◎ If you have 11 cookies and give 4 away, how many do you have left?

Understanding Student Response	Practice and Improvement
Student adds instead of subtracts.	Review lesson 5 and discuss key words that indicate subtraction is necessary in a problem.
Student gives a reasonable, but incorrect, response.	Review lesson 5 and then have the student count back 4 from 11 on the number line. Assign examples like those at the end of lesson 5.

Chapter-1 Journal Writing

Encourage students to generate their own journal entries related to math ideas in general or to concepts in this chapter. Present the following journal prompt and have students share their drawing/writing with a partner:

⊚ Write down 5 + 2 = 7, and then write the turnaround fact. Draw a picture showing why the sum does not change when you turn the addends around.

(Responses should show two sets of seven objects, one indicating 5 added to 2, the other indicating 2 added to 5. Students should be able to explain why the sum does not change.)

FOLLOW UP

To follow up, review the concept of turnaround facts. Ask students to think of any times that day when you or they had occasion to add two quantities (for example, adding points during a game at recess.) Use counters to show the turnaround facts for the sum.

Have students find all the turnaround facts for 3 consecutive sums (such as for 4, 5, and 6 or for 10, 11, and 12 depending on ability). Have the students draw conclusions about the number of facts for each sum and also write about how they found all the facts. Have students share their conclusions with a math partner.

Chapter-1 Monitoring Student Progress

☐ Form A   ☐ Form B

Student Name _____ Date _____

Directions: For each item that is answered incorrectly, cross out the item number. Then record the number of correct responses in the appropriate Student Score column. If the student has not met the Criterion Score for an objective, circle the student's score. Recommended assignments are listed in the Prescription Table on the next page.

Objective	Item Numbers	Criterion Score	Student Score
A. Add, facts to 12.	1, 3, 8, 10, 11, 13, 14	6/7	/7
B. Subtract, facts to 12.	2, 4, 5, 6, 7, 9, 12, 15, 16	8/9	/9
C. Solve problems, including those that involve drawing a picture.	17, 18, 19, 20	3/4	/4
Total Test Score		17/20	/20
Total Percent Correct			%

Chapter-1 Prescription Table

The following chart correlates the tested objectives for this chapter to supplementary materials that meet the individual needs of the students. The Practice and Reteach pages are designed for students who need further instruction in the math concepts taught in this chapter. The Enrich pages are designed for students who need advanced challenges.

Objective	Practice	Reteach	Enrich
A. Add, facts to 12.	1, 4, 16, 19	2, 5, 17, 20	3, 6, 18, 21
B. Subtract, facts to 12.	13, 16, 19	14, 17, 20	15, 18, 21
C. Solve problems, including those that involve drawing a picture.	7–10	11–12	

Choose the correct answer.

1.
$$5$$
$$+ 1$$

Ⓐ 4

Ⓑ 5

Ⓒ 6

Ⓓ 7

2.
$$12$$
$$- 4$$

Ⓕ 6   Ⓗ 9

Ⓖ 8   Ⓙ 10

3.
$$8$$
$$+ 3$$

Ⓐ 9   Ⓒ 11

Ⓑ 10   Ⓓ 12

4.
$$10$$
$$- 3$$

Ⓕ 6

Ⓖ 7

Ⓗ 8

Ⓙ 9

5. Look at this fact family triangle. Which fact belongs in this family?

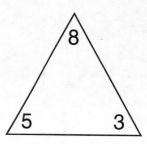

Ⓐ $5 - 3 = 2$

Ⓑ $11 - 3 = 8$

Ⓒ $8 - 3 = 5$

Ⓓ $3 + 8 = 11$

GO ON

6. $7 - 1 = \blacksquare$

   Ⓕ 4

   Ⓖ 5

   Ⓗ 6

   Ⓙ 7

7.
$$\begin{array}{r} 5 \\ -\,3 \\ \hline \blacksquare \end{array}$$

   Ⓐ 1

   Ⓑ 2

   Ⓒ 3

   Ⓓ 4

8. $6 + 6 = \blacksquare$

   Ⓕ 9

   Ⓖ 10

   Ⓗ 11

   Ⓙ 12

9. Which is a related subtraction fact for $6 + 2 = 8$?

   Ⓐ $8 - 8 = 0$

   Ⓑ $8 - 6 = 2$

   Ⓒ $6 - 2 = 4$

   Ⓓ $2 + 6 = 8$

10. What is the turnaround fact for $5 + 4 = 9$?

   Ⓕ $3 + 6 = 9$

   Ⓖ $8 + 1 = 9$

   Ⓗ $4 + 5 = 9$

   Ⓙ $9 - 1 = 8$

GO ON ➡

11. $4 + \boxed{} = 11$

Ⓐ 5

Ⓑ 6

Ⓒ 7

Ⓓ 8

12. $8 - 2 = \boxed{}$

Ⓕ 5

Ⓖ 6

Ⓗ 7

Ⓙ 8

13. Which of these is a doubles fact?

Ⓐ $6 + 2$

Ⓑ $3 + 3$

Ⓒ $4 + 1$

Ⓓ $1 + 2$

14.
$$\begin{array}{r} 5 \\ + 4 \\ \hline \boxed{} \end{array}$$

Ⓕ 1

Ⓖ 8

Ⓗ 9

Ⓙ 10

15.
$$\begin{array}{r} 12 \\ - 3 \\ \hline \boxed{} \end{array}$$

Ⓐ 5

Ⓑ 7

Ⓒ 8

Ⓓ 9

GO ON

16. The ▪ of 5 − 4 is 1.

(F) fact family

(G) difference

(H) addend

(J) sum

Solve.

17. There are 6 frogs in the pond. Then 6 more frogs jump in. How many frogs are in the pond now?

(A) 6 frogs

(B) 7 frogs

(C) 11 frogs

(D) 12 frogs

18. There are 6 bugs on a leaf. 2 bugs fly away. How many bugs are left?

(F) 3 bugs   (H) 5 bugs

(G) 4 bugs   (J) 6 bugs

19. Kayla has 4 stickers. Sam has 4 stickers. How many stickers do they have altogether?

(A) 6 stickers

(B) 7 stickers

(C) 8 stickers

(D) 9 stickers

20. Ana has 9 trucks. She gives 4 trucks to Rob. How many trucks does Ana have left?

(F) 4 trucks

(G) 5 trucks

(H) 7 trucks

(J) 8 trucks

STOP

Write the answer.

1.   5
     + 1
   _____

2.   12
     − 4
   _____

3.   8
     + 3
   _____

4.   10
     − 3
   _____

5. Look at this fact family triangle. Circle the fact that belongs in this family.

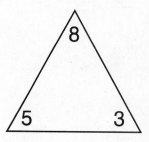

$5 - 3 = 2$

$11 - 3 = 8$

$8 - 3 = 5$

$3 + 8 = 11$

GO ON

6. $7 - 1 =$ _____

---

7. $\begin{array}{r} 5 \\ -\ 3 \\ \hline \end{array}$

---

8. $6 + 6 =$ _____

9. Circle the related subtraction fact for $6 + 2 = 8$.

$8 - 8 = 0$

$8 - 6 = 2$

$6 - 2 = 4$

$2 + 6 = 8$

---

10. What is the turnaround fact for $5 + 4 = 9$?

_____

 GO ON

11. $4 + \underline{\hspace{1.5cm}} = 11$

12. $8 - 2 = \underline{\hspace{1.5cm}}$

13. Which of these is a doubles fact?
Circle the answer.

$6 + 2$

$3 + 3$

$4 + 1$

$1 + 2$

14. $\begin{array}{r} 5 \\ + \ 4 \\ \hline \end{array}$

15. $\begin{array}{r} 12 \\ - \ 3 \\ \hline \end{array}$

16. Complete the sentence using one of the following: fact family, difference, addend, or sum.

The _____ of 5 − 4 is 1.

19. Kayla has 4 stickers.
Sam has 4 stickers.
How many stickers do they have altogether?

_____ stickers

Solve.

17. There are 6 frogs in the pond. Then 6 more frogs jump in. How many frogs are in the pond now?

_____ frogs

20. Ana has 9 trucks.
She gives 4 trucks to Rob.
How many trucks does Ana have left?

_____ trucks

18. There are 6 bugs on a leaf. 2 bugs fly away. How many bugs are left?

_____ bugs

STOP

Choose the correct answer.

1.   4
   + 5
   ⬛

   Ⓐ 7

   Ⓑ 8

   Ⓒ 9

   Ⓓ 10

2.   9
   − 3
   ⬛

   Ⓕ 2

   Ⓖ 3

   Ⓗ 4

   Ⓙ 6

3. 3 + 2 = ⬛

   Ⓐ 5   Ⓒ 7

   Ⓑ 6   Ⓓ 8

4.   12
   − 2
   ⬛

   Ⓕ 9

   Ⓖ 10

   Ⓗ 11

   Ⓙ 12

5. Look at this fact family triangle. Which fact belongs in this family?

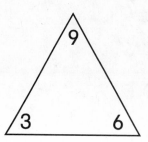

   Ⓐ 3 + 3 = 6

   Ⓑ 6 + 3 = 9

   Ⓒ 5 + 4 = 9

   Ⓓ 6 + 6 = 12

GO ON ➡

6. $12 - 6 =$ ▨

    (F) 3

    (G) 4

    (H) 5

    (J) 6

7.
$$\begin{array}{r} 10 \\ -\ 2 \\ \hline \end{array}$$
▨

    (A) 8

    (B) 7

    (C) 6

    (D) 5

8. $7 + 1 =$ ▨

    (F) 7

    (G) 8

    (H) 9

    (J) 10

9. Which is a related subtraction fact for $5 + 7 = 12$?

    (A) $7 - 5 = 2$

    (B) $2 + 5 = 7$

    (C) $7 + 5 = 12$

    (D) $12 - 7 = 5$

10. What is the turnaround fact for $1 + 3 = 4$?

    (F) $3 + 1 = 4$

    (G) $4 - 1 = 3$

    (H) $2 + 2 = 4$

    (J) $4 - 3 = 1$

GO ON ➡

11. $5 + \blacksquare = 7$

    Ⓐ 1

    Ⓑ 2

    Ⓒ 3

    Ⓓ 4

12. $11 - 3 = \blacksquare$

    Ⓕ 8

    Ⓖ 9

    Ⓗ 10

    Ⓙ 11

13. Which of these is a doubles fact?

    Ⓐ 7 + 1

    Ⓑ 8 + 4

    Ⓒ 4 + 4

    Ⓓ 9 + 3

14.
$$\begin{array}{r} 8 \\ + 4 \\ \hline \blacksquare \end{array}$$

    Ⓕ 8

    Ⓖ 9

    Ⓗ 10

    Ⓙ 12

15.
$$\begin{array}{r} 6 \\ + 5 \\ \hline \blacksquare \end{array}$$

    Ⓐ 1

    Ⓑ 8

    Ⓒ 11

    Ⓓ 12

GO ON

16. The ▢ of 4 + 1 is 5.

(F) fact family

(G) difference

(H) addend

(J) sum

Solve.

17. There are 9 frogs in the pond. Two more frogs hop in. How many frogs are in the pond?

(A) 5 frogs

(B) 6 frogs

(C) 11 frogs

(D) 12 frogs

18. There are 10 birds in the tree. One flies away. How many are left?

(F) 6 birds (H) 8 birds

(G) 7 birds (J) 9 birds

19. Lee has 6 dog stickers. He buys 5 more. How many dog stickers does Lee have?

(A) 1 dog sticker

(B) 9 dog stickers

(C) 11 dog stickers

(D) 12 dog stickers

20. Miguel has 11 fish. He gave 7 fish to his friends. How many fish does Miguel have left?

(F) 3 fish

(G) 4 fish

(H) 5 fish

(J) 6 fish

STOP

© McGraw-Hill School Division

Name _____

Write the answer.

1.   4
    + 5

2.   9
    − 3

3.   3
    + 2

4.   12
    − 2

5. Look at this fact family triangle. Circle the fact that belongs in this family.

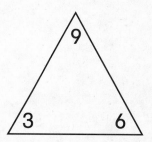

$3 + 3 = 6$

$6 + 3 = 9$

$5 + 4 = 9$

$6 + 6 = 12$

GO ON

6.
$$\begin{array}{r} 12 \\ -\ 6 \\ \hline \end{array}$$

7.
$$\begin{array}{r} 10 \\ -\ 2 \\ \hline \end{array}$$

8.
$$\begin{array}{r} 7 \\ +\ 1 \\ \hline \end{array}$$

9. Circle the related subtraction fact for $5 + 7 = 12$.

$7 - 5 = 2$

$2 + 5 = 7$

$7 + 5 = 12$

$12 - 7 = 5$

10. What is the turnaround fact for $1 + 3 = 4$?

_____

GO ON ➡

11. $5 +$ _____ $= 7$

12. $11 - 3 =$ _____

13. Which of these is a
doubles fact?
Circle the answer.

$7 + 1$

$8 + 4$

$4 + 4$

$9 + 3$

14. $\begin{array}{r} 8 \\ + 4 \\ \hline \end{array}$

15. $\begin{array}{r} 6 \\ + 5 \\ \hline \end{array}$

GO ON

16. Complete the sentence using one of the following: *fact family*, *difference*, *addend*, *sum*.

The _____ of 4 + 1 is 5.

Solve.

17. There are 9 frogs in the pond. Two more frogs hop in. How many frogs are in the pond?

_____ frogs

18. There are 10 birds in the tree. One flies away. How many are left?

_____ birds

19. Lee has 6 dog stickers. He buys 5 more. How many dog stickers does Lee have?

_____ dog stickers

20. Miguel has 11 fish. He gave 7 fish to his friends. How many fish does Miguel have left?

_____ fish

STOP

Chapter-2 Teacher Interview

Core Concept: *Addition and Subtraction Strategies and Facts to 20*

Student Activity: The student demonstrates an understanding of adding and subtracting facts to 20. Have 20 small objects, such as coins, buttons, or markers, and a number line available for the student. Ask the student to use strategies such as doubles facts and fact families to add and subtract.

Teacher Question 1:

◎ What is a doubles fact that will help you find the sum of 9 and 8?

Understanding Student Response	Practice and Improvement
Student does not know what a doubles fact is or how it may help to find the sum.	Review doubles facts as presented in lesson 1. Have the student practice increasing or decreasing various doubles facts by 1.
Student does not know which of the addends to double.	Review lesson 1 to practice doubling the larger addend and subtracting 1 and then doubling the smaller addend and adding 1. Ask the student to create similar examples for extra practice.

Teacher Question 2:

◎ What is the fact family that relates 15, 11, and 4?

Understanding Student Response	Practice and Improvement
Student gives addition facts correctly, but not subtraction facts.	Review lesson 9 and then use the number line to count down from 15 to 11 and then from 15 to 4. Record the results. Use examples like Fast Facts after lesson 9 for further practice.
Student does not understand "fact families."	Review lesson 9, or return to lesson 7 in Chapter 1 if necessary. Ask the student to use a number line or counters to help find members of the fact families.

Teacher Question 3:

◎ Newell painted 14 pictures in two days. He painted 8 on one day. How many did he paint on the second day?

Understanding Student Response	Practice and Improvement
Student tries to add 14 and 8.	Review lesson 8 to point out that this is a "missing addend" problem and then have the student review the fact family relating 8 and 14. Use counters to demonstrate.
Student gives a reasonable, but incorrect, response.	Have the student count back on the number line and ask the student to write (or say) the addition and subtraction fact families relating 14 and 8. Use similar examples to help the student understand the process involved.

Chapter-2 Journal Writing

Encourage students to generate their own journal entries related to math ideas in general or to concepts in this chapter. Present the following journal prompt and have students share their drawing/writing with a partner:

🌀 Bill and Susan have just started to collect baseball cards. Bill has 4 and Susan has 7. How many do they have together? Write a number sentence that will tell the sum and illustrate it with a picture.

(Responses should show one set of 4 cards and another set of 7, along with the number sentence 4 + 7 = 11.)

FOLLOW UP

Later in the day, review the idea of adding facts to 20. Present students with a set of 20 like items, such as counters or pennies. Have students use the items to create and solve addition problems. Encourage students to write number sentences from their problems.

Have students write at least 5 number sentences with an explanation of what they added. Ask the students to make a picture story with one of their number sentences in their journals. Have students share their picture stories and sentences with a math partner.

Chapter-2 Monitoring Student Progress

☐ Form A   ☐ Form B

Student Name _____ Date _____

Directions: For each item that is answered incorrectly, cross out the item number. Then record the number of correct responses in the appropriate Student Score column. If the student has not met the Criterion Score for an objective, circle the student's score. Recommended assignments are listed in the Prescription Table on the next page.

Objective	Item Numbers	Criterion Score	Student Score
A. Add, facts to 20	1, 2, 3, 4	3/4	/4
B. Subtract, facts to 20	5, 6, 7, 8	3/4	/4
C. Use related facts to add and subtract	9, 10, 11, 12	3/4	/4
D. Add three or more 1-digit numbers	13, 14, 15, 16	3/4	/4
E. Solve problems, including those that involve writing a number sentence	17, 18, 19, 20	3/4	/4
Total Test Score		15/20	/20
Total Percent Correct			%

© McGraw-Hill School Division

Chapter-2 Prescription Table

The following chart correlates the tested objectives for this chapter to supplementary materials that meet the individual needs of the students. The Practice and Reteach pages are designed for students who need further instruction in the math concepts taught in this chapter. The Enrich pages are designed for students who need advanced challenges.

Objective	Practice	Reteach	Enrich
A. Add, facts to 20 .	25, 28, 40, 46	26, 29, 41, 47	27, 30, 48
B. Subtract, facts to 20.	40, 46	41, 47	42, 48
C. Use related facts to add and subtract.	40, 43, 46, 49	41, 44, 47, 50	45, 48, 51
D. Add three or more 1-digit numbers.	31	32	33
E. Solve problems, including those that involve writing a number sentence.	34–37	38–39	

Choose the correct answer.

1. $8 + 8 = $ ▪

(A) 15

(B) 16

(C) 17

(D) 18

4. $6 + $ ▪ $ = 15$

(F) 7

(G) 8

(H) 9

(J) 10

2. $\begin{array}{r} 7 \\ + 6 \\ \hline \end{array}$ ▪

(F) 11 (H) 13

(G) 12 (J) 14

5. $\begin{array}{r} 16 \\ - 8 \\ \hline \end{array}$ ▪

(A) 6

(B) 7

(C) 8

(D) 9

3. $\begin{array}{r} 9 \\ + 4 \\ \hline \end{array}$ ▪

(A) 5 (C) 13

(B) 12 (D) 14

6. $14 - 9 = $ ▪

- Ⓕ 4
- Ⓖ 5
- Ⓗ 6
- Ⓙ 7

7.
$$\begin{array}{r} 14 \\ -\ 5 \\ \hline \end{array}$$
▪

- Ⓐ 8
- Ⓑ 9
- Ⓒ 10
- Ⓓ 11

8. $15 - $ ▪ $= 7$

- Ⓕ 6
- Ⓖ 7
- Ⓗ 8
- Ⓙ 9

9. Which subtraction fact relates to $5 + 9 = 14$?

- Ⓐ $14 - 5 = 9$
- Ⓑ $14 - 14 = 0$
- Ⓒ $9 - 5 = 4$
- Ⓓ $14 - 6 = 8$

10. Which addition fact relates to $13 - 6 = 7$?

- Ⓕ $6 + 7 = 13$
- Ⓖ $6 + 1 = 7$
- Ⓗ $9 + 4 = 13$
- Ⓙ $3 + 4 = 7$

GO ON ▶

11. $9 + 3 = $ ■

■ $- 9 = 3$

(A) 10   (C) 12

(B) 11   (D) 13

12.
$$\begin{array}{r} 17 \\ -\ 8 \\ \hline \blacksquare \end{array}$$

$$\begin{array}{r} 8 \\ +\ \blacksquare \\ \hline 17 \end{array}$$

(F) 7   (H) 9

(G) 8   (J) 10

13. $5 + 5 + 3 = $ ■

(A) 10

(B) 11

(C) 12

(D) 13

14.
$$\begin{array}{r} 3 \\ 2 \\ +\ 6 \\ \hline \blacksquare \end{array}$$

(F) 9

(G) 10

(H) 11

(J) 12

15. $4 + 7 + 3 = $ ■

(A) 11   (C) 13

(B) 12   (D) 14

16.
$$\begin{array}{r} 4 \\ 1 \\ +\ 5 \\ \hline \blacksquare \end{array}$$

(F) 9   (H) 11

(G) 10   (J) 12

GO ON

Solve.

17. Jan has 8 pencils. She buys 7 more. Which number sentence tells how many pencils Jan has in all?

Ⓐ $8 + 7 = 15$

Ⓑ $9 - 6 = 15$

Ⓒ $15 - 7 = 8$

Ⓓ $15 - 8 = 7$

18. Ken has 14 pretzels in his lunchbox. He eats 5 of them. Which number sentence tells how many pretzels Ken has left?

Ⓕ $5 + 9 = 14$

Ⓖ $9 + 5 = 14$

Ⓗ $14 - 5 = 9$

Ⓙ $14 - 9 = 5$

19. Dawn has 2 dogs, 5 fish, and 1 cat. How many pets does Dawn have altogether?

Ⓐ 7 pets

Ⓑ 8 pets

Ⓒ 9 pets

Ⓓ 10 pets

20. There were 13 cookies on a plate. Erik puts all but 6 of them in his lunchbox. How many cookies did Erik put in his lunchbox?

Ⓕ 5 cookies

Ⓖ 6 cookies

Ⓗ 7 cookies

Ⓙ 8 cookies

STOP

Write the answer.

1. $8 + 8 =$

4. $6 + $ _____ $= 15$

2. $\begin{array}{r} 7 \\ + 6 \\ \hline \end{array}$

5. $\begin{array}{r} 16 \\ - 8 \\ \hline \end{array}$

3. $\begin{array}{r} 9 \\ + 4 \\ \hline \end{array}$

6. $14 - 9 =$ _____

7. $\begin{array}{r} 14 \\ -\ 5 \\ \hline \end{array}$

8. $15 -$ _____ $= 7$

9. What is the subtraction fact that relates to $5 + 9 = 14$?

_____

10. What is the addition fact that relates to $13 - 6 = 7$?

_____

GO ON ➡️

© McGraw-Hill School Division

11. $9 + 3 =$ _____

_____ $- 9 = 3$

12. $\begin{array}{r} 17 \\ -\ 8 \\ \hline \end{array}$ $\begin{array}{r} 8 \\ +\ \square \\ \hline 17 \end{array}$

13. $5 + 5 + 3 =$ _____

14. $\begin{array}{r} 3 \\ 2 \\ +\ 6 \\ \hline \end{array}$

15. $4 + 7 + 3 =$ _____

16. $\begin{array}{r} 4 \\ 1 \\ +\ 5 \\ \hline \end{array}$

GO ON

Solve.

17. Jan has 8 pencils. She buys 7 more. How many pencils does she have altogether? Circle the number sentence that you would use to solve this problem.

$8 + 7 = 15$

$9 - 6 = 15$

$15 - 7 = 8$

$15 - 8 = 7$

18. Ken has 14 pretzels in his lunchbox. He eats 5 of them. How many pretzels does Ken have now? Circle the number sentence that you would use to solve this problem.

$5 + 9 = 14$

$9 + 5 = 14$

$14 - 5 = 9$

$14 - 9 = 5$

19. Dawn has 2 dogs, 5 fish, and 1 cat. How many pets does Dawn have altogether?

_____ pets

20. There were 13 cookies on a plate. Erik puts all but 6 of them in his lunchbox. How many cookies did Erik put in his lunchbox?

_____ cookies

STOP

Choose the correct answer.

1. $9 + 6 =$ ▨

Ⓐ 15

Ⓑ 16

Ⓒ 17

Ⓓ 18

4. $4 +$ ▨ $= 12$

Ⓕ 7

Ⓖ 8

Ⓗ 9

Ⓙ 10

2. $\begin{array}{r} 7 \\ + 7 \\ \hline \end{array}$ ▨

Ⓕ 12 Ⓗ 14

Ⓖ 13 Ⓙ 15

5. $\begin{array}{r} 14 \\ - 7 \\ \hline \end{array}$ ▨

Ⓐ 6

Ⓑ 7

Ⓒ 8

Ⓓ 9

3. $\begin{array}{r} 9 \\ + 5 \\ \hline \end{array}$ ▨

Ⓐ 5 Ⓒ 13

Ⓑ 12 Ⓓ 14

GO ON ➤

6. $16 - 9 = $ ▣

Ⓕ 4

Ⓖ 5

Ⓗ 6

Ⓙ 7

7. $\begin{array}{r} 13 \\ -\ 5 \\ \hline \end{array}$ ▣

Ⓐ 8

Ⓑ 9

Ⓒ 10

Ⓓ 13

8. $14 - $ ▣ $= 8$

Ⓕ 6

Ⓖ 7

Ⓗ 8

Ⓙ 9

9. Which subtraction fact relates to $6 + 7 = 13$?

Ⓐ $13 - 13 = 0$

Ⓑ $13 - 7 = 6$

Ⓒ $13 - 5 = 8$

Ⓓ $7 - 6 = 1$

10. Which addition fact relates to $16 - 7 = 9$?

Ⓕ $7 + 2 = 9$

Ⓖ $8 + 8 = 16$

Ⓗ $9 + 7 = 16$

Ⓙ $2 + 7 = 9$

GO ON ➡

11. $8 + 6 = \blacksquare$

   $\blacksquare - 8 = 6$

   Ⓐ 10   Ⓒ 14

   Ⓑ 12   Ⓓ 15

12.
$$\begin{array}{r} 17 \\ -\ 9 \\ \hline \blacksquare \end{array}$$
$$\begin{array}{r} 9 \\ +\ \blacksquare \\ \hline 17 \end{array}$$

   Ⓕ 7   Ⓗ 9

   Ⓖ 8   Ⓙ 10

13. $6 + 3 + 4 = \blacksquare$

   Ⓐ 10

   Ⓑ 11

   Ⓒ 12

   Ⓓ 13

14.
$$\begin{array}{r} 4 \\ 5 \\ +\ 2 \\ \hline \blacksquare \end{array}$$

   Ⓕ 9

   Ⓖ 10

   Ⓗ 11

   Ⓙ 12

15. $2 + 7 + 7 = \blacksquare$

   Ⓐ 13   Ⓒ 15

   Ⓑ 14   Ⓓ 16

16.
$$\begin{array}{r} 3 \\ 5 \\ +\ 2 \\ \hline \blacksquare \end{array}$$

   Ⓕ 9   Ⓗ 11

   Ⓖ 10   Ⓙ 12

GO ON ➡

Name _____

Solve.

17. Fran has 4 pencils.
She buys 8 more.
Which number sentence
tells how many pencils Fran
has in all?

Ⓐ 8 + 6 = 14

Ⓑ 12 − 8 = 4

Ⓒ 4 + 8 = 12

Ⓓ 12 − 4 = 8

18. Spencer has 16 pretzels
in his lunchbox. He eats 7
of them. Which number
sentence tells how many
pretzels Spencer has left?

Ⓕ 7 + 9 = 16

Ⓖ 9 + 7 = 16

Ⓗ 16 − 9 = 7

Ⓙ 16 − 7 = 9

19. Kayla has 1 dog, 6 fish, and
2 cats. How many pets does
Kayla have altogether?

Ⓐ 7 pets

Ⓑ 8 pets

Ⓒ 9 pets

Ⓓ 10 pets

20. There were 15 cookies on a
plate. Tim puts all but 9 of
them in his lunchbox. How
many cookies did Tim put in
his lunchbox?

Ⓕ 5 cookies

Ⓖ 6 cookies

Ⓗ 7 cookies

Ⓙ 8 cookies

STOP

© McGraw-Hill School Division

Write the answer.

1. $9 + 6 =$

4. $4 + \underline{\hspace{1.5cm}} = 12$

2.
$$\begin{array}{r} 7 \\ + 7 \\ \hline \end{array}$$

5.
$$\begin{array}{r} 14 \\ - 7 \\ \hline \end{array}$$

3.
$$\begin{array}{r} 9 \\ + 5 \\ \hline \end{array}$$

GO ON

6. $16 - 9 = $ _____

7.
$$\begin{array}{r} 13 \\ -\ 5 \\ \hline \end{array}$$

8. $14 - $ _____ $= 8$

9. What is the subtraction fact that relates to $6 + 7 = 13$?

_____

_____

10. What is the addition fact that relates to $16 - 7 = 9$?

_____

GO ON →

11. $8 + 6 =$ _____

12. $\begin{array}{r} 17 \\ -\ 9 \\ \hline \end{array}$

13. $6 + 3 + 4 =$ _____

14. $\begin{array}{r} 4 \\ 5 \\ +\ 2 \\ \hline \end{array}$

15. $2 + 7 + 7 =$ _____

16. $\begin{array}{r} 3 \\ 5 \\ +\ 2 \\ \hline \end{array}$

GO ON

Solve.

17. Fran has 4 pencils.
She buys 8 more.
How many pencils does she
have altogether?
Circle the number sentence
that you would use to solve
this problem.

$8 + 6 = 15$

$12 - 8 = 4$

$4 + 8 = 12$

$12 - 4 = 8$

18. Spencer has 16 pretzels in
his lunchbox. He eats 7 of
them. How many pretzels
does Spencer have now?
Circle the number sentence
that you would use to solve
this problem.

$7 + 9 = 16$

$9 + 7 = 16$

$16 - 9 = 7$

$16 - 7 = 9$

19. Kayla has 1 dog, 6 fish, and
2 cats. How many pets does
Kayla have altogether?

_____ pets

20. There were 15 cookies on a
plate. Tim puts all but 9 of
them in his lunchbox. How
many cookies did Tim put in
his lunchbox?

_____ cookies

STOP

Chapter-3 Teacher Interview

Core Concept: Place Value to 100s

Student Activity: The student demonstrates an understanding of reading, writing, comparing, and ordering numbers to 100. Have available a collection of small objects, such as coins, buttons, or markers; tens and ones models; a number line; and pencils and paper for the student to use. Ask the student questions such as, "Which number comes before 37?"

Teacher Question 1:

⊚ Think about the number 14. How many tens and how many ones are in 14?

Understanding Student Response	Practice and Improvement
Student refers only to 14 ones.	Review lesson 2 to reinforce place value. Have student count out 14 objects and then group 10 of the objects together. Show that there is one group of 10 and 4 ones left over. Repeat using other numbers.
Student reverses the places, saying 4 tens and one 1.	Do the counting exercise above. Point out that 4 groups of 10 make 40. Repeat with another number. Use items like those in **Practice** at the end of lesson 3.

Teacher Question 2:

⊚ What are the numbers just **before** and just **after** the number 37?

Understanding Student Response	Practice and Improvement
Student says the wrong numbers or knows just one number.	Review ordering numbers in lesson 9. Have the student make '37' with tens and ones models. Take one ones model away or add one more ones model and name the number.
Student responds with 27 and 47.	Review lesson 9. Count back to 27 from 37 on a number line and then count on to 47 from 37. Show that those numbers are 10 away from 37. Assign from the **Practice** section of lesson 9.

Teacher Question 3:

⊚ Write down the numbers twenty-five, forty-two, and seventeen. Now put them in the correct order.

Understanding Student Response	Practice and Improvement
Student cannot write the numbers correctly.	Review lesson 4. Assign practice items from among those given in lesson 4.
Student writes the numbers correctly, but orders them incorrectly.	Review lesson 8 to remind student that ordering means to write the numbers from smallest to largest. Give student another group of three 2-digit numbers to write and order.

Chapter-3 Journal Writing

Encourage students to generate their own journal entries related to math ideas in general or to concepts in this chapter. Present the following journal prompt and have students share their drawing/writing with a partner:

⊚ Even numbers are those that end with 0, 2, 4, 6, and 8 in the ones place, and odd numbers are those that end with 1, 3, 5, 7, and 9 in the ones place. If you add 2 even numbers, is the result odd or even? If you add 2 odd numbers, is the result odd or even? What numbers could you add to get an odd result?

(Responses should indicate that adding two even or two odd numbers together gives an even result, while adding an even number and an odd number gives an odd result.)

FOLLOW UP

To follow up, review the meaning of odd and even numbers. Have students skip-count by 2 starting at 2, and note that the numbers that they are naming are all even numbers. Then have students skip-count by 2 starting at 1, and note that these numbers are all odd numbers.

Now have the students find and count objects in the room and decide if there is an even or an odd number of that object. Have the students write the name of the object, how many they found, and if they found an even or an odd number. With an object they found, or with counters, have students divide them into two groups of equal size. Ask students to write about even and odd numbers based on this activity. They may draw pictures to illustrate. Have students share their pictures with a math partner.

Chapter-3 Monitoring Student Progress

☐ **Form A**   ☐ **Form B**

Student Name _____ Date _____

Directions: For each item that is answered incorrectly, cross out the item number. Then record the number of correct responses in the appropriate Student Score column. If the student has not met the Criterion Score for an objective, circle the student's score. Recommended assignments are listed in the Prescription Table on the next page.

Objective	Item Numbers	Criterion Score	Student Score
A. Count, read, write, and represent numbers to 100.	1, 2, 3, 4	3/4	/4
B. Identify the place value for each digit for numbers to 100.	5, 6, 7	2/3	/3
C. Compare and order numbers to 100.	8, 9, 10	2/3	/3
D. Skip count to 100.	11, 12, 13	2/3	/3
E. Identify odd and even numbers.	14, 15, 16	2/3	/3
F. Solve problems, including those that involve using logical reasoning.	17, 18, 19, 20	3/4	/4
Total Test Score		14/20	/20
Total Percent Correct			%

Pages 88–90 involve ordinal numbers.

Chapter-3 Prescription Table

The following chart correlates the tested objectives for this chapter to supplementary materials that meet the individual needs of the students. The Practice and Reteach pages are designed for students who need further instruction in the math concepts taught in this chapter. The Enrich pages are designed for students who need advanced challenges.

Objective	Practice	Reteach	Enrich
A. Count, read, write, and represent numbers to 100.	55, 64	56, 65	57, 66
B. Identify the place value for each digit for numbers to 100.	61, 67	62, 68	63, 69
C. Compare and order numbers to 100.	76, 79	77, 80	78, 81
D. Skip-count to 100.	82	83	84
E. Identify odd and even numbers.	85	86	87
F. Solve problems, including those that involve using logical reasoning.	70–73	74–75	

Pages 58–60 involve estimation.
Pages 88–90 involve ordinal numbers.

© McGraw-Hill School Division

Choose the correct answer.

1. What number does the picture show?

tens	ones

Ⓐ 7

Ⓑ 34

Ⓒ 43

Ⓓ 44

2. What number does the picture show?

tens	ones

Ⓕ 13

Ⓖ 57

Ⓗ 75

Ⓙ 76

3. How do you write the number sixteen?

Ⓐ 6   Ⓒ 60

Ⓑ 16   Ⓓ 70

4. What is 93 in expanded form?

Ⓕ 12 + 0

Ⓖ 30 + 9

Ⓗ 30 − 9

Ⓙ 90 + 3

5. How many tens are in 62?

Ⓐ 2 tens

Ⓑ 6 tens

Ⓒ 20 tens

Ⓓ 60 tens

6. How many ones are in 72?

    F 2 ones

    G 7 ones

    H 20 ones

    J 70 ones

7. What number is the same as 4 tens and 3 ones?

    A 7

    B 34

    C 43

    D 44

8. Which is true?

    F $18 > 34$

    G $72 > 59$

    H $21 > 28$

    J $34 > 43$

9. What number comes just before 83?

    A 80

    B 81

    C 82

    D 84

10. What number comes just after 39?

    F 37

    G 38

    H 40

    J 41

GO ON

11. Skip count by threes.
Which number comes next?

3 6 9

Ⓐ 10

Ⓑ 11

Ⓒ 12

Ⓓ 18

12. Skip count by fives.
Which number comes next?

15 20 25

Ⓕ 26

Ⓖ 27

Ⓗ 30

Ⓙ 35

13. Skip count by fours.
Which number comes next?

4 8 12

Ⓐ 14   Ⓒ 17

Ⓑ 16   Ⓓ 18

14. Which is an odd number?

Ⓕ 16

Ⓖ 23

Ⓗ 48

Ⓙ 54

15. Which is an even number?

Ⓐ 38

Ⓑ 63

Ⓒ 71

Ⓓ 89

GO ON

16. What are the next three even numbers?

16   18

(F) 19, 20, 21

(G) 20, 21, 22

(H) 19, 21, 23

(J) 20, 22, 24

Solve.

17. Tony has 6 tens and 4 ones. Sal has 4 tens and 4 ones. How many more tens does Tony have than Sal?

(A) 0 tens   (C) 4 tens

(B) 2 tens   (D) 6 tens

18. Mr. Ruiz's students are standing in line. How many people are in front of the fifth person in line?

(F) 4 people   (H) 11 people

(G) 5 people   (J) 16 people

19. How many books are on the shelf?
The number is between 25 and 29.
It is an odd number.

(A) 24 books

(B) 26 books

(C) 27 books

(D) 28 books

20. How many children are on the bus?
The number is between 31 and 46.
There are 4 tens in the number.
The ones digit is greater than the tens digit.

(F) 43 children

(G) 45 children

(H) 47 children

(J) 35 children

STOP

Write the answer.

1. What number does the picture show?

tens	ones

_____

2. What number does the picture show?

tens	ones

_____

3. How do you write the number sixteen?

_____

4. Write 93 in expanded form.

_____

5. How many tens are in 62?

_____ tens

6. How many ones are in 72?

_____ ones

_____

7. Write the number that is the same as 4 tens and 3 ones.

_____

8. Circle the comparison that is true.

18 > 34

72 > 59

21 > 28

34 > 43

9. What number comes just before 83?

_____

_____

10. What number comes just after 39?

_____

GO ON

11. Skip count by threes.
Which number comes next?

3   6   9   _____

12. Skip count by fives.
Which number comes next?

15   20   25   _____

13. Skip count by fours.
Which number comes next?

4   8   12   _____

14. Which is an odd number:
16, 23, 48, or 54?

_____

15. Which is an even number:
38, 63, 71, or 89?

_____

GO ON

16. Write the next three even numbers.

16 18 ____ ____ ____

Solve.

17. Tony has 6 tens and 4 ones. Sal has 4 tens and 4 ones. How many more tens does Tony have than Sal?

_____ tens

---

18. Mr. Ruiz's students are standing in line. How many people are in front of the fifth person in line?

_____ people

19. How many books are on the shelf?
The number is between 25 and 29.
It is an odd number.

_____ books

---

20. How many children are on the bus?
The number is between 31 and 46.
There are 4 tens in the number.
The ones digit is greater than the tens digit.

_____ children

STOP

Choose the correct answer.

1. What number does the picture show?

tens	ones

Ⓐ 13

Ⓑ 67

Ⓒ 76

Ⓓ 86

2. What number does the picture show?

tens	ones

Ⓕ 10

Ⓖ 28

Ⓗ 72

Ⓙ 82

3. How do you write the number eighteen?

Ⓐ 8   Ⓒ 18

Ⓑ 11   Ⓓ 80

4. What is 47 in expanded form?

Ⓕ 4 + 7

Ⓖ 11 + 0

Ⓗ 40 + 7

Ⓙ 70 + 4

5. How many tens are in 79?

Ⓐ 7 tens

Ⓑ 9 tens

Ⓒ 70 tens

Ⓓ 90 tens

GO ON

6. How many ones are in 91?

 Ⓕ 1 one

 Ⓖ 9 ones

 Ⓗ 10 ones

 Ⓙ 90 ones

7. What number is the same as 3 tens and 5 ones?

 Ⓐ 8

 Ⓑ 35

 Ⓒ 53

 Ⓓ 54

8. Which is true?

 Ⓕ 50 < 49

 Ⓖ 62 < 85

 Ⓗ 65 < 40

 Ⓙ 95 < 85

9. What number comes just before 37?

 Ⓐ 35

 Ⓑ 36

 Ⓒ 38

 Ⓓ 39

10. What number comes just after 59?

 Ⓕ 57

 Ⓖ 58

 Ⓗ 60

 Ⓙ 61

GO ON

11. Skip count by threes.
Which number comes next?

15   18   21

(A) 20

(B) 22

(C) 23

(D) 24

12. Skip count by fives.
Which number comes next?

45   50   55

(F) 56

(G) 57

(H) 60

(J) 65

13. Skip count by fours.
Which number comes next?

8   12   16

(A) 18   (C) 20

(B) 19   (D) 21

14. Which is an odd number?

(F) 29

(G) 56

(H) 82

(J) 98

15. Which is an even number?

(A) 36

(B) 41

(C) 67

(D) 83

GO ON

16. What are the next three even numbers?

26   28

 (F) 29, 30, 31

 (G) 30, 31, 32

 (H) 30, 32, 34

 (J) 31, 33, 35

Solve.

17. Evan has 4 tens and 6 ones. Joe has 4 tens and 3 ones. How many more ones does Evan have than Joe?

 (A) 0 ones (C) 4 ones

 (B) 3 ones (D) 8 ones

---

18. Mrs. Cho's class is standing in line. How many people are in front of the seventh person in line?

 (F) 6 people (H) 14 people

 (G) 8 people (J) 17 people

---

19. How many books are on the shelf?
The number is between 33 and 37.
It is an odd number.

 (A) 34 books

 (B) 35 books

 (C) 36 books

 (D) 39 books

---

20. How many children are on the bus?
The number is between 52 and 68.
There are 6 tens in the number.
The ones digit is greater than the tens digit.

 (F) 65 children

 (G) 67 children

 (H) 69 children

 (J) 57 chldren

STOP

Write the answer.

1. What number does the picture show?

tens	ones

_____

2. What number does the picture show?

tens	ones

_____

3. How do you write the number eighteen?

_____

4. Write 47 in expanded form.

_____

5. How many tens are in 79?

_____ tens

GO ON

6. How many ones are in 91?

_____ ones

_____

7. Write the number that is the same as 3 tens and 5 ones.

_____

8. Circle the comparison that is true.

50 < 49

62 < 85

65 < 40

95 < 85

9. What number comes just before 37?

_____

_____

10. What number comes just after 59?

_____

GO ON

11. Skip count by threes.
Which number comes next?

15   18   21   _____

12. Skip count by fives.
Which number comes next?

45   50   55   _____

13. Skip count by fours.
Which number comes next?

8   12   16   _____

14. Which is an odd number:
29, 56, 82, or 98?

_____

15. Which is an even number:
36, 41, 67, or 83?

_____

GO ON ➡

16. Write the next three even numbers.

26 28 ____ ____ ____

_____

Solve.

17. Evan has 4 tens and 6 ones. Joe has 4 tens and 3 ones. How many more ones does Evan have than Joe?

_____ ones

_____

18. Mrs. Cho's class is standing in line. How many people are in front of the seventh person in line?

_____ people

19. How many books are on the shelf?
The number is between 33 and 37.
It is an odd number.

_____ books

_____

20. How many children are on the bus?
The number is between 52 and 68.
There are 6 tens in the number.
The ones digit is greater than the tens digit.

_____ children

STOP

Chapters 1–3 Performance Assessment

Pack Your Bags!

⊚ *Target Skill:*   Addition and subtraction facts to 15.

⊚ *Additional Skills:* Fact families for 15; solving problems using addition and subtraction; commutative property (optional).

Task
Description: This task requires students to separate 15 books into two bags and determine how many different ways this can be done.

Preparing: You may wish to have students use the commutative property (turnaround facts) and say, for example, that 1 in Tara's bag and 14 in Tim's bag is a *different* way than 14 in Tara's bag and 1 in Tim's bag.

Materials	Group Size	Time on Task
Pencil Paper Counters	2 to 3 students	1–2 days

Guiding: Remind students that they must put at least one book in each bag (15 in one, none in the other is not an option). Suggest to students that they think of all the addends for 15.

Observing/
Monitoring: As you move among the students, pose the following questions:

How do you know you found all the ways to separate 15 books into two bags?

How do addition facts help you solve this problem?

Chapters 1–3 Performance Assessment Scoring Rubric

Pack Your Bags!

Score	Explanation
3	Students demonstrate an efficient strategy and a thorough approach that enables them to solve the problem completely. Students may: ◉ include all the ways to take 15 books in two bags (7 if you do not include the commutative options or 14 if you do). 1 and 14, 2 and 13, 3 and 12, 4 and 11, 5 and 10, 6 and 9, and 7 and 8 Students are able to complete the problem quickly and have all of the above correct solutions.
2	Students demonstrate a strategy that enables them to solve most of the problem correctly. The strategy is somewhat disorganized, making it less efficient. A solution is found, but errors are contained. Students may: ◉ find most of the options; ◉ find all of the options, but have no method or organization. Students may have some difficulty determining all solutions correctly but demonstrate an understanding of general concepts.
1	Students demonstrate a confused strategy, which leads to difficulty solving the problem. Most answers are incorrect, but students do demonstrate knowledge of at least one concept being assessed. Students may: ◉ find 3 options.

Pack Your Bags!

You will need

- counters

- a piece of paper

- a pencil

Tara and Tim are going on a trip with their family. They decide to bring 15 books to read in the car. All 15 books will not fit into one bag. How many different ways can they sort the books into two bags? _____

1. Place 15 counters on a table or desk.

2. Draw two large squares on your paper. Label one Tara's Bag. Label the other Tim's Bag.

3. See how many different ways you can sort the counters into the two bags.

4. Write a number sentence for each way.

_____

_____

_____

Chapters 1–3 Monitoring Student Progress Cumulative Test 1

Student Name _____ Date _____

Directions: This test targets selected objectives. For each item that is answered incorrectly, cross out the item number. Then record the number of correct responses for each strand in the column labeled **Number of Correct Responses**. Add to find the **Total Number of Correct Responses** and record the total. Use this total to determine the **Total Test Score** and the **Total Percent Correct.**

Strand • Objective(s)	Item Numbers	Number of Correct Responses
Number Sense		
⊚ Add, facts to 12.	1, 4, 6	
⊚ Subtract, facts to 12.	2, 5	
⊚ Add, facts to 20.	11	
⊚ Subtract, facts to 20.	8	
⊚ Use related facts to add and subtract.	3, 9	
⊚ Add three or more 1-digit numbers.	13	
⊚ Count, read, write, and represent numbers to 100.	7, 10	
⊚ Identify place value for each digit for numbers to 100.	12	
⊚ Compare and order numbers to 100.	14	
⊚ Skip count to 100.	15	
⊚ Identify odd and even numbers.	16	
Mathematical Reasoning		
⊚ Solve problems, including those that involve drawing a picture.	18	
⊚ Solve problems, including those that involve writing number sentences.	19, 20	
⊚ Solve problems, including those that involve logical reasoning.	17	
Total Number of Correct Responses		
Total Test Score		/20
Total Percent Correct		%

Choose the correct answer.

1. $9 + 2 = \blacksquare$

- (A) 7
- (B) 11
- (C) 12
- (D) 13

2. $10 - 6 = \blacksquare$

- (F) 3
- (G) 4
- (H) 5
- (J) 6

3. Which is a related subtraction fact for $4 + 5 = 9$?

- (A) $5 - 1 = 4$
- (B) $5 + 9 = 14$
- (C) $9 - 5 = 4$
- (D) $9 - 9 = 0$

4. $3 + \blacksquare = 11$

- (F) 7
- (G) 8
- (H) 9
- (J) 14

5.
$$\begin{array}{r} 12 \\ -\ 4 \\ \hline \blacksquare \end{array}$$

- (A) 6
- (B) 7
- (C) 8
- (D) 16

6.
$$
\begin{array}{r}
7 \\
+\ 5 \\
\hline
\end{array}
$$

(F) 9 (H) 11

(G) 10 (J) 12

7. What number does the picture show?

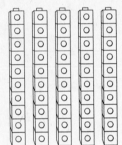

(A) 9 (C) 54

(B) 45 (D) 55

8. $17 - 8 =$

(F) 8 (H) 10

(G) 9 (J) 11

9. Which is a related addition fact for $15 - 9 = 6$?

(A) $9 + 7 = 16$

(B) $16 - 15 = 1$

(C) $7 + 8 = 15$

(D) $9 + 6 = 15$

10. How do you write the number thirty-two?

(F) 32

(G) 30

(H) 13

(J) 3

GO ON

11.
$$\begin{array}{r} 8 \\ + 7 \\ \hline \end{array}$$

Ⓐ 1

Ⓑ 14

Ⓒ 15

Ⓓ 16

12. How many tens are in 482?

Ⓕ 2 tens

Ⓖ 4 tens

Ⓗ 6 tens

Ⓙ 8 tens

13. $8 + 2 + 3 =$

Ⓐ 11

Ⓑ 12

Ⓒ 13

Ⓓ 14

14. Which sign makes the number sentence true?

49 ◯ 67

Ⓕ <

Ⓖ >

Ⓗ +

Ⓙ =

15. Skip count by 4s. Which number comes next?

16, 20, ▢, 28, 32

Ⓐ 23

Ⓑ 24

Ⓒ 25

Ⓓ 26

16. Which is an odd number?

Ⓕ 28   Ⓗ 64

Ⓖ 57   Ⓙ 72

GO ON

Solve.

17. How many balls are in the net? The number is between 18 and 21. It is an even number.

    Ⓐ 17 balls

    Ⓑ 18 balls

    Ⓒ 19 balls

    Ⓓ 20 balls

18. There are 14 people in line. How many people are in front of the seventh person?

    Ⓕ 5

    Ⓖ 6

    Ⓗ 7

    Ⓙ 8

19. Carl picked 8 carrots. He also picked 5 peppers. How many vegetables did he pick in all?

    Ⓐ 3 vegetables

    Ⓑ 12 vegetables

    Ⓒ 13 vegetables

    Ⓓ 14 vegetables

20. There were 15 crackers on a plate. Bill put all but 9 of them in his lunchbox. How many crackers did Bill put in his lunchbox?

    Ⓕ 6 crackers

    Ⓖ 7 crackers

    Ⓗ 9 crackers

    Ⓙ 15 crackers

STOP

Chapter-4 Teacher Interview

Core Concept: *Identifying and Counting Money*

Student Activity: The student demonstrates an understanding of coins and their values. Have a collection of real or realistic play money available for the student. A number line should also be available. Ask the student questions such as, "How can you make 25¢ using different coin combinations?"

Teacher Question 1:

⊚ Chul has two dimes, and Erin has four nickels. Who has more money? Why do you think so?

Understanding Student Response	Practice and Improvement
Student says Chul has more because dimes are worth more than nickels.	Review lesson 2 to help the student write the number of cents each person has. Show that 5¢ + 5¢ = 10¢ = one dime and therefore 2 dimes equal 4 nickels.
Student says Erin has more because she has 4 coins while Chul has only 2 coins.	Review lesson 2 and then use the procedure above. Use pennies, nickels, and dimes to show that size of a coin is not necessarily related to its value.

Teacher Question 2:

⊚ If you buy candy for 25¢, with what different coin combinations can you pay for it?

Understanding Student Response	Practice and Improvement
Student just says a quarter.	Review lesson 7 before asking the student what coins make a quarter. Prompt the student by saying "How many pennies in 25¢?" Then prompt for other coins. If necessary, student may use real or realistic play money.
Student gives one or two correct answers, but cannot produce others.	Review lesson 7 to prompt the student to think of other combinations that will make 25¢. If student does not think of others then ask such questions as, "How many pennies are in 25¢?"

Teacher Question 3:

⊚ At the school bake sale, cupcakes are 35¢ each. If Becky has 3 quarters, how many can she buy?

Understanding Student Response	Practice and Improvement
Student says Becky can buy just one cupcake.	Review lesson 1. Prompt student to find how many cents Becky has. Then ask how much 2 cupcakes will cost. Review lesson 5. Ask how much change Becky will receive.
Student says Becky can buy 3 or more cupcakes.	Review lesson 9. Then have the student determine the cost of 2 cupcakes and of 3 cupcakes. Point out that 3 cupcakes cost more than $1, and it takes 4 quarters to make $1. Assign practice from lesson 9.

Chapter-4 Journal Writing

Encourage students to generate their own journal entries related to math ideas in general or to concepts in this chapter. Present the following journal prompt and have students share their drawing/writing with a partner:

◎ Georgina buys 2 pieces of candy and a ball. What do you have to know to tell whether she has enough money to pay for it and whether or not she will get any change back?

(Responses should mention how much one piece of candy costs, how much the ball costs, and how much money she has with her. Responses should suggest that if she has more money with her than the items cost, she will get change back.)

FOLLOW UP

At an appropriate time, review ways of showing money amounts (Lesson 4) and making change (Lesson 5). Students may practice making change using real or play money, and write or draw a picture about the experience in their journals.

Have students work in pairs. The first student will think of three items to buy. The partner will write down the items and the cost of each item. They will total the cost of the items and the first student will "pay" for the items. If change is needed they will calculate it together and record it in the journal. One student should use addition to check the answer. Students will then reverse roles.

Chapter - 4 Monitoring Student Progress

☐ Form A   ☐ Form B

Student Name _____ Date _____

Directions: For each item that is answered incorrectly, cross out the item number. Then record the number of correct responses in the appropriate Student Score column. If the student has not met the Criterion Score for an objective, circle the student's score. Recommended assignments are listed in the Prescription Table on the next page.

Objective	Item Numbers	Criterion Score	Student Score
A. Identify coins, bills and their value.	1, 2, 5, 7	3/4	/4
B. Give the value of a set of coins or a set of bills and coins.	3, 6, 12, 14, 15, 16	5/6	/6
C. Compare money amounts.	4, 8, 9, 10, 11, 13	5/6	/6
D. Solve problems, including those that involve acting it out.	17, 18, 19, 20	3/4	/4
Total Test Score		16/20	/20
Total Percent Correct			%

Chapter-4 Prescription Table

The following chart correlates the tested objectives for this chapter to supplementary materials that meet the individual needs of the students. The Practice and Reteach pages are designed for students who need further instruction in the math concepts taught in this chapter. The Enrich pages are designed for students who need advanced challenges.

Objective	Practice	Reteach	Enrich
A. Identify coins, bills and their value.	94, 97, 115	95, 98, 116	96, 99, 117
B. Give the value of a set of coins or a set of bills and coins.	100, 103, 106	101, 104, 107	102, 105, 108
C. Compare money amounts.	118	119	120
D. Solve problems, including those that involve acting it out.	109–112	113–114	

Choose the correct answer.

1. How many cents are in a nickel?

- Ⓐ 1¢
- Ⓑ 5¢
- Ⓒ 10¢
- Ⓓ 25¢

2. How many cents are in a quarter?

- Ⓕ 5¢
- Ⓗ 10¢
- Ⓖ 25¢
- Ⓙ 50¢

3. Count. How much money?

- Ⓐ 35¢
- Ⓒ 26¢
- Ⓑ 30¢
- Ⓓ 25¢

4. Which set of coins has the greatest value?

Ⓕ

Ⓖ

Ⓗ

Ⓙ

5. Which of these coins is a dime?

- Ⓐ
- Ⓑ
- Ⓒ
- Ⓓ

GO ON →

6. Count. How much money?

F 48¢   H 93¢

G 73¢   J 98¢

7. Which of these coins is a half dollar?

A   C   B   D

8. Which set of coins has the greatest value?

F   G   H   J

9. Which toy costs the most?

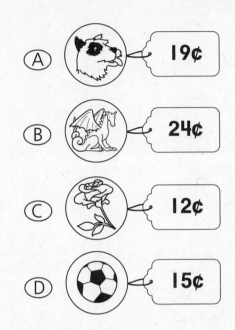

A 19¢

B 24¢

C 12¢

D 15¢

10. Which set of coins has the least value?

F   G   H   J

GO ON

11. Which set of coins has the least value?

Ⓐ

Ⓑ

Ⓒ

Ⓓ

12. Count. How much money?

Ⓕ $1.80

Ⓖ $3.15

Ⓗ $3.21

Ⓙ $3.50

13. Which toy costs the least?

Ⓐ  $1.59

Ⓑ 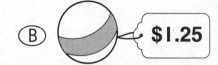 $1.25

Ⓒ  $1.05

Ⓓ 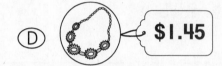 $1.45

14. Count. How much money?

Ⓕ 5¢   Ⓗ 62¢

Ⓖ 57¢   Ⓙ 65¢

15. Count. How much money?

Ⓐ 5¢   Ⓒ 81¢

Ⓑ 46¢   Ⓓ 86¢

16. Count. How much money?

(F) $1.05

(G) $1.17

(H) $1.32

(J) $1.50

Solve.

17. Kyle has 6 dimes. He buys a drink for 55¢. How much change should he get back?

(A) 1¢   (C) 10¢

(B) 5¢   (D) 50¢

18. Denise has dimes and nickels. How many ways can she buy a cookie for 25¢?

(F) 1 way   (H) 3 ways

(G) 2 ways   (J) 4 ways

19. Ted buys some candy for 65¢. He only has nickels. How many nickels does he need?

(A) 5

(B) 6

(C) 11

(D) 13

20. Evan wants to buy a glass of juice for 20¢. How many nickels does he need?

(F) 2

(G) 3

(H) 4

(J) 5

STOP

Write the answer.

1. How many cents are in a nickel?

_____ ¢

2. How many cents are in a quarter?

_____ ¢

3. Count. How much money?

_____ ¢

4. Circle the set of coins with the greatest value.

5. Circle the dime.

GO ON ▶

6. Count. How much money?

_____ ¢

7. Circle the half dollar.

8. Circle the set of coins with the greatest value.

9. Circle the toy which costs the most.

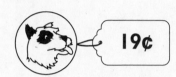   19¢

   24¢

   12¢

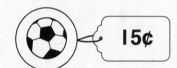   15¢

10. Circle the set of coins with the least value.

GO ON ▶

11. Circle the set of coins with the least value.

12. Count. How much money?

$ _____

13. Circle the toy that costs the least.

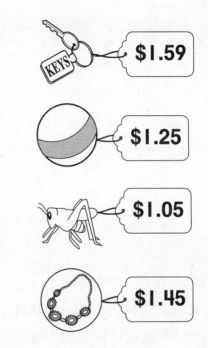

$1.59

$1.25

$1.05

$1.45

14. Count. How much money?

_____ ¢

15. Count. How much money?

_____ ¢

GO ON

16. Count. How much money?

$ _____

_____

Solve.

17. Kyle has 6 dimes. He buys a drink for 55¢. How much change should he get back?

_____ ¢

_____

18. Denise has dimes and nickels. How many ways can she buy a cookie for 25¢?

_____ ways

19. Ted buys some candy for 65¢. He only has nickels. How many nickels does he need?

_____ nickels

_____

20. Evan wants to buy a glass of juice for 20¢. How many nickels does he need?

_____ nickels

STOP

Choose the correct answer.

1. How many cents are in a quarter?

    Ⓐ 1¢

    Ⓑ 5¢

    Ⓒ 10¢

    Ⓓ 25¢

2. How many cents are in a dime?

    Ⓕ 5¢

    Ⓖ 10¢

    Ⓗ 25¢

    Ⓙ 50¢

3. Count. How much money?

    Ⓐ 22¢   Ⓒ 35¢

    Ⓑ 30¢   Ⓓ 40¢

4. Which set of coins has the greatest value?

    Ⓕ

    Ⓖ

    Ⓗ

    Ⓙ

5. Which of these coins is a penny?

    Ⓐ

    Ⓑ

    Ⓒ

    Ⓓ

GO ON

6. Count. How much money?

(F) 42¢   (H) 65¢

(G) 62¢   (J) 67¢

7. Which of these coins is a nickel?

(A)   (C)

(B)   (D)

8. Which set of coins has the greatest value?

(F)

(G)

(H)

(J)

9. Which toy costs the most?

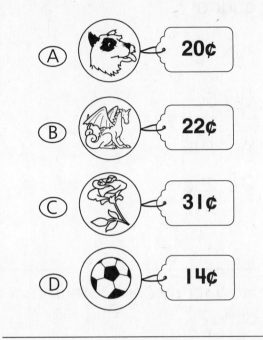

(A) 20¢

(B) 22¢

(C) 31¢

(D) 14¢

10. Which set of coins has the least value?

(F)

(G)

(H)

(J)

GO ON →

11. Which set of coins has the least value?

(A)

(B)

(C)

(D)

12. Count. How much money?

(F) $1.76

(G) $2.04

(H) $2.12

(J) $2.16

13. Which toy costs the least?

(A)  $1.45

(B) 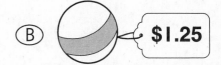 $1.25

(C)  $1.05

(D)  $1.59

14. Count. How much money?

(F) 6¢

(G) 71¢

(H) 96¢

(J) 97¢

GO ON

15. Count. How much money?

Ⓐ 8¢   Ⓒ 50¢

Ⓑ 40¢   Ⓓ 55¢

16. Count. How much money?

Ⓕ $1.35

Ⓖ $1.30

Ⓗ $1.26

Ⓙ $1.10

Solve.

17. Byron has 8 dimes. He buys a drink for 75¢. How much change should he get back?

Ⓐ 1¢   Ⓒ 10¢

Ⓑ 5¢   Ⓓ 40¢

18. Kristen has quarters and nickels. How many ways can she buy a ticket for 35¢?

Ⓕ 1 way   Ⓗ 3 ways

Ⓖ 2 ways   Ⓙ 4 ways

19. Lee buys some candy for 40¢. He only has nickels. How many nickels does he need?

Ⓐ 4 nickels

Ⓑ 5 nickels

Ⓒ 7 nickels

Ⓓ 8 nickels

20. Jan wants to buy a glass of juice for 50¢. How many dimes does she need?

Ⓕ 2 dimes

Ⓖ 3 dimes

Ⓗ 4 dimes

Ⓙ 5 dimes

STOP

Write the answer.

1. How many cents are in a quarter?

_____ ¢

2. How many cents are in a dime?

_____ ¢

3. Count. How much money?

_____ ¢

4. Circle the set of coins with the greatest value.

5. Circle the penny.

GO ON

6. Count. How much money?

_____ ¢

7. Circle the nickel.

8. Circle the set of coins with the greatest value.

9. Circle the toy that costs the most.

20¢

22¢

31¢

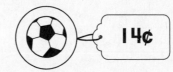

14¢

10. Circle the set of coins with the least value.

GO ON ➡

11. Circle the set of coins with the least value.

12. Count. How much money?

$ _____

13. Circle the toy that costs the least.

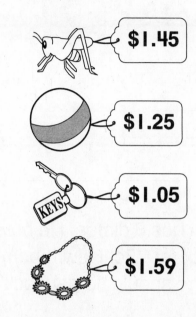

$1.45

$1.25

$1.05

$1.59

14. Count. How much money?

_____ ¢

15. Count. How much money?

_____ ¢

GO ON

16. Count. How much money?

$ _____

19. Lee buys some candy for 40¢. He only has nickels. How many nickels does he need?

_____ nickels

Solve.

17. Byron has 8 dimes. He buys a drink for 75¢. How much change should he get back?

_____ ¢

20. Jan wants to buy a glass of juice for 50¢. How many dimes does she need?

_____ dimes

---

18. Kristen has quarters and nickels. How many ways can she buy a ticket for 35¢?

_____ ways

STOP

Chapter-5 Teacher Interview

Core Concept: *Adding 2-Digit Numbers and Money Amounts*

Student Activity: The student demonstrates an understanding of adding two 2-digit numbers and three 2-digit numbers (including money amounts totaling less than $1), with and without regrouping. Have a collection of small objects, tens models and ones models, and a number line available for student use. Ask the student questions such as, "What is the sum of 15 + 26?"

Teacher Question 1:

◎ What is the sum of 15 + 26?

Understanding Student Response	Practice and Improvement
Student finds an incorrect sum.	Review lesson 2 to reinforce addition facts. Find the sum together using counters. Assign practice from **Facts Practice** after lesson 1.
Student does not know when to regroup, or does not regroup correctly.	Review lessons 5 and 6 to show how to use place-value models to add ones. Ask the student to trade ten ones for a ten and then put it in the tens place to be counted.

Teacher Question 2:

◎ There are 19 boys and 17 girls in Ms. Rivera's room. How many students does she have in all?

Understanding Student Response	Practice and Improvement
Student does not know how to proceed.	Review lesson 7 to help students choose the correct procedure (addition) for solving the problem. Use counters or a number line to arrive at the total.
Student does not realize regrouping is necessary, or does not know how to carry it out.	Review regrouping from lesson 5. Have the student put 19 red counters and 17 green counters in 1 pile and then separate them into groups of 10. Count and write the number 36.

Teacher Question 3:

◎ Sayeed spent 1 quarter on crackers, 3 dimes on a carton of milk, and 3 nickels on a pencil. How much money did he spend in all?

Understanding Student Response	Practice and Improvement
Student is not able to write the money amounts from the information given.	Review lesson 1, Chapter 4, to convert the value of the coins and write down the problem.
Student is confused with the regrouping because of dealing with three addends.	Review lesson 12 and then use counters or the number line to perform the addition; then use real or realistic play coins to further illustrate the result.

Chapter-5 Journal Writing

Encourage students to generate their own journal entries related to math ideas in general or to concepts in this chapter. Present the following journal prompt and have students share their drawing/writing with a partner:

◎ Mr. Salimi's class went on a nature hike at the reservoir. They saw 12 birds, 8 turtles, and 16 fish. How many animals did they see in all? Explain how to estimate the number first and then find the exact answer. Was your estimate close?

(Responses should describe rounding to the nearest ten and adding mentally. Students may want to sketch the animals first and then do an exact count, but encourage them to estimate and then report on how near they came to the exact count.)

FOLLOW UP

To follow up, review the concept of adding 2 digit numbers and regrouping. Ask students to think of anytime that day when they had to add groups of items (for example, the cost of buying two snacks at lunchtime.)

Have the student pretend that they will be going on a field trip tomorrow with another 2nd grade class. They will need to bring 58 sandwiches, 18 bananas, 17 oranges, 23 peaches, 28 boxes of apple juice, 13 boxes of grape juice, and 17 boxes of fruit punch. Have the students answer how many pieces of fruit they will be bringing, how many boxes of juice they will be bringing, and how many items they will be bringing in all. Ask them to write about what they noticed with the sums. Students can then use the information to add in some other healthy snacks to bring on the trip.

Chapter-5 Monitoring Student Progress

☐ **Form A**   ☐ **Form B**

Student Name _____ Date _____

Directions: For each item that is answered incorrectly, cross out the item number. Then record the number of correct responses in the appropriate Student Score column. If the student has not met the Criterion Score for an objective, circle the student's score. Recommended assignments are listed in the Prescription Table on the next page.

Objective	Item Numbers	Criterion Score	Student Score
A. Add 2-digit numbers.	1, 5, 6, 8, 9, 14, 15, 16	7/8	/8
B. Add money amounts.	2, 10, 12, 13	3/4	/4
C. Add three 2-digit numbers.	3, 4, 7, 11	3/4	/4
D. Solving problems, including those that involve drawing a picture.	17, 18, 19, 20	3/4	/4
Total Test Score		16/20	/20
Total Percent Correct			%

Chapter-5 Prescription Table

The following chart correlates the tested objectives for this chapter to supplementary materials that meet the individual needs of the students. The Practice and Reteach pages are designed for students who need further instruction in the math concepts taught in this chapter. The Enrich pages are designed for students who need advanced challenges.

Objective	Practice	Reteach	Enrich
A. Add 2-digit numbers.	124, 127, 130, 133, 136, 139, 148	125, 128, 131, 134, 137, 140, 149	126, 129, 132, 135, 138, 141, 150
B. Add money amounts.	154	155	156
C. Add three 2-digit numbers.	157	158	159
D. Solving problems, including those that involve drawing a picture.	142–145	146–147	

Pages 151–153 involve estimating sums.

© McGraw-Hill School Division

Name_____

Choose the correct answer.

1. $46 + 20 =$ ▨

- Ⓐ 26
- Ⓑ 60
- Ⓒ 66
- Ⓓ 70

2. $17¢ + 28¢ =$ ▨

- Ⓕ 31¢
- Ⓖ 35¢
- Ⓗ 40¢
- Ⓙ 45¢

3.
$$\begin{array}{r} 34 \\ 4 \\ +26 \\ \hline \end{array}$$
▨

- Ⓐ 50
- Ⓒ 64
- Ⓑ 54
- Ⓓ 65

4.
$$\begin{array}{r} 27 \\ 23 \\ +31 \\ \hline \end{array}$$
▨

- Ⓕ 70
- Ⓖ 71
- Ⓗ 81
- Ⓙ 91

5. $30 + 60 =$ ▨

- Ⓐ 30
- Ⓑ 70
- Ⓒ 80
- Ⓓ 90

GO ON

6. $37 + 41 = $ ◼

- Ⓕ 16
- Ⓗ 76
- Ⓖ 70
- Ⓙ 78

7.
$$\begin{array}{r} 42 \\ 38 \\ +19 \\ \hline \end{array}$$
◼

- Ⓐ 87
- Ⓒ 98
- Ⓑ 89
- Ⓓ 99

8.
$$\begin{array}{r} 18 \\ +29 \\ \hline \end{array}$$
◼

- Ⓕ 37
- Ⓖ 38
- Ⓗ 47
- Ⓙ 48

9.
$$\begin{array}{r} 45 \\ +11 \\ \hline \end{array}$$
◼

- Ⓐ 11
- Ⓑ 34
- Ⓒ 56
- Ⓓ 92

10. $52¢ + 16¢ = $ ◼

- Ⓕ 28¢
- Ⓖ 64¢
- Ⓗ 68¢
- Ⓙ 78¢

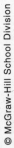© McGraw-Hill School Division

GO ON

11.
$$\begin{array}{r} 15 \\ 36 \\ + 25 \\ \hline \end{array}$$

Ⓐ 66   Ⓒ 86

Ⓑ 76   Ⓓ 96

12.
$$\begin{array}{r} 52¢ \\ + 36¢ \\ \hline \end{array}$$

Ⓕ 24¢   Ⓗ 88¢

Ⓖ 79¢   Ⓙ 98¢

13.
$$\begin{array}{r} 74¢ \\ + 19¢ \\ \hline \end{array}$$

Ⓐ 83¢   Ⓒ 93¢

Ⓑ 85¢   Ⓓ 94¢

14.
$$\begin{array}{r} 25 \\ + 6 \\ \hline \end{array}$$

Ⓕ 21

Ⓖ 28

Ⓗ 31

Ⓙ 32

15.
$$\begin{array}{r} 54 \\ + 5 \\ \hline \end{array}$$

Ⓐ 51

Ⓑ 57

Ⓒ 59

Ⓓ 60

16.

$$47$$
$$+ \ 33$$
$$\blacksquare$$

Ⓕ 70   Ⓗ 80

Ⓖ 74   Ⓙ 84

Solve.

17. On Tuesday, 18 boys and 16 girls visit the library. How many children visit the library in all?

Ⓐ 22 children

Ⓑ 27 children

Ⓒ 34 children

Ⓓ 40 children

18. There are 15 books about dogs and 12 books about cats on the shelf. How many books are on the shelf?

Ⓕ 3 books   Ⓗ 27 books

Ⓖ 13 books   Ⓙ 28 books

19. There are 10 children playing at the park. Then 18 more children join them. How many children are at the park in all?

Ⓐ 12 children

Ⓑ 28 children

Ⓒ 30 children

Ⓓ 38 children

20. Mr. Smith is at the store. He buys 12 red apples and 19 green apples. How many apples does he buy in all?

Ⓕ 20 apples

Ⓖ 21 apples

Ⓗ 27 apples

Ⓙ 31 apples

STOP

Write the correct answer.

1. 46 + 20 = _____

2. 17¢ + 28¢ = ____ ¢

3.
```
   34
    4
 + 26
```

4.
```
   27
   23
 + 31
```

5. 30 + 60 = _____

6. $37 + 41 =$ _____

9.
$$\begin{array}{r} 45 \\ + 11 \\ \hline \end{array}$$

7.
$$\begin{array}{r} 42 \\ 38 \\ + 19 \\ \hline \end{array}$$

10. $52¢ + 16¢ =$ ____ $¢$

8.
$$\begin{array}{r} 18 \\ + 29 \\ \hline \end{array}$$

GO ON

11.
```
   15
   36
+ 25
```

14.
```
   25
+   6
```

12.
```
   52¢
+ 36¢

    ¢
```

15.
```
   54
+   5
```

13.
```
   74¢
+ 19¢

    ¢
```

16.   47
          + 33

Solve.

17. On Tuesday, 18 boys and 16 girls visit the library. How many children are at the library?

_____ children

---

18. There are 15 books about dogs and 12 books about cats on the shelf. How many books are on the shelf?

_____ books

19. There are 10 children playing at the park. Then 18 more children join them. How many children are at the park in all?

_____ children

---

20. Mr. Smith is at the store. He buys 12 red apples and 19 green apples. How many apples does he buy in all?

_____ apples

STOP

Choose the correct answer.

1. $52 + 20 =$

- Ⓐ 9
- Ⓑ 32
- Ⓒ 72
- Ⓓ 90

2.
$$\begin{array}{r} 32¢ \\ + 29¢ \\ \hline \end{array}$$

- Ⓕ 17¢
- Ⓖ 51¢
- Ⓗ 61¢
- Ⓙ 71¢

---

3. $27 + 3 + 35 =$

- Ⓐ 55
- Ⓒ 62
- Ⓑ 60
- Ⓓ 65

4.
$$\begin{array}{r} 46 \\ 23 \\ + 17 \\ \hline \end{array}$$

- Ⓕ 23
- Ⓖ 85
- Ⓗ 86
- Ⓙ 96

---

5. $20 + 40 =$

- Ⓐ 20
- Ⓑ 40
- Ⓒ 60
- Ⓓ 70

GO ON

6. $43 + 51 =$ ▪

(F) 12 (H) 94

(G) 13 (J) 95

7.
$$\begin{array}{r} 35 \\ 29 \\ + 15 \\ \hline \end{array}$$
▪

(A) 34 (C) 79

(B) 69 (D) 80

8.
$$\begin{array}{r} 17 \\ + 18 \\ \hline \end{array}$$
▪

(F) 21

(G) 25

(H) 35

(J) 38

9.
$$\begin{array}{r} 64 \\ + 12 \\ \hline \end{array}$$
▪

(A) 13

(B) 52

(C) 66

(D) 76

10. $31¢ + 34¢ =$ ▪

(F) 38¢

(G) 41¢

(H) 65¢

(J) 66¢

GO ON

11.
$$
\begin{array}{r}
16 \\
25 \\
+ \ 35 \\
\hline
\end{array}
$$

Ⓐ 64   Ⓒ 76

Ⓑ 66   Ⓓ 86

12.
$$
\begin{array}{r}
73¢ \\
+ \ 24¢ \\
\hline
\end{array}
$$

Ⓕ 51¢   Ⓗ 97¢

Ⓖ 91¢   Ⓙ 98¢

13.
$$
\begin{array}{r}
54¢ \\
+ \ 28¢ \\
\hline
\end{array}
$$

Ⓐ 66¢   Ⓒ 82¢

Ⓑ 72¢   Ⓓ 92¢

14.
$$
\begin{array}{r}
22 \\
+ \ 7 \\
\hline
\end{array}
$$

Ⓕ 15

Ⓖ 19

Ⓗ 25

Ⓙ 29

15.
$$
\begin{array}{r}
52 \\
+ \ 6 \\
\hline
\end{array}
$$

Ⓐ 54

Ⓑ 56

Ⓒ 58

Ⓓ 59

GO ON ➤

16.

$$\begin{array}{r} 64 \\ + 19 \\ \hline \end{array}$$

Ⓕ 75 Ⓗ 83

Ⓖ 78 Ⓙ 84

Solve.

17. On Friday, 19 boys and 15 girls visit the library. How many children visit the library in all?

Ⓐ 16 children

Ⓑ 24 children

Ⓒ 34 children

Ⓓ 40 children

---

18. There are 14 books about dogs and 15 books about cats on the shelf. How many books are on the shelf?

Ⓕ 28 books Ⓗ 30 books

Ⓖ 29 books Ⓙ 39 books

19. There are 17 children playing at the park. Then 11 more children join them. How many children are at the park in all?

Ⓐ 14 children

Ⓑ 28 children

Ⓒ 30 children

Ⓓ 36 children

---

20. Mr. Smith is at the store. He buys 15 red apples and 28 green apples. How many apples does he buy in all?

Ⓕ 34 apples

Ⓖ 42 apples

Ⓗ 43 apples

Ⓙ 44 apples

STOP

Name _____

Write the correct answer.

1. $52 + 20 =$ _____

2.
$$
\begin{array}{r}
32¢ \\
+ 29¢ \\
\hline
¢
\end{array}
$$

3. $27 + 3 + 35 =$ ____

4.
$$
\begin{array}{r}
46 \\
23 \\
+ 17 \\
\hline
\end{array}
$$

5. $20 + 40 =$ _____

GO ON

6. $43 + 51 =$ _____

7.
$$
\begin{array}{r}
35 \\
29 \\
+\ 15 \\
\hline
\end{array}
$$

8.
$$
\begin{array}{r}
17 \\
+\ 18 \\
\hline
\end{array}
$$

9.
$$
\begin{array}{r}
64 \\
+\ 12 \\
\hline
\end{array}
$$

10. $31¢ + 34¢ =$ ____ ¢

GO ON

11.
```
   16
   25
 + 35
```

14.
```
   22
 +  7
```

12.
```
  73¢
+ 24¢

   ¢
```

15.
```
  52
+  6
```

13.
```
  54¢
+ 28¢

   ¢
```

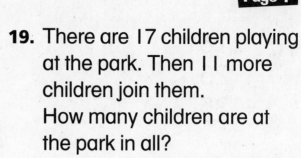
16.   64
          + 19

Solve.

17. On Friday, 19 boys and 15 girls visit the library. How many children are at the library?

_____ children

---

18. There are 14 books about dogs and 15 books about cats on the shelf. How many books are on the shelf?

_____ books

19. There are 17 children playing at the park. Then 11 more children join them. How many children are at the park in all?

_____ children

---

20. Mr. Smith is at the store. He buys 15 red apples and 28 green apples. How many apples does he buy in all?

_____ apples

STOP

© McGraw-Hill School Division

Chapter-6 Teacher Interview

Core Concept: *Subtracting 2-digit Numbers and Money Amounts*

Student will correctly subtract two 2-digit numbers (including money amounts totaling less than $1), with and without regrouping.

Student Activity: Work with student individually or in small groups. Have a collection of small objects, tens models and ones models, and a number line available for student to use.

Teacher Question 1:

What is the difference between 23 and 16?

Understanding Student Response	Practice and Improvement
Student does not know that difference means subtraction.	Review lesson 1 to review what "difference" means. If they do not know subtraction facts, assign practice from **Facts Practice** following lesson 1 and/or use number line.
Student does not know when to regroup, or does not regroup correctly.	Review lessons 3 to 5. Have the student make the number 23 with 2 tens models and 3 ones models. Next have the student exchange 1 tens model for 10 ones models. The student should remove 16 and count what is left to arrive at 7.

Teacher Question 2:

How can you tell when regrouping will be needed in subtraction? Give an example.

Understanding Student Response	Practice and Improvement
Student knows when regrouping is required, but does not know how to carry it out.	Review easy examples such as 21–19 from lessons 5 and 6. Have student use tens models and ones models to visualize the regrouping. Assign practice from lessons 5 and 6.
Student cannot give an example of when regrouping is necessary for subtraction.	Review lesson 3 and show examples of the ones place in the subtrahend being greater than the ones in the minuend. Show why it is necessary to regroup a 10 to allow subtraction.

Teacher Question 3:

A ballpoint pen costs 45¢ while a pencil costs 19¢. How much more does the pen cost than the pencil?

Understanding Student Response	Practice and Improvement
Student adds the numbers instead of subtracting the numbers.	Review lesson 11 to reinforce subtracting money amounts. Point out that subtraction is used when the question asks the difference between two prices.
Student subtracts correctly, but does not write the ¢ sign.	Review lesson 11 to remind student that since this is a money problem, the ¢ sign is required.

Chapter-6 Journal Writing

Encourage students to generate their own journal entries related to math ideas in general or to concepts in this chapter. Present the following journal prompt and have students share their drawing/writing with a partner:

⊚ Frankie read 76 pages of a book last week and Johnny read 59 pages. How many more pages did Frankie read? Tell how to solve this problem and then do the work. Write or draw your solution. Check your work.

(Responses should state that subtraction is the process required. Students may do the solution graphically. They may check their work by estimating, or by adding the exact difference to the subtrahend as in Lesson 9.)

FOLLOW UP

At the end of the day, review the concept of subtraction. Ask the students to think of any times that day when you or they had to use subtraction (for example, subtracting objects for a science experiment.)

For the next few days, have the class help take attendance. Each day write the number of students enrolled in the class. See how many students are absent. In their math journals, have the students construct a number sentence for the problem and solve it.

Chapter-6 Monitoring Student Progress

☐ **Form A**   ☐ **Form B**

Student Name _____ Date _____

Directions: For each item that is answered incorrectly, cross out the item number. Then record the number of correct responses in the appropriate Student Score column. If the student has not met the Criterion Score for an objective, circle the student's score. Recommended assignments are listed in the Prescription Table on the next page.

Objective	Item Numbers	Criterion Score	Student Score
A. Subtract 2-digit numbers.	2, 4, 5, 9, 10, 13, 14, 16	7/8	/8
B. Subtract money amounts.	1, 6, 8, 15	3/4	/4
C. Use addition to check subtraction.	3, 7, 11, 12	3/4	/4
D. Solve problems, including those that involve choosing the operation.	17, 18, 19, 20	3/4	/4
Total Test Score		16/20	/20
Total Percent Correct			%

Chapter-6 Prescription Table

The following chart correlates the tested objectives for this chapter to supplementary materials that meet the individual needs of the students. The Practice and Reteach pages are designed for students who need further instruction in the math concepts taught in this chapter. The Enrich pages are designed for students who need advanced challenges.

Objective	Practice	Reteach	Enrich
A. Subtract 2-digit numbers.	163, 166, 169, 172, 175, 178	164, 167, 170, 173, 176, 179	165, 168, 171, 174, 177, 180
B. Subtract money amounts.	193	194	195
C. Use addition to check subtraction.	187	188	189
D. Solve problems, including those that involve choosing the operation.	181–184	185–186	

Pages 190–192 involve estimating differences.

Choose the correct answer.

1.   83¢
       − 27¢

   Ⓐ 56¢

   Ⓑ 64¢

   Ⓒ 66¢

   Ⓓ 90¢

2. $57 - 10 = \blacksquare$

   Ⓕ 40

   Ⓖ 47

   Ⓗ 57

   Ⓙ 67

3. How can you add to check
$45 - 13 = 32$?

   Ⓐ $30 + 15 = 45$

   Ⓑ $32 - 13 = 19$

   Ⓒ $32 + 13 = 45$

   Ⓓ $45 + 32 = 77$

4.   65
       − 43

   Ⓕ 22

   Ⓖ 28

   Ⓗ 32

   Ⓙ 98

5. $80 - 30 = \blacksquare$

   Ⓐ 20

   Ⓑ 40

   Ⓒ 50

   Ⓓ 60

GO ON ▶

6.   50¢
     − 25¢

   Ⓕ 24¢   Ⓗ 35¢

   Ⓖ 25¢   Ⓙ 75¢

7. How can you add to check
36 − 9 = 27?

   Ⓐ 9 + 27 = 36

   Ⓑ 13 + 23 = 36

   Ⓒ 36 + 27 = 63

   Ⓓ 36 − 27 = 9

8.   68¢
     − 30¢

   Ⓕ 17¢   Ⓗ 90¢

   Ⓖ 38¢   Ⓙ 98¢

9. For which number sentence
do you need to regroup?

   Ⓐ 87 − 6 = 81

   Ⓑ 78 − 5 = 73

   Ⓒ 64 − 9 = 55

   Ⓓ 56 − 2 = 5

10.   74
      − 27

   Ⓕ 47

   Ⓖ 53

   Ⓗ 57

   Ⓙ 93

GO ON ➡

11. How can you add to check
83 − 57 = 26?

Ⓐ 26 + 57 = 83

Ⓑ 30 + 53 = 83

Ⓒ 83 − 26 = 57

Ⓓ 32 + 51 = 83

12. How can you add to check
90 − 46 = 44?

Ⓕ 46 − 44 = 2

Ⓖ 45 + 45 = 90

Ⓗ 46 + 44 = 90

Ⓙ 90 − 44 = 46

13. 58 − 39 = ▢

Ⓐ 19   Ⓒ 81

Ⓑ 29   Ⓓ 97

14.
$$\begin{array}{r} 43 \\ -\ 34 \\ \hline \end{array}$$

Ⓕ 9   Ⓗ 19

Ⓖ 17   Ⓙ 77

15.
$$\begin{array}{r} 34¢ \\ -\ 8¢ \\ \hline \end{array}$$

Ⓐ 26¢   Ⓒ 36¢

Ⓑ 32¢   Ⓓ 42¢

16.
$$\begin{array}{r} 37 \\ -\ 5 \\ \hline \end{array}$$

Ⓕ 22   Ⓗ 34

Ⓖ 32   Ⓙ 42

GO ON

Solve.

17. Chen plants 18 flower seeds and 24 tomato seeds. Which number sentence shows how many seeds she planted in all?

(A) $18 + 24 = 42$

(B) $42 - 18 = 24$

(C) $42 - 24 = 18$

(D) $42 + 18 = 60$

18. There are 24 crackers on a plate. Then 7 crackers are eaten. Which number sentence shows how many crackers are on the plate now?

(F) $7 + 17 = 24$

(G) $27 + 7 = 34$

(H) $24 - 7 = 17$

(J) $7 + 7 = 14$

19. There are 15 children in Mr. Brown's class who say red is their favorite color. There are 18 children who say blue is their favorite color. How many more children like blue than red?

(A) 3 children

(B) 15 children

(C) 18 children

(D) 33 children

20. There are 27 children picking up trash. Then 14 children leave. Now how many children are picking up trash?

(F) 11 children

(G) 13 children

(H) 19 children

(J) 21 children

STOP

Name _____

Write the answer.

1.
$$\begin{array}{r} 83¢ \\ -\ 27¢ \\ \hline ¢ \end{array}$$

4.
$$\begin{array}{r} 65 \\ -\ 43 \\ \hline \end{array}$$

2. $57 - 10 =$ _____

5. $80 - 30 =$ _____

3. Show how you can add to
check $45 - 13 = 32$.

_____

6.
$$\begin{array}{r} 50¢ \\ -\ 25¢ \\ \hline ¢ \end{array}$$

9. For which number sentence do you need to regroup? Circle the answer.

$$87 - 6 = 81$$

$$78 - 5 = 73$$

$$64 - 9 = 55$$

$$56 - 2 = 5$$

7. Show how you can add to check $36 - 9 = 27$.

_____

10.
$$\begin{array}{r} 74 \\ -\ 27 \\ \hline \end{array}$$

8.
$$\begin{array}{r} 68¢ \\ -\ 30¢ \\ \hline ¢ \end{array}$$

GO ON →

11. How can you add to check
83 − 57 = 26?

_____

_____

12. How can you add to check
90 − 46 = 44?

_____

_____

13. 58 − 39 = _____

14. 43
     − 34
     _____

15. 34¢
     − 8¢
     _____
        ¢

16. 37
     − 5
     _____

GO ON

Solve.

17. Chen plants 18 flower seeds and 24 tomato seeds. Which number sentence shows how many seeds she planted in all? Circle the answer.

$18 + 24 = 42$

$42 - 18 = 24$

$42 - 24 = 18$

$42 + 18 = 60$

18. There are 24 crackers on a plate. Then 7 crackers are eaten. Which number sentence shows how many crackers are on the plate now? Circle the answer.

$7 + 17 = 24$

$27 + 7 = 34$

$24 - 7 = 17$

$7 + 7 = 14$

19. There are 15 children in Mr. Brown's class who say red is their favorite color. There are 18 children who say blue is their favorite color. How many more children like blue than red?

_____ children

20. There are 27 children picking up trash. Then 14 children leave. Now how many children are picking up trash?

_____ children

© McGraw-Hill School Division

STOP

Choose the correct answer.

1.   63¢
      − 28¢

   Ⓐ 25¢

   Ⓑ 35¢

   Ⓒ 45¢

   Ⓓ 85¢

2. $65 - 10 =$ ▣

   Ⓕ 45

   Ⓖ 50

   Ⓗ 55

   Ⓙ 75

3. How can you add to check
$67 - 14 = 53$?

   Ⓐ $50 + 17 = 67$

   Ⓑ $53 + 14 = 67$

   Ⓒ $67 - 53 = 14$

   Ⓓ $67 + 14 = 81$

4.   85
      − 24

   Ⓕ 36

   Ⓖ 61

   Ⓗ 67

   Ⓙ 69

5. $90 - 20 =$ ▣

   Ⓐ 40

   Ⓑ 50

   Ⓒ 60

   Ⓓ 70

GO ON

6.   50¢
       − 15¢

  (F) 24¢   (H) 35¢

  (G) 25¢   (J) 65¢

7. How can you add to check
44 − 8 = 36?

  (A) 44 + 36 = 80

  (B) 36 + 8 = 44

  (C) 39 + 5 = 44

  (D) 36 − 8 = 28

8.   76¢
       − 20¢

  (F) 46¢   (H) 56¢

  (G) 54¢   (J) 96¢

9. For which number sentence
do you need to regroup?

  (A) 65 − 3 = 62

  (B) 89 − 8 = 81

  (C) 57 − 6 = 51

  (D) 74 − 7 = 67

10.   86
        − 39

  (F) 47

  (G) 53

  (H) 55

  (J) 57

GO ON ➡

© McGraw-Hill School Division

11. How can you add to check
92 − 48 = 44?

(A) 38 + 54 = 92

(B) 48 + 44 = 92

(C) 52 + 40 = 92

(D) 92 − 44 = 48

12. How can you add to check
80 − 52 = 28?

(F) 46 + 34 = 80

(G) 52 + 28 = 80

(H) 80 − 28 = 52

(J) 72 + 10 = 82

13. 87 − 49 = ▨

(A) 28 (C) 42

(B) 38 (D) 48

14.
$$54$$
$$- 35$$

(F) 19 (H) 29

(G) 21 (J) 89

15.
$$43¢$$
$$- 7¢$$

(A) 26¢ (C) 46¢

(B) 36¢ (D) 50¢

16. 48 − 6 = ▨

(F) 32 (H) 42

(G) 38 (J) 44

Solve.

17. Kayla plants 14 flower seeds and 37 tomato seeds. Which number sentence shows how many seeds she planted in all?

Ⓐ $37 - 14 = 23$

Ⓑ $14 + 37 = 51$

Ⓒ $51 - 14 = 37$

Ⓓ $51 + 14 = 65$

18. There are 32 crackers on a plate. Then 9 are eaten. Which number sentence shows how many crackers are on the plate now?

Ⓕ $32 - 9 = 23$

Ⓖ $23 - 9 = 14$

Ⓗ $23 + 9 = 32$

Ⓙ $9 - 9 = 0$

19. There are 20 children in Mr. Chester's class who say green is their favorite color. There are 15 children who say yellow is their favorite color. How many more children like green than yellow?

Ⓐ 5 children

Ⓑ 15 children

Ⓒ 20 children

Ⓓ 35 children

20. There are 24 children picking up trash. Then 19 children leave. Now how many children are picking up trash?

Ⓕ 5 children

Ⓖ 8 children

Ⓗ 11 children

Ⓙ 15 children

STOP

Write the answer.

1.
$$
\begin{array}{r}
63¢ \\
- 28¢ \\
\hline
¢
\end{array}
$$

2. $65 - 10 =$ _____

3. How can you add to check
$67 - 14 = 53$?

_____

4.
$$
\begin{array}{r}
85 \\
- 24 \\
\hline
\end{array}
$$

5. $90 - 20 =$ _____

GO ON

6.
$$
\begin{array}{r}
50¢ \\
- 15¢ \\
\hline
¢
\end{array}
$$

7. Show how you can add to check $44 - 8 = 36$.

_____

8.
$$
\begin{array}{r}
76¢ \\
- 20¢ \\
\hline
¢
\end{array}
$$

9. For which number sentence do you need to regroup? Circle the answer.

$65 - 3 = 62$

$89 - 8 = 81$

$57 - 6 = 51$

$74 - 7 = 67$

_____

10.
$$
\begin{array}{r}
86 \\
- 39 \\
\hline
\end{array}
$$

GO ON

11. Show how you can add to check $92 - 48 = 44$.

_____

_____

12. Show how you can add to check $80 - 52 = 28$.

_____

_____

13. $87 - 49 =$ _____

14. $\begin{array}{r} 54 \\ -\ 35 \\ \hline \end{array}$

_____

15. $\begin{array}{r} 43¢ \\ -\ 7¢ \\ \hline ¢ \end{array}$

_____

16. $48 - 6 =$ _____

Solve.

17. Kayla plants 14 flower seeds and 37 tomato seeds. Which number sentence shows how many seeds she planted in all? Circle the answer.

$37 - 14 = 23$

$14 + 37 = 51$

$51 - 14 = 37$

$51 + 14 = 65$

18. There are 32 crackers on a plate. Then 9 crackers are eaten. Which number sentence shows how many crackers are on the plate now?

$32 - 9 = 23$

$23 - 9 = 14$

$23 + 9 = 32$

$9 - 9 = 0$

19. There are 20 children in Mr. Chester's class who say green is their favorite color. There are 15 children who say yellow is their favorite color. How many more children like green than yellow?

_____ children

20. There are 24 children picking up trash. Then 19 children leave. Now how many children are picking up trash?

_____ children

STOP

Chapters 1–6 Performance Assessment

School Supply Sale

◎ **Target Skill:** Solve problems that involve money

◎ **Additional Skills:** Identify coins and bills and their value; add money amounts; subtract money amounts; compare money amounts; add two and three 2-digit numbers.

Task Description: This task requires students to select items from a list to purchase with $12.50. They are to spend as much of the money as they can.

Preparing: You may wish to have students list items that they think are needed in a classroom. Explain that they will be trying to get as much for the classroom as possible with $12.50. Stress that this does not necessarily mean the greatest number of items. They should try to spend as close to $12.50 as they can, without going over.

Materials	Group Size	Time on Task
Paper Pencil Play money (optional)	2 to 3 students	1–2 days

Guiding: Remind students that they can purchase multiples of any item. If students finish early, suggest to students that they try a different variety of items.

Observing/ Monitoring: As you move among the students, pose the following questions:

How do you know you added the costs correctly?

How do you decide if you can buy something else or not?

Chapters 1–6 Performance Assessment Scoring Rubric

School Supply Sale

Score	Explanation
3	Students demonstrate an efficient strategy and a thorough approach that enables them to solve the problem completely. Students may: ⦿ include money amounts and the number of items to be purchased with the total being exactly or close to $12.50. Students are able to complete the problem quickly and have all of the above correct solutions.
2	Students demonstrate a strategy that enables them to solve most of the problem correctly. The strategy is somewhat disorganized, making it less efficient. A solution is found, but errors are contained. Students may: ⦿ be unable to get total close to $12.50, but all calculations are correct; ⦿ get total close to $12.50, but are not organized. Students may have some difficulty determining all solutions correctly but demonstrate an understanding of general concepts.
1	Students demonstrate a confused strategy, which leads to difficulty solving the problem. Most answers are incorrect, but students demonstrate knowledge of at least one concept being assessed. Students may: ⦿ add some money amounts; OR ⦿ make a reasonable list of items without costs.

School Supply Sale

You will need

- a pencil

- a piece of paper

- play money (optional)

Liam is the class treasurer. One of his jobs is to buy classroom supplies. He has $12.50 to spend on items for his classroom.

The store has the following items for sale.

Pencils	**. . . . . 50¢ each**
Erasers	**. . . . . 25¢ each**
Folders	**. . . . . 75¢ each**
Notepads	**. . $1.25 each**
Markers	**. . . $2.30 each**

Use the sign shown above.

1. Make a list or table of possible supplies.

2. Show the total cost.

Remember, Liam may buy more than one of any item. Liam must spend as much of the money as possible.

Chapters 1–6 Monitoring Student Progress Cumulative Test 2

Student Name _____ Date _____

Directions: This test targets selected objectives. For each item that is answered incorrectly, cross out the item number. Then record the number of correct responses for each strand in the column labeled **Number of Correct Responses**. Add to find the **Total Number of Correct Responses** and record the total. Use this total to determine the **Total Test Score** and the **Total Percent Correct**.

Strand • Objective(s)	Item Numbers	Number of Correct Responses
Number Sense		
⦿ Add, facts to 12.	1	
⦿ Subtract, facts to 12.	2	
⦿ Add, facts to 20.	5	
⦿ Count, read, write, and represent numbers to 100.	4	
⦿ Identify coins and bills; and their value.	6, 8	
⦿ Give the value of a set of coins or a set of bills and coins.	3, 13	
⦿ Compare money amounts.	11	
⦿ Add 2-digit numbers.	7, 16	
⦿ Add money amounts.	14	
⦿ Add three 2-digit numbers.	12	
⦿ Subtract 2-digit numbers.	10, 15	
⦿ Subtract money amounts.	9	
Mathematical Reasoning		
⦿ Solve problems, including those that involve writing number sentences.	18	
⦿ Solve problems, including those that involve money and acting it out.	20	
⦿ Solve problems, including those that involve addition and drawing a picture.	19	
⦿ Solve problems, including those that involve choosing the operation.	17	
Total Number of Correct Responses		
Total Test Score		/20
Total Percent Correct		%

© McGraw-Hill School Division

Choose the correct answer.

1. $4 + 6 = $ ■

   (A) 12

   (B) 11

   (C) 10

   (D) 9

2.
$$\begin{array}{r} 12 \\ -\ 5 \\ \hline \end{array}$$
■

   (F) 6   (H) 8

   (G) 7   (J) 9

3. How much money is shown?

   (A) 83¢   (C) 93¢

   (B) 88¢   (D) 98¢

4. What number does the picture show?

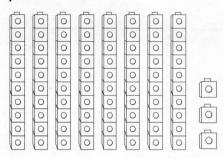

   (F) 11

   (G) 38

   (H) 73

   (J) 83

5.
$$\begin{array}{r} 5 \\ +\ 8 \\ \hline \end{array}$$

   (A) 11

   (B) 12

   (C) 13

   (D) 14

GO ON

6. How many cents are in a quarter?

- Ⓕ 5¢
- Ⓗ 25¢
- Ⓖ 10¢
- Ⓙ 50¢

7.
$$18 + 63$$

- Ⓐ 71
- Ⓒ 82
- Ⓑ 81
- Ⓓ 711

8. Stan pays 65¢ for an ice cream cone.
Which coins does he use?

- Ⓕ 2 quarters, 1 nickel
- Ⓖ 2 quarters, 5 pennies
- Ⓗ 1 half dollar, 1 nickel
- Ⓙ 1 half dollar, 3 nickels

9.
$$59¢ - 38¢$$

- Ⓐ 11¢
- Ⓑ 21¢
- Ⓒ 31¢
- Ⓓ 97¢

10. $70 - 20 = \blacksquare$

- Ⓕ 40
- Ⓖ 50
- Ⓗ 60
- Ⓙ 90

GO ON

11. Which set of coins has the least value?

13. How much money is shown?

Ⓐ 63¢   Ⓒ 75¢

Ⓑ 66¢   Ⓓ 90¢

---

12.   34
          41
        + 19

Ⓕ 84

Ⓖ 85

Ⓗ 94

Ⓙ 95

---

14.   46¢
        + 38¢

Ⓕ 12¢   Ⓗ 75¢

Ⓖ 74¢   Ⓙ 84¢

---

15.   82
        − 51

Ⓐ 30

Ⓑ 31

Ⓒ 32

Ⓓ 33

GO ON

16. $26 + 52 = $ ■

(F) 34 (H) 74

(G) 38 (J) 78

Solve.

17. There are 15 stickers on the table. Erin puts all but 7 of them in a book.
How many stickers does Erin put in her book?

(A) 7 (C) 15

(B) 8 (D) 22

---

18. Debbie is planting 12 tulip seeds and 23 daffodil seeds in a garden.
Which number sentence shows how many seeds she is planting in all?

(F) $35 - 12 = 23$

(G) $23 - 12 = 11$

(H) $35 + 12 = 47$

(J) $12 + 23 = 35$

19. Today 19 boys and 14 girls will visit the farm.
How many children will visit the farm in all?

(A) 23 children

(B) 32 children

(C) 33 children

(D) 34 children

---

20. Cameron has 7 dimes.
He bought a drink for 60¢.
How much money will he have left?

(F) 1¢ left

(G) 10¢ left

(H) 13¢ left

(J) 67¢ left

STOP

Chapter-7 Teacher Interview

Core Concept: *Telling Time and Finding the Duration of Various Intervals of Time*

Student Activity: The student demonstrates an understanding of reading analog clocks and using addition and subtraction to state durations of time. Have worksheets with analog clock faces available for the student, as well as worksheets of current calendar pages. A demonstration clock is desirable. Ask the student questions such as, "What is another name for quarter past 8 in the morning?"

Teacher Question 1:

◉ What is another name for quarter past 8 in the morning?

Understanding Student Response	Practice and Improvement
Student says "8:15," but does not add "A.M."	Review lesson 3 to point out that since 8:15 occurs twice each day, they must specify A.M. or P.M. to be correct.
Student gives an incorrect response, such as "8:30" or "7:45."	Review lesson 3 to prompt the student for the meaning of "quarter past." Have the student count 15 minutes on an analog clock face and draw hands to illustrate 8:15.

Teacher Question 2:

◉ Here is a calendar showing that today is Wednesday, October 4th (or whatever the current date is). One week from today, what will be the date?

Understanding Student Response	Practice and Improvement
Student does not know that one week in the future will be the same day of the week as today.	Review lesson 8 to remind the student that one week contains 7 days. Have the student note that seven days will be the same day of the week as today. Give other examples.
Student knows that it will be Wednesday, but cannot give the date.	Review lesson 8 to point out that since today is the 4th and a week contains 7 days, one week will be Wednesday, the (4 + 7)th or the 11th. Practice items like those following lesson 8.

Teacher Question 3:

◉ If Khalid can do 10 arithmetic problems in 10 minutes, how many can he do in a half-hour?

Understanding Student Response	Practice and Improvement
Student does not know that there are 30 minutes in a half-hour.	Review lessons 1-4 to help the student see that there are 30 minutes in a half-hour. Ask how many problems Khalid can do in 30 minutes.
Student knows there are 30 minutes in a half-hour, but does not see that Khalid can do one problem each minute, hence 30 problems in 30 minutes.	Review lessons 1-4 to help students determine how many problems Khalid can do in 5 minutes, 20 minutes, and other durations leading up to 30 minutes. Create additional items for practice and improvement.

Chapter-7 Journal Writing

Encourage students to generate their own journal entries related to math ideas in general or to concepts in this chapter. Present the following journal prompt and have students share their drawing/writing with a partner:

⑥ Dorothy practices her music lessons for 20 minutes in the morning and 20 minutes in the afternoon on Monday, Wednesday, and Friday. How many hours does she practice in a week?

(Responses should state that adding the numbers of minutes is the process required. Students may solve the problem by using a demonstration clock or by drawing on an analog clock face. Students should convert the total minutes to hours, and should be able to explain how they arrived at a solution.)

FOLLOW UP

At the end of the day, review the concept of time and of elapsed time. Ask students to think of a time when they used a clock today (for example, knowing when it was time for music.)

Have the students show what time they have special classes, like art and music, on analog clocks. Have them skip count by fives to figure out how long each class lasts. Add the times together. Students should show all of their work in their journals and share their entry with a math partner.

© McGraw-Hill School Division

Chapter-7 Monitoring Student Progress

☐ Form A   ☐ Form B

Student Name _____ Date _____

Directions: For each item that is answered incorrectly, cross out the item number. Then record the number of correct responses in the appropriate Student Score column. If the student has not met the Criterion Score for an objective, circle the student's score. Recommended assignments are listed in the Prescription Table on the next page.

Objective	Item Numbers	Criterion Score	Student Score
A. Tell and write time to 5-minute intervals.	1, 10, 12, 15	3/4	/4
B. Read a calendar.	5, 6, 7, 8	3/4	/4
C. Know relationships of time.	2, 4, 9, 11	3/4	/4
D. Find elapsed time.	3, 13, 14, 16	3/4	/4
E. Solve problems, including those that involve acting it out.	17, 18, 19, 20	3/4	/4
Total Test Score		15/20	/20
Total Percent Correct			%

Chapter-7 Prescription Table

The following chart correlates the tested objectives for this chapter to supplementary materials that meet the individual needs of the students. The Practice and Reteach pages are designed for students who need further instruction in the math concepts taught in this chapter. The Enrich pages are designed for students who need advanced challenges.

Objective	Practice	Reteach	Enrich
A. Tell and write time to 5-minute intervals.	199, 202, 205	200, 203, 206	201, 204, 207
B. Read a calendar.	220	221	222
C. Know relationships of time.	208	209	210
D. Find elapsed time.	217	218	219
E. Solve problems, including those that involve acting it out.	211–214	215–216	

Choose the correct answer.

1. What time does the clock show?

- Ⓐ 12:00
- Ⓑ 12:20
- Ⓒ 4:00
- Ⓓ 4:12

2. How many minutes are in a half hour?

- Ⓕ 5 minutes
- Ⓖ 15 minutes
- Ⓗ 30 minutes
- Ⓙ 60 minutes

3. How many hours have passed?

- Ⓐ 1 hour
- Ⓒ 3 hours
- Ⓑ 2 hours
- Ⓓ 4 hours

4. What is the same as 60 minutes?

- Ⓕ one second
- Ⓖ a quarter hour
- Ⓗ a half hour
- Ⓙ one hour

GO ON

Name _____

Use the calendar to answer exercises 5–8.

April 2002

Sun	Mon	Tues	Wed	Thurs	Fri	Sat
				1	2	3
4	5	6	7	8	9	10
11	12	13	14	15	16	17
18	19	20	21	22	23	24
25	26	27	28	29	30	

5. On which day of the week is April 1?

Ⓐ Sunday   Ⓒ Tuesday

Ⓑ Monday   Ⓓ Thursday

6. What is the date of the second Tuesday in April?

Ⓕ April 8   Ⓗ April 13

Ⓖ April 12   Ⓙ April 15

7. How many days are there between April 15 and April 26?

Ⓐ 8 days   Ⓒ 10 days

Ⓑ 9 days   Ⓓ 11 days

8. How many days are there in April?

Ⓕ 28 days   Ⓗ 30 days

Ⓖ 29 days   Ⓙ 31 days

9. How many minutes are in a quarter hour?

Ⓐ 5 minutes

Ⓑ 10 minutes

Ⓒ 15 minutes

Ⓓ 30 minutes

10. What time does the clock show?

Ⓕ 4:35   Ⓗ 7:04

Ⓖ 5:35   Ⓙ 7:20

GO ON ▶

11. What is the same as 60 seconds?

Ⓐ one minute

Ⓑ a quarter hour

Ⓒ a half hour

Ⓓ one hour

12. What time does the clock show?

Ⓕ 3:55

Ⓖ 10:15

Ⓗ 11:15

Ⓙ 12:15

13. How many hours have passed?

Ⓐ 2 hours   Ⓒ 5 hours

Ⓑ 3 hours   Ⓓ 7 hours

14. How many hours have passed?

Ⓕ 2 hours   Ⓗ 4 hours

Ⓖ 3 hours   Ⓙ 10 hours

15. What time does the clock show?

Ⓐ 1:35

Ⓑ 2:35

Ⓒ 7:05

Ⓓ 12:35

16. How many hours have passed?

Ⓕ 1 hour   Ⓗ 3 hours

Ⓖ 2 hours   Ⓙ 4 hours

GO ON

Solve.

17. Mrs. Ahart's class puts on puppet shows. Each show is 30 minutes long. How many minutes does it take to put on 2 puppet shows?

Ⓐ 30 minutes

Ⓑ 40 minutes

Ⓒ 50 minutes

Ⓓ 60 minutes

18. It takes 10 minutes to tell one puppet story. How long does it take to tell 3 puppet stories?

Ⓕ 10 minutes

Ⓖ 20 minutes

Ⓗ 30 minutes

Ⓙ 40 minutes

19. The puppets sing in the puppet show. It takes 4 minutes to sing each song. How long does it take to sing 5 puppet songs?

Ⓐ 5 minutes

Ⓑ 10 minutes

Ⓒ 20 minutes

Ⓓ 25 minutes

20. The students eat lunch at 12:30. They finish 30 minutes later. At what time do they finish?

Ⓕ 12:00

Ⓖ 12:30

Ⓗ 1:00

Ⓙ 1:30

STOP

Write the answer.

1. What time does the clock show?

_____ : _____

2. How many minutes are in a half hour?

_____ minutes

3. How many hours have passed?

_____ hour(s)

4. Circle the answer that is the same as 60 minutes.

one second

a quarter hour

a half hour

one hour

GO ON ▶

Use the calendar to answer exercises 5–8.

April 2002

Sun	Mon	Tues	Wed	Thurs	Fri	Sat
				1	2	3
4	5	6	7	8	9	10
11	12	13	14	15	16	17
18	19	20	21	22	23	24
25	26	27	28	29	30	

5. On which day of the week is April 1?

_____

6. What is the date of the second Tuesday in April?

_____

7. How many days are there between April 15 and April 26?

_____ days

8. How many days are there in April?

_____ days

9. How many minutes are in a quarter hour?

_____ minutes

10. What time does the clock show?

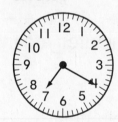

_____ : _____

11. Circle the answer that is the same as 60 seconds.

one minute

a quarter hour

a half hour

one hour

12. What time does the clock show?

_____ : _____

13. How many hours have passed?

_____ hours

14. How many hours have passed?

_____ hours

15. What time does the clock show?

_____ : _____

16. How many hours have passed?

_____ hours

GO ON

Solve.

17. Mrs. Ahart's class puts on puppet shows. Each show is 30 minutes long. How many minutes does it take to put on 2 puppet shows?

_____ minutes

18. It takes 10 minutes to tell one puppet story. How long does it take to tell 3 puppet stories?

_____ minutes

19. The puppets sing in the puppet show. It takes 4 minutes to sing each song. How long does it take to sing 5 puppet songs?

_____ minutes

20. The students eat lunch at 12:30. They finish 30 minutes later. At what time do they finish?

_____ : _____

STOP

Choose the correct answer.

1. What time does the clock show?

(A) 12:00

(B) 12:20

(C) 7:00

(D) 7:12

2. How many minutes are in one hour?

(F) 1 minute

(G) 15 minutes

(H) 30 minutes

(J) 60 minutes

3. How many hours have passed?

(A) 1 hour (C) 3 hours

(B) 2 hours (D) 4 hours

4. What is the same as 30 minutes?

(F) one second

(G) a half hour

(H) a quarter hour

(J) one hour

GO ON

Use the calendar to answer exercises 5–8.

June 2002

Sun	Mon	Tues	Wed	Thurs	Fri	Sat
					1	2
3	4	5	6	7	8	9
10	11	12	13	14	15	16
17	18	19	20	21	22	23
24	25	26	27	28	29	30

5. On which day of the week is June 1?

Ⓐ Sunday   Ⓒ Tuesday

Ⓑ Monday   Ⓓ Friday

6. What is the date of the third Tuesday in June?

Ⓕ June 8   Ⓗ June 15

Ⓖ June 14   Ⓙ June 19

7. How many days are there between June 16 and June 27?

Ⓐ 8 days   Ⓒ 10 days

Ⓑ 9 days   Ⓓ 27 days

8. How many days are there in June?

Ⓕ 28 days   Ⓗ 30 days

Ⓖ 29 days   Ⓙ 31 days

9. How many seconds are there in one minute?

Ⓐ 1 second

Ⓑ 15 seconds

Ⓒ 30 seconds

Ⓓ 60 seconds

10. What time does the clock show?

Ⓕ 4:40   Ⓗ 8:20

Ⓖ 5:40   Ⓙ 9:20

GO ON ➡

11. What is the same as 15 minutes?

Ⓐ one minute

Ⓑ a quarter hour

Ⓒ a half hour

Ⓓ one hour

12. What time does the clock show?

Ⓕ 3:45

Ⓖ 9:15

Ⓗ 10:15

Ⓙ 11:15

13. How many hours have passed?

Ⓐ 2 hours Ⓒ 5 hours

Ⓑ 3 hours Ⓓ 7 hours

14. How many hours have passed?

Ⓕ 2 hours Ⓗ 4 hours

Ⓖ 3 hours Ⓙ 10 hours

15. What time does the clock show?

Ⓐ 1:35

Ⓑ 3:35

Ⓒ 4:25

Ⓓ 5:25

16. How many hours have passed?

Ⓕ 1 hour Ⓗ 3 hours

Ⓖ 2 hours Ⓙ 4 hours

GO ON

Solve.

17. Mrs. Jackson's class puts on puppet shows. Each show is 20 minutes long. How many minutes does it take to put on 3 puppet shows?

Ⓐ 30 minutes

Ⓑ 40 minutes

Ⓒ 50 minutes

Ⓓ 60 minutes

18. It takes 5 minutes to tell one puppet story. How long does it take to tell 3 puppet stories?

Ⓕ 10 minutes

Ⓖ 15 minutes

Ⓗ 20 minutes

Ⓙ 30 minutes

19. The puppets sing in the puppet show. It takes 10 minutes to sing each song. How long does it take to sing 2 puppet songs?

Ⓐ 5 minutes

Ⓑ 10 minutes

Ⓒ 20 minutes

Ⓓ 25 minutes

20. The students eat lunch at 12:30. They finish 30 minutes later. At what time do they finish?

Ⓕ 12:00

Ⓖ 12:30

Ⓗ 1:00

Ⓙ 1:30

STOP

© McGraw-Hill School Division

Write the answer.

1. What time does the clock show?

_____ : _____

2. How many minutes are in one hour?

_____ minutes

3. How many hours have passed?

_____ hour(s)

4. Circle the answer that is the same as 30 minutes.

one second

a quarter hour

a half hour

one hour

Use the calendar to answer exercises 5–8.

June 2002

Sun	Mon	Tues	Wed	Thurs	Fri	Sat
					1	2
3	4	5	6	7	8	9
10	11	12	13	14	15	16
17	18	19	20	21	22	23
24	25	26	27	28	29	30

5. On which day of the week is June 1?

_____

6. What is the date of the third Thursday in June?

_____

7. How many days are there between June 16 and June 27?

_____ days

8. How many days are in June?

_____ days

9. How many seconds are there in one minute?

_____ seconds

10. What time does the clock show?

_____ : _____

11. Circle the time that is the same as 15 minutes.

one minute

a quarter hour

a half hour

one hour

GO ON

© McGraw-Hill School Division

12. What time does the clock show?

_____ : _____

13. How many hours have passed?

_____ hours

14. How many hours have passed?

_____ hours

15. What time does the clock show?

_____ : _____

16. How many hours have passed?

_____ hours

GO ON

Solve.

17. Mrs. Jackson's class puts on puppet shows. Each show is 20 minutes long. How many minutes does it take to put on 3 puppet shows?

_____ minutes

18. It takes 5 minutes to tell one puppet story. How long does it take to tell 3 puppet stories?

_____ minutes

19. The puppets sing in the puppet show. It takes 10 minutes to sing each song. How long does it take to sing 2 puppet songs?

_____ minutes

20. The students eat lunch at 12:30. They finish 30 minutes later. At what time do they finish?

_____ : _____

STOP

Chapter-8 Teacher Interview

Core Concept: *Recording Data in Graphs; Reading and Interpreting Graphs*

Student Activity: The student will demonstrate an understanding of making graphs and interpreting data presented in graphic form. Have graph paper, crayons or markers, pencils, and scratch paper available for the student. Ask the student questions such as, "What is the difference between a pictograph and a bar graph?"

Teacher Question 1:

☺ Ms. Tollefsen's class made a pictograph in which a small square represents 10 books. If the "animal stories" category showed 3 of these small squares, how many books are represented?

Understanding Student Response	Practice and Improvement
Student does not know what a pictograph is and how it represents data.	Review lesson 1 to explain pictographs and how each square represents 10 books. Have the student skip count by 10s for the squares to find how many books. Ask the student to recalculate based on 1 square = 2 books.
Student understands that one square means 10 books, but cannot interpret 3 squares.	Review lesson 1. Have the student assume each square = 2 books, then skip count to find 6 books. Go back and skip count by 10s to get 30.

Teacher Question 2:

☺ What is the difference between a pictograph and a bar graph?

Understanding Student Response	Practice and Improvement
Student is unable to explain how a pictograph and bar graph differ.	Review lessons 1 and 3 to clarify that in pictographs, each picture represents a certain number of things, while in bar graphs, the length of a bar shows how many.
Student confuses the graph types, or "mixes up" the ways of displaying data.	Review lessons 1, 3, and 6. Point out that the same data can be shown by either method, but that it may be easier to read a bar graph.

Teacher Question 3:

☺ How can you find the range of a set of data?

Understanding Student Response	Practice and Improvement
Student does not understand the term range.	Review lesson 7 to point out that the range is simply the difference between the greatest and least numbers in the set of data.
Student confuses the range and the mode.	Review lesson 7 and discuss the difference between range and mode.

Chapter-8 Journal Writing

Encourage students to generate their own journal entries related to math ideas in general or to concepts in this chapter. Present the following journal prompt and have students share their drawing/writing with a partner:

◎ Imagine that you are going to make a pictograph showing how many books your class has read over a whole year. You want to show how many adventure books, biographies, mysteries, and so on have been read. How will you collect the data? What would be a good picture to use? How many books should each picture stand for?

(Responses should describe several categories of books. The picture suggested should be appropriate. One way of collecting data would be to survey the class; another would be to put every learner's name on a chart and put a tally mark for every book read. Have students sketch what the pictograph might look like in their journals.)

FOLLOW UP

At the end of the day, review the concept of representing quantities with pictures. Ask students to think of classroom activities other than reading that might be recorded on a pictograph or bar graph. Have students draw some symbols that would represent those activities, and share with their math partners.

Have students think of out-of-school events that could be shown graphically, and propose ways to record and interpret the data. Students should share their pictures and stories with a math partner.

Chapter-8 Monitoring Student Progress

☐ Form A   ☐ Form B

Student Name _____ Date _____

Directions: For each item that is answered incorrectly, cross out the item number. Then record the number of correct responses in the appropriate Student Score column. If the student has not met the Criterion Score for an objective, circle the student's score. Recommended assignments are listed in the Prescription Table on the next page.

Objective	Item Numbers	Criterion Score	Student Score
A. Read and interpret graphs.	5, 6, 7, 8	3/4	/4
B. Record numerical data in systematic ways.	1, 2, 3, 4	3/4	/4
C. Represent the same data set in more than one way.	9, 10, 11, 12	3/4	/4
D. Identify range and mode.	13, 14, 15, 16	3/4	/4
E. Solve problems, including those that involve making a table.	17, 18, 19, 20	3/4	/4
Total Test Score		15/20	/20
Total Percent Correct			%

Chapter-8 Prescription Table

The following chart correlates the tested objectives for this chapter to supplementary materials that meet the individual needs of the students. The Practice and Reteach pages are designed for students who need further instruction in the math concepts taught in this chapter. The Enrich pages are designed for students who need advanced challenges.

Objective	Practice	Reteach	Enrich
A. Read and interpret graphs.	226, 232	227, 233	228, 234
B. Record numerical data in systematic ways.	229	230	231
C. Represent the same data set in more than one way.	241	242	243
D. Identify range and mode.	244	245	246
E. Solve problems, including those that involve making a table.	235–238	239–240	

Choose the correct answer.

Use the data from the chart to answer items 1, 2, and 3.

Favorite Recess Activity

swings	IIII
tag	JHH I
kickball	JHH III
seesaw	JHH

1. How many children voted for kickball?

Ⓐ 10 children

Ⓑ 8 children

Ⓒ 6 children

Ⓓ 4 childen

2. How many more children chose the seesaw than the swings?

Ⓕ 4 more

Ⓖ 3 more

Ⓗ 2 more

Ⓙ 1 more

3. Which activity was chosen the most?

Ⓐ tag

Ⓑ swings

Ⓒ seesaw

Ⓓ kickball

4. Jerry brought lunch to school 4 days this month. Which group of tally marks shows how many days Jerry brought lunch to school?

Ⓕ IIII

Ⓖ JHH

Ⓗ JHH I

Ⓙ JHH II

GO ON

Use the graph below to answer items 5, 6, 7, and 8. The graph shows how many minutes three friends ride their bikes on Saturday mornings.

Saturday Morning Bike Rides

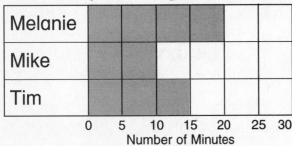

Number of Minutes

5. How many minutes in all do the three friends ride on Saturday morning?

Ⓐ 60 minutes

Ⓑ 55 minutes

Ⓒ 50 minutes

Ⓓ 45 minutes

6. Mike rides his bike for 10 minutes more after lunch. Which bar shows how much time he rides altogether?

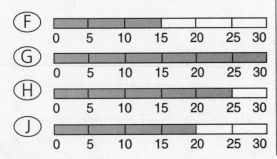

7. Tim rides his bike for 15 minutes more after lunch. Which bar shows how much time he rides altogether?

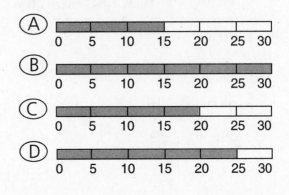

8. Melanie rides her bike for 5 minutes more after lunch. Which bar shows how much time she rides altogether?

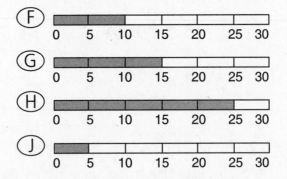

GO ON ▶

Sam and Janet took a survey. They asked their classmates which snack they liked best. Then they showed the data in a tally chart and a graph. Use the data to answer items 9–12.

Favorite Snacks

Apples	ЖЖ |||
Carrots	|||
Crackers	||||
Popcorn	ЖЖ ЖЖ

Favorite Snacks

Apples	o o o o o o o o
Carrots	o o o
Crackers	o o o o
Popcorn	o o o o o o o o o o

Each o stands for 1 vote.

9. How many children voted for carrots?

Ⓐ 2   Ⓒ 4

Ⓑ 3   Ⓓ 5

10. How many children voted for crackers?

Ⓕ 6   Ⓗ 4

Ⓖ 5   Ⓙ 3

11. How many more children voted for popcorn than apples?

Ⓐ 4   Ⓒ 2

Ⓑ 3   Ⓓ 1

12. Which snack received 8 votes?

Ⓕ Apples   Ⓗ Crackers

Ⓖ Carrots   Ⓙ Popcorn

In five swim meets Billy swam this many laps.
1 7 6 6 5

13. What is the greatest and the least number of laps he swam?

Ⓐ 7, 1   Ⓒ 6, 1

Ⓑ 7, 5   Ⓓ 5, 1

GO ON

14. What is the range of the numbers?

- Ⓕ 7
- Ⓗ 5
- Ⓖ 6
- Ⓙ 1

15. Which number is shown more than once?

- Ⓐ 7
- Ⓒ 5
- Ⓑ 6
- Ⓓ 2

16. What is the mode of the numbers?

- Ⓕ 7
- Ⓗ 5
- Ⓖ 6
- Ⓙ 2

Fill in the table. Then answer items 17–20.

Sally is saving money for a gift. She saved $3 in week 1 and $2 in week 2. She saved $5 in week 3 and $4 in week 4.

Sally's Gift Money

Week	1	2	3	4
How Much				

17. How much money does Sally save during week 2?

- Ⓐ $8
- Ⓒ $2
- Ⓑ $6
- Ⓓ $3

18. How much more money does Sally save in week 3 than in week 1?

- Ⓕ $9
- Ⓗ $5
- Ⓖ $6
- Ⓙ $2

19. Sally has enough money to buy a gift that costs which amount?

- Ⓐ $20
- Ⓒ $15
- Ⓑ $18
- Ⓓ $12

20. How much money did Sally save in all?

- Ⓕ $15
- Ⓗ $11
- Ⓖ $14
- Ⓙ $8

STOP

Name _____

Write the correct answer.

Use the data from the chart to answer items 1, 2, and 3.

Favorite Recess Activity

swings	||||
tag	ЖІ
kickball	Ж |||
seesaw	Ж

1. How many children voted for kickball?

_____ children

2. How many more children chose the seesaw than the swings?

_____ more

3. Which activity was chosen the most?

_____

_____

4. Jerry brought lunch to school 4 days this month. Draw tally marks to show how many days Jerry brought lunch to school.

_____

GO ON

Use the graph below to answer items 5, 6, 7, and 8. The graph shows how many minutes three friends ride their bikes on Saturday mornings.

Saturday Morning Bike Rides

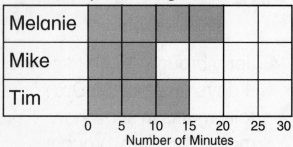

Number of Minutes

5. How many minutes in all do the three friends ride on Saturday morning?

_____ minutes

6. Mike rides his bike for 10 minutes more after lunch. Circle the bar that shows how much time he rides altogether.

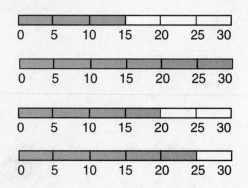

7. Tim rides his bike for 15 minutes more after lunch. Circle the bar that shows how much time he rides altogether.

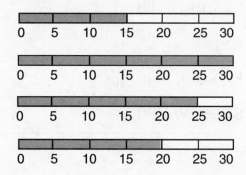

8. Melanie rides her bike for 5 minutes more after lunch. Circle the bar that shows how much time she rides altogether.

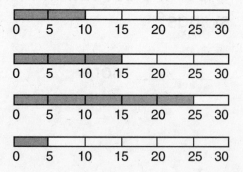

GO ON

Sam and Janet took a survey. They asked their classmates which snack they liked best. Then they showed the data in a tally chart and a graph. Use the data to answer items 9–12.

Favorite Snacks

Apples	ЖΙ ΙΙΙ
Carrots	ΙΙΙ
Crackers	ΙΙΙΙ
Popcorn	ЖΙ ЖΙ

Favorite Snacks

Apples	o o o o o o o o
Carrots	o o o
Crackers	o o o o
Popcorn	o o o o o o o o o o

Each o stands for 1 vote.

9. How many children voted for carrots?

_____ children

10. How many children voted for crackers?

_____ children

11. How many more children voted for popcorn than apples?

_____ more children

12. Which snack received 8 votes?

_____

In five swim meets Billy swam this many laps.
Ι 7 6 6 5

13. What is the greatest and the least number of laps he swam?

Greatest number of laps: ____

Least number of laps: ____

14. What is the range of the numbers?

_____

15. Which number is shown more than once?

_____

16. What is the mode of the numbers?

_____

Fill in the table. Then answer items 17–20.
Sally is saving money for a gift. She saved $3 in week 1 and $2 in week 2. She saved $5 in week 3 and $4 in week 4.

Sally's Gift Money

Week	1	2	3	4
How Much				

17. How much money does Sally save during week 2?

$ _____

18. How much more money does Sally save in week 3 than in week 1?

$ _____

19. Which book does Sally have enough money to buy—$20, $18, $15, $12?

$ _____

20. How much money did Sally save in all?

$ _____

STOP

Choose the correct answer.

Use the data from the chart to answer items 1, 2, and 3.

Favorite Recess Activity

swings	|||
tag	~~||||~~
kickball	~~||||~~ ||
seesaw	||||

1. How many children voted for the seesaw?

Ⓐ 10 children

Ⓑ 8 children

Ⓒ 6 children

Ⓓ 4 children

2. How many more children chose kickball than the seesaw?

Ⓕ 4 more   Ⓗ 2 more

Ⓖ 3 more   Ⓙ 1 more

3. Which activity was chosen the least?

Ⓐ tag

Ⓑ swings

Ⓒ seesaw

Ⓓ kickball

4. Jerry brought lunch to school 6 days this month. Which group of tally marks shows how many days Jerry brought lunch to school?

Ⓕ |||| Ⓗ ~~||||~~ |

Ⓖ ~~||||~~   Ⓙ ~~||||~~ ||

Use the graph below to answer items 5, 6, 7, and 8. The graph shows how many minutes three friends swing on the swing set.

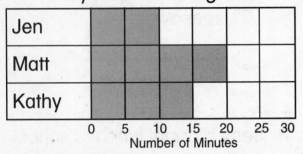

Playtime on Swing Set

Jen							
Matt							
Kathy							

0   5   10   15   20   25   30
Number of Minutes

5. How many minutes in all do the three friends swing on the swing set?

Ⓐ 15 minutes

Ⓑ 30 minutes

Ⓒ 45 minutes

Ⓓ 60 minutes

6. Kathy plays on the swings for 5 more minutes after school. Which bar shows how much she plays on the swings altogether?

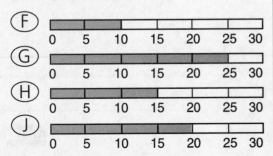

7. Jen plays on the swings for 10 more minutes after school. Which bar shows how much Jen plays on the swings altogether?

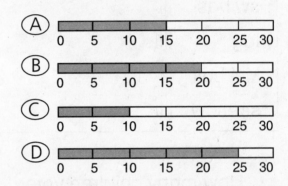

8. Matt plays on the swings for 5 minutes more after school. Which bar shows how much he plays on the swings altogether?

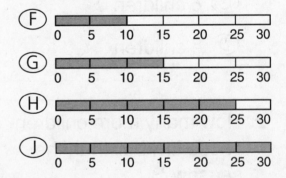

© McGraw-Hill School Division

GO ON

Joey and Lucy took a survey. They asked their classmates which snack they liked best. Then they showed the data in a tally chart and a graph. Use the data to answer items 9–12.

Favorite Snacks

Oranges	IIII
Grapes	JHH IIII
Pretzels	JHH I
Bananas	JHH II

Favorite Snacks

Oranges	o o o o
Grapes	o o o o o o o o o
Pretzels	o o o o o o
Bananas	o o o o o o o

Each o stands for 1 vote.

9. How many children voted for oranges?

Ⓐ 3   Ⓒ 5

Ⓑ 4   Ⓓ 6

10. How many children voted for grapes?

Ⓕ 6   Ⓗ 8

Ⓖ 7   Ⓙ 9

11. How many more children voted for bananas than pretzels?

Ⓐ 5   Ⓒ 2

Ⓑ I   Ⓓ 6

12. Which snack received 6 votes?

Ⓕ oranges   Ⓗ pretzels

Ⓖ grapes   Ⓙ bananas

In five swim meets Billy swam this many laps.
2 7 6 5 5

13. What is the greatest and the least number of laps he swam?

Ⓐ 7, 2   Ⓒ 6, 2

Ⓑ 7, 5   Ⓓ 5, 2

GO ON

14. What is the range of the numbers?

(F) 7　　　(H) 5

(G) 6　　　(J) 1

15. Which number is shown more than once?

(A) 7　　　(C) 5

(B) 6　　　(D) 2

16. What is the mode of the numbers?

(F) 7　　　(H) 5

(G) 6　　　(J) 2

Fill in the table. Then answer items 17–20.
Sally is saving money for a gift. She saved $1 in week 1 and $3 in week 2. She saved $8 in week 3 and $6 in week 4.

Sally's Gift Money

Week	1	2	3	4
How Much				

17. How much money did Sally save during week 2?

(A) $8　　　(C) $5

(B) $6　　　(D) $3

18. How much more money did Sally save in week 3 than in week 2?

(F) $9　　　(H) $4

(G) $5　　　(J) $1

19. During which week did Sally save the least amount of money?

(A) Week 4

(B) Week 3

(C) Week 2

(D) Week 1

20. How much money did Sally save in all?

(F) $20　　　(H) $12

(G) $18　　　(J) $8

STOP

Write the answer.

Use the data from the chart to answer items 1, 2, and 3.

Favorite Recess Activity

swings				
tag	~~				~~
kickball	~~||||~~ ||
seesaw					

1. How many children voted for the seesaw?

_____ children

2. How many more children chose kickball than the seesaw?

_____ more children

3. Which activity was chosen the least?

_____

4. Jerry brought lunch to school 6 days this month. Draw tally marks to show how many days Jerry brought lunch to school.

_____

Use the graph below to answer items 5, 6, 7, and 8. The graph shows how many minutes three friends swing on the swing set.

Playtime on Swing Set

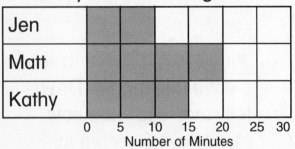

Number of Minutes

5. How many minutes in all do the three friends swing on the swing set?

_____ minutes

6. Kathy plays on the swings for 5 more minutes after school. Circle the bar that shows how much time she plays on the swings all together.

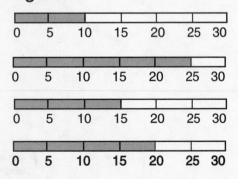

7. Jen plays on the swings for 10 more minutes after school. Circle the bar that shows how much Jen plays on the swings all together.

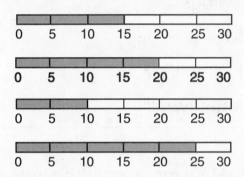

8. Matt plays on the swings for 5 minutes more after school. Circle the bar that shows how much he plays on the swings all together.

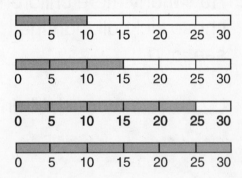

GO ON ➡

Joey and Lucy took a survey. They asked their classmates which snack they liked best. Then they showed the data in a tally chart and a graph. Use the data to answer items 9–12.

Favorite Snacks

Oranges	IIII
Grapes	卌 IIII
Pretzels	卌 I
Bananas	卌 II

Favorite Snacks

Oranges	o o o o
Grapes	o o o o o o o o
Pretzels	o o o o o o
Bananas	o o o o o o o

Each o stands for 1 vote.

9. How many children voted for oranges?

_____ children

10. How many children voted for grapes?

_____ children

11. How many more children voted for bananas than pretzels?

_____ more

12. Which snack received 6 votes?

_____

In five swim meets Billy swam this many laps.
2 7 6 5 5

13. What is the greatest and the least number of laps he swam?

Greatest number of laps: __

Least number of laps: __

GO ON

14. What is the range of the numbers?

_____

_____

15. Which number is shown more than once?

_____

_____

16. What is the mode of the numbers?

_____

_____

Fill in the table. Then answer items 17–20.

Sally is saving money for a gift. She saved $1 in week 1 and $3 in week 2. She saved $8 in week 3 and $6 in week 4.

Sally's Gift Money

Week	1	2	3	4
How Much				

17. How much money did Sally save during week 2?

$ _____

_____

18. How much more money did Sally save in week 3 than in week 2?

$ _____

_____

19. During which week did Sally save the least amount of money?

_____

_____

20. How much money did Sally save in all?

$ _____

STOP

Chapter-9 Teacher Interview

Core Concept: *Measuring Length, Weight, Capacity, Perimeter, and Area; Reading Temperatures*

Student Activity: The student will demonstrate an understanding of measuring length, weight, capacity, perimeter and area, and reading temperatures. Have yardsticks and/or meter sticks (so student can measure in inches or centimeters), pencils, and paper available for student use. Ask the student questions such as, "What is the best tool to use to measure the length of your family's car?"

Teacher Question 1:

Sam and Rose have put 3 cups of water into a bottle. Does the bottle hold more than a pint?

Understanding Student Response	Practice and Improvement
Student says there is not enough information to tell.	Review lesson 3 to compare cups and pints. Ask the student if more information is needed. Point out that 2 cups = 1 pint, so the bottle must hold more than 1 pint. Assign examples like those following lesson 3.
Student says that the bottle does not hold more than a pint.	Review lesson 3, in which it is noted that 2 cups = 1 pint. Point out that if Sam and Rose have put more than 2 cups into it, it must hold more than a pint.

Teacher Question 2:

What is the perimeter of a photo that is 3 inches wide and 5 inches high?

Understanding Student Response	Practice and Improvement
Student says "15 square units" or some other value indicating an attempt to calculate area.	Review lesson 5, including the definition of "perimeter." Have student cut out a 3" × 5" piece of paper, and measure. Then show how to find perimeter as (2 × length) + (2 × width).
Student says "8 inches," adding length and width values but not for all sides.	Use procedure above, reinforcing the idea that perimeter means to measure around all sides.

Teacher Question 3:

What is the best tool to use to measure the length of your family's car?

Understanding Student Response	Practice and Improvement
Student identifies an inappropriate tool (such as thermometer or measuring cup).	Review lesson 2 and the concept of length. Assign practice from items at end of lesson 2.
Student identifies an inappropriate tool for measuring length (such as an inch or centimeter ruler).	Review lesson 2 and give examples of what you may measure in inches (pencil) or in feet (a desk). Point out that it is better to use a measuring tool closer to the length of the object to be measured, such as a yardstick or meter stick. (A measuring tape is an acceptable tool as well.)

Chapter-9 Journal Writing

Encourage students to generate their own journal entries related to math ideas in general or to concepts in this chapter. Present the following journal prompt and have students share their drawing/writing with a partner:

⟡ How good are you at estimating length? Estimate the length of three classroom items, and have your math partner measure them with a ruler. Record your estimates and the measurements. Then have your partner estimate the length of three other items, while you measure them. Record these estimates and measurements, too. How could you improve your estimates?

(Make some common items available to students, such as crayons, chalk, chalkboard erasers, paper clips, books, etc. Students should record the discrepancies between their estimates and actual measurements in their journals. Vary the units of measurement between metric and customary units, and ask students which are easiest to use and why.)

FOLLOW UP

At the end of the day, review the basic measurement concepts, such as beginning measurement with the end of the ruler, measuring to the nearest whole (or half) unit, using successive measurements to measure something longer than the ruler, etc. Ask students to label their measurements appropriately in inches, centimeters, etc.

Ask students to think of when estimates of linear measures are sufficient, and when accuracy is required. Students should share their writing and drawing with a math partner.

Chapter-9 Monitoring Student Progress

☐ Form A   ☐ Form B

Student Name _____ Date _____

Directions: For each item that is answered incorrectly, cross out the item number. Then record the number of correct responses in the appropriate Student Score column. If the student has not met the Criterion Score for an objective, circle the student's score. Recommended assignments are listed in the Prescription Table on the next page.

Objective	Item Numbers	Criterion Score	Student Score
A. Measure length in customary and metric units.	1, 2, 3, 4	3/4	/4
B. Measure weight, mass and capacity in customary and metric units.	5, 6, 7, 8	3/4	/4
C. Read temperatures.	9, 10, 11, 12	3/4	/4
D. Find the perimeter and area of a figure.	13, 14, 15,16	3/4	/4
E. Solve problems, including those that involve using guess and check.	17, 18, 19, 20	3/4	/4
Total Test Score		15/20	/20
Total Percent Correct			%

Chapter-9 Prescription Table

The following chart correlates the tested objectives for this chapter to supplementary materials that meet the individual needs of the students. The Practice and Reteach pages are designed for students who need further instruction in the math concepts taught in this chapter. The Enrich pages are designed for students who need advanced challenges.

Objective	Practice	Reteach	Enrich
A. Measure length in customary and metric units.	250, 253, 274	251, 254, 275	252, 255, 276
B. Measure weight, mass and capacity in customary and metric units.	256, 259, 277, 280, 286	257, 260, 278, 281, 287	258, 261, 279, 282, 288
C. Read temperatures.	283	284	285
D. Find the perimeter and area of a figure.	262, 265	263, 266	264, 267
E. Solve problems, including those that involve using guess and check.	268–271	272–273	

Choose the correct answer.

Find the length.

1.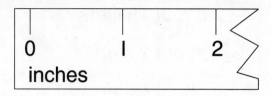

Ⓐ 4 inches

Ⓑ 3 inches

Ⓒ 2 inches

Ⓓ 1 inch

2.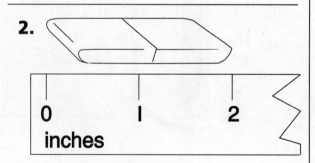

Ⓕ 5 inches

Ⓖ 4 inches

Ⓗ 3 inches

Ⓙ 2 inches

3.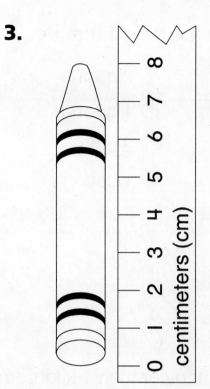

Ⓐ 10 cm   Ⓒ 8 cm

Ⓑ 9 cm   Ⓓ 7 cm

4.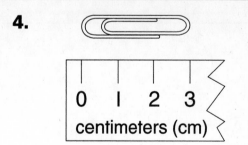

Ⓕ 4 cm   Ⓗ 2 cm

Ⓖ 3 cm   Ⓙ 1 cm

GO ON ➡

Choose the best estimate.

5.
- Ⓐ 2 quarts
- Ⓑ 1 quart
- Ⓒ 2 pints
- Ⓓ 1 cup

6.
- Ⓕ heavier than 1 kilogram
- Ⓖ about 1 kilogram
- Ⓗ lighter than 1 gram
- Ⓙ about 1 gram

7.
- Ⓐ more than 1 pound
- Ⓑ the same as 1 pound
- Ⓒ more than 1 ounce
- Ⓓ less than 1 ounce

8.
- Ⓕ about 15 liters
- Ⓖ about 2 liters
- Ⓗ about 1 liter
- Ⓙ less than 1 liter

What is the temperature?

9.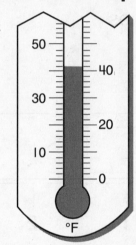
- Ⓐ 52°F
- Ⓑ 42°F
- Ⓒ 50°F
- Ⓓ 32°F

10.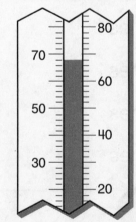
- Ⓕ 78°F
- Ⓖ 70°F
- Ⓗ 68°F
- Ⓙ 58°F

GO ON

11.

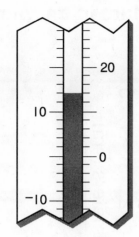

Ⓐ 20°C

Ⓑ 14°C

Ⓒ 10°C

Ⓓ 4°C

14.

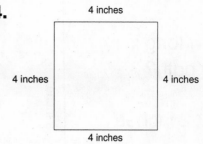

4 inches
4 inches   4 inches
4 inches

Ⓕ 20 in.   Ⓗ 12 in.

Ⓖ 16 in.   Ⓙ 4 in.

Find the area of each shape.

15.

Ⓐ 13 square units

Ⓑ 12 square units

Ⓒ 7 square units

Ⓓ 3 square units

12.

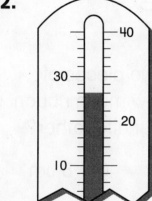

Ⓕ 36°C

Ⓖ 30°C

Ⓗ 26°C

Ⓙ 20°C

Find the perimeter of each shape.

13.

6 inches

2 inches   2 inches

6 inches

Ⓐ 20 inches

Ⓑ 18 inches

Ⓒ 16 inches

Ⓓ 8 inches

16.

Ⓕ 13 square units

Ⓖ 9 square units

Ⓗ 6 square units

Ⓙ 3 square units

GO ON

Solve.

17. How long is the path?

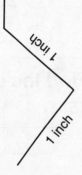

Ⓐ 2 inches

Ⓑ 3 inches

Ⓒ 4 inches

Ⓓ 5 inches

18. How long is the path?

Ⓕ 6 inches

Ⓖ 5 inches

Ⓗ 3 inches

Ⓙ 2 inches

Use this picture to answer 19–20.

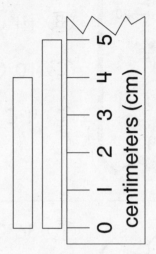

19. Amy cut two pieces of ribbon. How much ribbon did Amy cut altogether?

Ⓐ 81 cm   Ⓒ 8 cm

Ⓑ 9 cm   Ⓓ 4 cm

20. How much longer was one piece of ribbon than the other?

Ⓕ 1 cm   Ⓗ 3 cm

Ⓖ 2 cm   Ⓙ 4 cm

STOP

Write the answer.
Write the length.

1.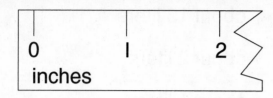

_____ inch

2.

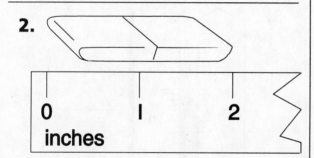

_____ inches

3.

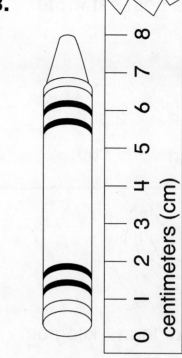

_____ cm

4.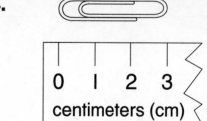

_____ cm

GO ON

Circle the best estimate.

5.

2 quarts   2 pints

1 quart   1 cup

6.

heavier than 1 kilogram

about 1 kilogram

lighter than 1 gram

about 1 gram

7.

more than 1 pound

about 1 pound

more than 1 ounce

less than 1 ounce

8.

about 15 liters

about 2 liters

about 1 liter

less than 1 liter

Write the temperature.

9.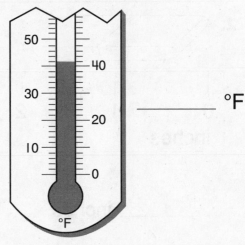

_____ °F

10.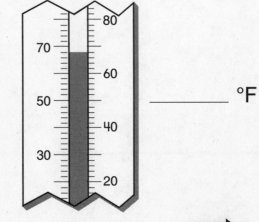

_____ °F

© McGraw-Hill School Division

GO ON

11.

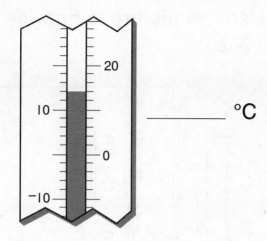

_____ °C

12.

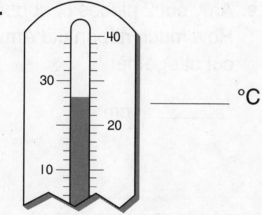

_____ °C

Find the perimeter of each shape.

13.

6 inches

2 inches   2 inches

6 inches

_____ inches

14.

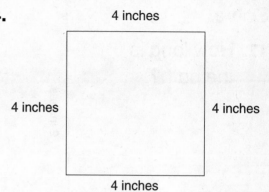

4 inches

4 inches   4 inches

4 inches

_____ inches

Find the area of each shape.

15.

_____ square units

16.

_____ square units

GO ON

Solve.

17. How long is the path?

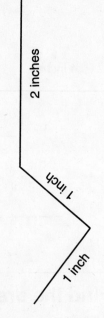

2 inches

1 inch

1 inch

_____ inches

18. How long is the path?

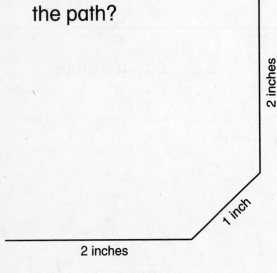

2 inches

1 inch

2 inches

_____ inches

Use this picture to answer 19–20.

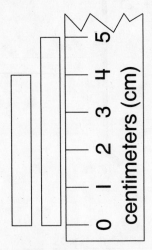

centimeters (cm)

19. Amy cut 2 pieces of ribbon. How much ribbon did Amy cut altogether?

_____ cm

20. How much longer was one piece of ribbon than the other?

_____ cm

STOP

● **Choose the answer.**

Find the length.

1.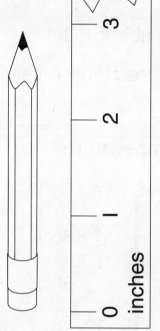

Ⓐ 4 inches

Ⓑ 3 inches

Ⓒ 2 inches

Ⓓ 1 inch

2.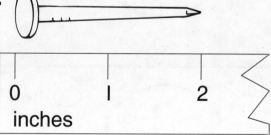

Ⓕ 5 inches

Ⓖ 4 inches

Ⓗ 3 inches

Ⓙ 2 inches

3.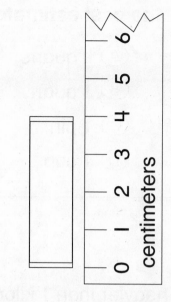

Ⓐ 6 cm   Ⓒ 4 cm

Ⓑ 5 cm   Ⓓ 3 cm

4.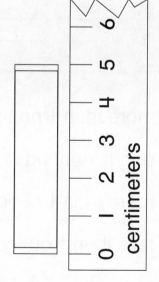

Ⓕ 9 cm   Ⓗ 5 cm

Ⓖ 8 cm   Ⓙ 6 cm

 GO ON

Choose the best estimate.

5.

- Ⓐ 4 quarts
- Ⓑ I quart
- Ⓒ I pint
- Ⓓ I cup

6.

- Ⓕ heavier than I kilogram
- Ⓖ about I kilogram
- Ⓗ lighter than I kilogram
- Ⓙ about I gram

7.

- Ⓐ more than I pound
- Ⓑ about I pound
- Ⓒ more than I ounce
- Ⓓ less than I ounce

8.

- Ⓕ about 10 liters
- Ⓖ about 2 liters
- Ⓗ about I liter
- Ⓙ less than I liter

What is the temperature?

9.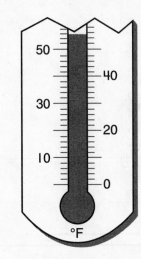

- Ⓐ 58°F
- Ⓑ 56°F
- Ⓒ 54°F
- Ⓓ 50°F

10.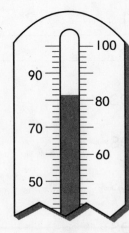

- Ⓕ 86°F
- Ⓖ 84°F
- Ⓗ 82°F
- Ⓙ 80°F

GO ON

11.

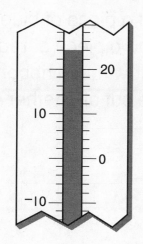

(A) 24°C

(B) 22°C

(C) 20°C

(D) 14°C

12.

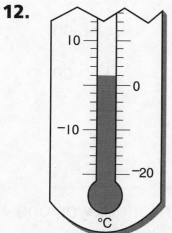

(F) 10°C

(G) 8°C

(H) 4°C

(J) 2°C

What is the perimeter?

13.

5 inches

1 inch   1 inch

5 inches

(A) 20 inches

(B) 12 inches

(C) 10 inches

(D) 8 inches

14.

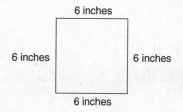

6 inches

6 inches   6 inches

6 inches

(F) 24 in.   (H) 20 in.

(G) 22 in.   (J) 12 in.

What is the area?

15.

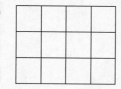

(A) 18 square units

(B) 16 square units

(C) 12 square units

(D) 8 square units

16.

(F) 25 square units

(G) 16 square units

(H) 10 square units

(J) 6 square units

GO ON

Solve.

17. How long is the path?

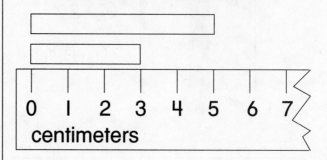

Ⓐ 2 inches

Ⓑ 3 inches

Ⓒ 4 inches

Ⓓ 6 inches

18. How long is the path?

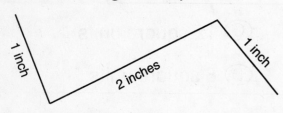

Ⓔ 3 inches

Ⓗ 4 inches

Ⓙ 6 inches

Ⓟ 8 inches

19. Annie cut a piece of blue ribbon and a piece of red ribbon. How much ribbon did Annie cut altogether?

```
    0   I   2   3   4   5   6   7
    centimeters
```

Ⓐ 8 cm   Ⓒ 6 cm

Ⓑ 7 cm   Ⓓ 5 cm

20. How much longer was one piece than the other?

Ⓔ I cm   Ⓗ 3 cm

Ⓘ 2 cm   Ⓟ 4 cm

© McGraw-Hill School Division

STOP

Write the answer.
Write the length.

1.

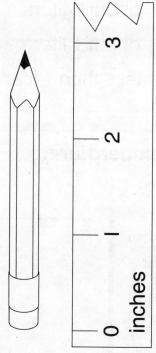

_____ inches

2.

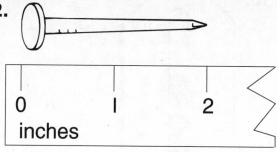

_____ inches

3.

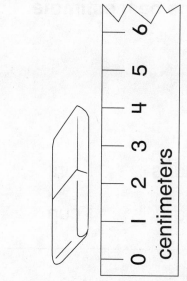

_____ centimeters

4.

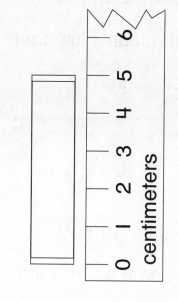

_____ centimeters

GO ON

Circle the best estimate.

5.

4 quarts   I pint

I quart   I cup

6.

heavier than I kilogram

about I kilogram

lighter than I kilogram

about I gram

7.

more than I pound

the same as I pound

more than I ounce

less than I ounce

8. about 10 liters

about 2 liters

about I liter

less than I liter

Write the temperature.

9. 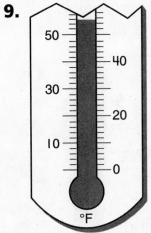 _____ °F

10. 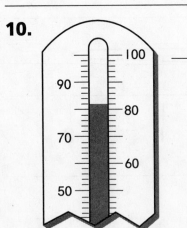 _____ °F

GO ON ➡

11. _____ °C

12. _____ °C

What is the perimeter?

13.

5 inches

1 inch | | 1 inch

5 inches

_____ inches

14.

6 inches

6 inches | | 6 inches

6 inches

_____ inches

What is the area?

15.

_____ square units

16.

_____ square units

GO ON

Solve.

17. How long is the path?

3 inches

1 inch

_____ inches

18. How long is the path?

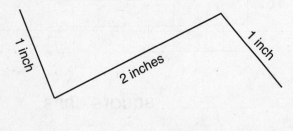

_____ inches

19. Annie cut two pieces of ribbon. How much ribbon did Annie cut altogether?

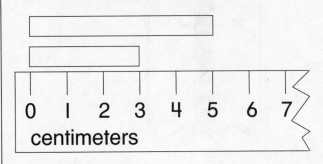

0 1 2 3 4 5 6 7

centimeters

_____ cm

20. How much longer was one piece than the other?

_____ cm

© McGraw-Hill School Division

STOP

Chapter-10 Teacher Interview

Core Concept: *Identifying and Describing Geometric Shapes*

Student Activity: The student will demonstrate an ability to identify common 2- and 3-dimensional figures, distinguish congruent and symmetrical figures, and use slides, flips, and turns of geometric figures. Have pencils and paper available for student use, along with several geometric shapes and solids.

Teacher Question 1:

What does it mean to say that two triangles are congruent?

Understanding Student Response	Practice and Improvement
Student cannot define congruent.	Review lesson 7 to point out that congruence requires the sides and angles of the two triangles to be exactly the same. Have student choose congruent shapes from manipulatives.
Student says that congruence requires the same size OR the same shape, but does not specify both.	Reinforce from lesson 7 that congruence means the figures are exactly the same in shape and size. Remind the student that all squares have the same shape but can be different sizes.

Teacher Question 2:

If you take 2 squares of the same size and place them next to each other, what figure results?

Understanding Student Response	Practice and Improvement
Student says a square.	Review the definition of "square" and "rectangle" as found in lesson 2. Have student use manipulatives to work out the idea that a rectangle will result.
Student guesses a figure other than a rectangle.	Review all of lesson 2, working with manipulatives or having student sketch figures on paper. Have student practice with all figures discussed in lesson 2.

Teacher Question 3:

How are the number of sides and the number of angles of triangles, squares, and other plane figures related?

Understanding Student Response	Practice and Improvement
Student does not know the shapes of various plane figures.	Review shapes shown in lesson 2. Have student sketch various plane figures, counting the sides and the angles in each. Reinforce with manipulatives.
Student states that there is no relationship, or give another incorrect response.	Use lesson 2 to prompt student to examine the sides and angles of figures as the basis of comparison.

Chapter-10 Journal Writing

Encourage students to generate their own journal entries related to math ideas in general or to concepts in this chapter. Present the following journal prompt and have students share their drawing/writing with a partner:

⊚ Draw one of each of these shapes in your journal: triangle, rectangle, pentagon, hexagon, octagon, trapezoid, and parallelogram. Think about your school, your home, and your town, and find examples of as many of those shapes as you can in those places. Work with your math partner and write these down.

(Responses should be fairly accurate. Some further prompting may be needed. Students may also look for examples in magazine advertisements, cut them out, and paste them in their journals.)

FOLLOW UP

At an appropriate time, have students discuss ways in which knowledge of shapes in the environment has value, such as in the shapes of traffic signs. Reinforce use of correct terminology in naming shapes.

Other activities may include combining or partitioning various shapes to form other shapes, such as flipping a trapezoid to form a hexagon, and counting the number of triangles formed by drawing diagonals of a square (there are 6!).

Chapter-10 Monitoring Student Progress

☐ Form A   ☐ Form B

Student Name _____ Date _____

Directions: For each item that is answered incorrectly, cross out the item number. Then record the number of correct responses in the appropriate Student Score column. If the student has not met the Criterion Score for an objective, circle the student's score. Recommended assignments are listed in the Prescription Table on the next page.

Objective	Item Numbers	Criterion Score	Student Score
A. Identify 3-dimensional figures and their attributes.	1, 4, 7, 10, 13,15	5/6	/6
B. Identify 2-dimensional figures and their attributes.	2, 5, 8, 11, 14, 16	5/6	/6
C. Identify congruent and symmetrical figures.	3, 6, 9, 12	3/4	/4
D. Solve problems, including those that involve acting it out.	17, 18, 19, 20	3/4	/4
Total Test Score		16/20	/20
Total Percent Correct			%

Chapter-10 Prescription Table

The following chart correlates the tested objectives for this chapter to supplementary materials that meet the individual needs of the students. The Practice and Reteach pages are designed for students who need further instruction in the math concepts taught in this chapter. The Enrich pages are designed for students who need advanced challenges.

Objective	Practice	Reteach	Enrich
A. Identify 3-dimensional figures and their attributes.	292, 295	293, 296	294, 297
B. Identify 2-dimensional figures and their attributes.	295, 298, 301	296, 299, 302	297, 300, 303
C. Identify congruent and symmetrical figures.	310, 313	311, 314	312, 315
D. Solve problems, including those that involve acting it out.	304–307	308–309	

Choose the correct answer.

1. Name the solid figure.

- Ⓐ cone
- Ⓒ cylinder
- Ⓑ cube
- Ⓓ pyramid

2. What is this figure?

- Ⓕ circle
- Ⓖ rectangle
- Ⓗ square
- Ⓙ triangle

3. Which shapes are congruent?

Ⓐ

Ⓑ

Ⓒ

Ⓓ

4. How many faces does this solid figure have?

- Ⓕ 8 faces
- Ⓖ 5 faces
- Ⓗ 6 faces
- Ⓙ 4 faces

5. Which of these figures is a quadrilateral?

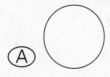
Ⓐ

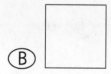
Ⓑ

Ⓒ

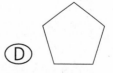
Ⓓ

GO ON

6. What is a matching part for the figure?

Ⓕ

Ⓖ ◯

Ⓗ ▱

Ⓙ ◺

7. How many edges does this solid figure have?

Ⓐ 16   Ⓒ 8

Ⓑ 12   Ⓓ 4

8. How many sides does this figure have?

Ⓕ 7   Ⓗ 6

Ⓖ 5   Ⓙ 4

9. Which shows a line of symmetry?

Ⓐ

Ⓑ

Ⓒ

Ⓓ ▢

10. How many vertices does this solid figure have?

Ⓕ 10   Ⓗ 6

Ⓖ 12   Ⓙ 8

11. What is this figure?

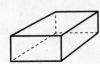

Ⓐ triangle

Ⓑ trapezoid

Ⓒ parallelogram

Ⓓ pentagon

 GO ON

12. Which shapes are congruent?

F

G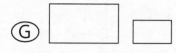

H

J

13. How many edges does this solid figure have?

Ⓐ 10 edges

Ⓑ 8 edges

Ⓒ 6 edges

Ⓓ 4 edges

14. How many angles does this figure have?

Ⓕ 6 angles   Ⓗ 5 angles

Ⓖ 4 angles   Ⓙ 3 angles

15. Name the solid figure.

Ⓐ cube   Ⓒ pyramid

Ⓑ cylinder   Ⓓ sphere

16. Which figure has 4 sides?

Ⓕ

Ⓖ

Ⓗ

Ⓙ

GO ON

Solve.

17. I have 3 sides and 3 angles. What am I?

Ⓐ circle

Ⓑ triangle

Ⓒ square

Ⓓ rectangle

18. I have 5 sides and 5 angles. What am I?

Ⓕ rectangle

Ⓖ hexagon

Ⓗ pentagon

Ⓙ trapezoid

19. How many of these triangles does it take to make this figure?

Ⓐ 4 triangles

Ⓑ 3 triangles

Ⓒ 2 triangles

Ⓓ I triangle

20. How many of these squares does it take to make this figure?

Ⓕ 4 squares

Ⓖ 3 squares

Ⓗ 2 squares

Ⓙ I square

STOP

Write the answer.

1. Name the solid figure.

_____

_____

2. What is this figure?

_____

_____

3. Circle the shapes that are congruent.

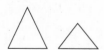

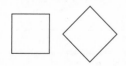

4. How many faces does this solid figure have?

_____ faces

_____

5. Which of these figures is a quadrilateral? Circle the figure.

GO ON

6. Circle the matching part for the figure.

7. How many edges does this solid figure have?

_____ edges

8. How many sides does this figure have?

_____ sides

9. Which shows a line of symmetry? Circle the figure.

10. How many vertices does this solid figure have?

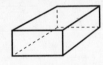

_____ vertices

11. What is this figure?

_____

GO ON

12. Circle the shapes that are congruent.

15. Name the solid figure.

_____

_____

13. How many edges does this solid figure have?

_____ edges

16. Which figure has 4 sides: a circle, a square, a triangle, or a pentagon?

_____

14. How many angles does this figure have?

_____ angles

Solve.

17. I have 3 sides and 3 angles. What am I?

_____

18. I have 5 sides and 5 angles. What am I?

_____

19. How many of these triangles does it take to make this figure?

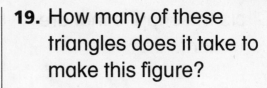

_____ triangles

20. How many of these squares does it take to make this figure?

_____ squares

STOP

Choose the correct answer.

1. Name the solid figure.

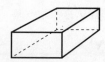

- Ⓐ cone
- Ⓑ rectangular prism
- Ⓒ cylinder
- Ⓓ pyramid

2. What is this figure?

- Ⓕ circle
- Ⓗ rectangle
- Ⓖ square
- Ⓙ triangle

3. Which shapes are congruent?

- Ⓐ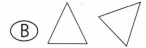
- Ⓑ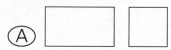
- Ⓒ
- Ⓓ

4. How many faces does this solid figure have?

- Ⓕ 2 faces
- Ⓖ 3 faces
- Ⓗ 4 faces
- Ⓙ 5 faces

5. Which of these figures is a quadrilateral?

- Ⓐ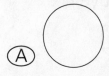
- Ⓑ
- Ⓒ
- Ⓓ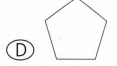

© McGraw-Hill School Division

GO ON

Name _____

6. What is a matching part for the figure?

F

G △

H ⬚

J ◿

7. How many edges does this solid figure have?

A 16   C 8

B 12   D 4

8. How many sides does this figure have?

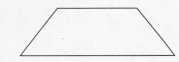

F 7   H 6

G 5   J 4

9. Which shows a line of symmetry?

A △

B ⏢

C ▢

D ▭

10. How many vertices does this solid figure have?

F 5   H 1

G 4   J 0

11. What is this figure?

A triangle

B trapezoid

C hexagon

D pentagon

GO ON

12. Which shapes are congruent?

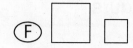 F

 G

 H

 J

13. How many edges does this solid figure have?

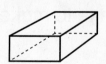

Ⓐ 12   Ⓒ 8

Ⓑ 10   Ⓓ 6

14. How many angles does this figure have?

Ⓕ 6   Ⓗ 4

Ⓖ 5   Ⓙ 3

15. Name the solid figure.

Ⓐ cube

Ⓑ cylinder

Ⓒ pyramid

Ⓓ sphere

16. Which figure has 3 sides?

 F

 G

 H

 J

GO ON

Solve.

17. I have 6 sides and 6 angles. What plane figure am I?

Ⓐ pentagon

Ⓑ triangle

Ⓒ square

Ⓓ hexagon

18. I have 4 sides and 4 angles. What plane figure am I?

Ⓕ rectangle

Ⓖ triangle

Ⓗ hexagon

Ⓙ circle

19. How many of these triangles does it take to make this figure?

Ⓐ 6 triangles

Ⓑ 5 triangles

Ⓒ 4 triangles

Ⓓ 3 triangles

20. How many of these squares does it take to make this figure?

Ⓕ 4 squares

Ⓖ 3 squares

Ⓗ 2 squares

Ⓙ I square

STOP

Write the answer.

1. Name the solid figure.

_____

2. What is this figure?

_____

3. Circle the shapes that are congruent.

4. How many faces does this solid figure have?

_____ faces

5. Which of these figures is a quadrilateral? Circle the figure.

6. Circle the matching part for the figure.

7. How many edges does this solid figure have?

_____ edges

8. How many sides does this figure have?

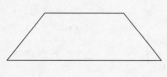

_____ sides

9. Which shows a line of symmetry? Circle the figure.

_____

10. How many vertices does this solid figure have?

_____ vertices

_____

11. What is this figure?

_____

GO ON ➡

12. Circle the shapes that are congruent.

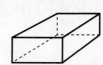

_____

13. How many edges does this solid figure have?

_____ edges

_____

14. How many angles does this figure have?

_____ angles

15. Name the solid figure.

_____

16. What figure has 3 sides?

_____

GO ON

Solve.

17. I have 6 sides and 6 angles. What plane figure am I?

_____

18. I have 4 sides and 4 angles. What plane figure am I?

_____

19. How many of these triangles does it take to make this figure?

_____ triangles

20. How many of these squares does it take to make this figure?

▭

_____ squares

STOP

Chapters 1–10 Performance Assessment

Picnic Plans

    ⊚ *Target Skill:*   Record numerical data in systematic ways.

    ⊚ *Additional Skills:* Create tally chart; solve problems that involve making a table and collecting data.

Task Description: This task requires students to ask 9 classmates which kind of fruit they would like for a picnic and to make a tally chart of this information. Students then need to decide which kind of fruit to bring and why.

Preparing: You may wish to have students list fruits that they know. Talk about how to decide which fruit to bring for a picnic.

Materials	Group Size	Time on Task
Pencil Paper for tally chart	1 to 2 students	1–2 days

Guiding: Suggest that the students collect all the data first and then create the tally chart once they know which kinds of fruit they will need to record.

Observing/ Monitoring: As you move among the students, pose the following questions:

How did you decide which fruit to bring?

Is there anything else you learned in class that can help you solve this problem?

Chapters 1–10 Performance Assessment Scoring Rubric

Picnic Plans

Score	Explanation
3	Students demonstrate an efficient strategy and a thorough approach that enables them to solve the problem completely. Students may: ⊚ include collected data from 9 classmates; ⊚ include an organized tally chart; ⊚ include a sentence that draws a conclusion from the information. Students are able to complete the problem quickly and have all of the above correct solutions.
2	Students demonstrate a strategy that enables them to solve most of the problem correctly. The strategy is somewhat disorganized, making it less efficient. A solution is found, but errors are contained. Students may: ⊚ make a tally chart that is missing some of the collected information; ⊚ make no decisions about the fruit or suggest that you purchase all the fruits. Students may have some difficulty determining all solutions correctly but demonstrate an understanding of general concepts.
1	Students demonstrate a confused strategy, which leads to difficulty solving the problem. Most answers are incorrect, but students do demonstrate knowledge of at least one concept being assessed. Students may: ⊚ collect some data; OR ⊚ begin a tally chart.

Picnic Plans

You will need

⌕ a pencil

⌕ a tally chart

You are helping to plan a class picnic.

Your job is to find out which kind of fruit to bring.

1. Ask nine classmates which kind of fruit they would like to have at the picnic.

2. Record your results in a tally chart.

3. Finally, write a sentence telling which kind of fruit you will buy and why.

_____

_____

_____

Chapters 1–10 Monitoring Student Progress Cumulative Test 3

Student Name _____ Date _____

Directions: This test targets selected objectives. For each item that is answered incorrectly, cross out the item number. Then record the number of correct responses for each strand in the column labeled **Number of Correct Responses.** Add to find the **Total Number of Correct Responses** and record the total. Use this total to determine the **Total Test Score** and the **Total Percent Correct.**

Strand • Objective(s)	Item Numbers	Number of Correct Responses
Number Sense		
⑥ Subtract, facts to 20.	1	
⑥ Compare and order numbers to 100.	2	
⑥ Give the value of a set of coins or a set of bills and coins.	3	
⑥ Add 2-digit numbers.	15	
⑥ Subtract money amounts.	5	
Measurement and Geometry		
⑥ Tell and write time to 5-minute intervals.	6	
⑥ Find elapsed time.	13	
⑥ Measure length in customary and metric units.	10	
⑥ Read temperatures.	11	
⑥ Identify 3-dimensional figures and their attributes.	7, 12	
⑥ Identify 2-dimensional figures and their attributes.	4, 14	
⑥ Identify congruent and symmetrical figures.	16	
Statistics, Data, and Probability		
⑥ Read and interpret graphs.	8, 9	
Mathematical Reasoning		
⑥ Solve problems, including those that involve writing number sentences.	17	
⑥ Solve problems, including those that involve choosing the operation.	18	
⑥ Solve problems, including those that involve time and acting it out.	19	
⑥ Solve problems, including those that involve measurement and guessing and checking.	20	
Total Number of Correct Responses		
Total Test Score		/20
Total Percent Correct		%

Choose the correct answer.

1. $14 - \blacksquare = 6$

   Ⓐ 9

   Ⓑ 8

   Ⓒ 7

   Ⓓ 6

2. Which sign makes the number sentence true?

83 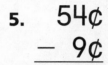 47

   Ⓕ <

   Ⓖ >

   Ⓗ +

   Ⓙ =

3. What is one way to show 33¢?

   Ⓐ 1 quarter, 1 dime

   Ⓑ 1 quarter, 8 pennies

   Ⓒ 3 dimes, 3 nickels

   Ⓓ 7 nickels

4. Name the shape.

   Ⓕ circle   Ⓗ triangle

   Ⓖ square   Ⓙ rectangle

5.
$$54¢$$
$$-\ 9¢$$

   Ⓐ 63¢   Ⓒ 45¢

   Ⓑ 55¢   Ⓓ 43¢

6. What time does the clock show?

   Ⓕ 3:30   Ⓗ 8:15

   Ⓖ 3:40   Ⓙ 8:30

GO ON

7. Name the figure.

Ⓐ cone

Ⓑ cube

Ⓒ cylinder

Ⓓ pyramid

Miss Carter's class made a tally chart of how children get to school. Use the chart to answer exercises 8 and 9.

How We Get to School

bus	卌 卌 卌 ‖
car	卌 卌 ‖

8. How many children take the bus to school?

Ⓕ 17 children

Ⓖ 12 children

Ⓗ 9 children

Ⓙ 5 children

9. How many more children get to school by bus than by car?

Ⓐ 23　　Ⓒ 11

Ⓑ 17　　Ⓓ 5

---

10. Find the length.

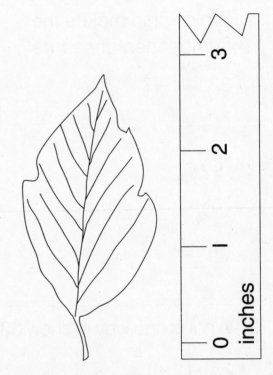

Ⓕ 4 inches

Ⓖ 3 inches

Ⓗ 2 inches

Ⓙ 1 inch

© McGraw-Hill School Division

11. What is the temperature?

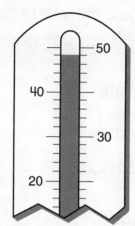

Ⓐ 58°C

Ⓑ 50°C

Ⓒ 48°C

Ⓓ 40°C

12. Name the figure.

Ⓕ cone   Ⓗ cylinder

Ⓖ cube   Ⓙ pyramid

13. How much time has passed?

Ⓐ 7 hours   Ⓒ 5 hours

Ⓑ 6 hours   Ⓓ 4 hours

14. Which shape has 3 sides?

Ⓕ circle

Ⓖ square

Ⓗ triangle

Ⓙ rectangle

15.   38
       + 45

Ⓐ 93

Ⓑ 83

Ⓒ 73

Ⓓ 13

16. Which shapes are congruent?

Ⓕ △ △

Ⓖ ▭ ▭

Ⓗ ▢ ▢

Ⓙ ○ ○

GO ON ➡

Solve.

17. Ashley has 9 pencils.
Leila has 8 pencils.
How many pencils do they
have in all?

ⓐ 98 pencils

ⓑ 19 pencils

ⓒ 18 pencils

ⓓ 17 pencils

18. There are 16 children in Mr.
Carl's class who like apples.
There are 17 children who
like oranges.
How many more children
like oranges than apples?

ⓕ 33 children

ⓖ 17 children

ⓗ 2 children

ⓙ 1 child

19. One puppet story takes 10
minutes to tell. How long does
it take to tell 5 puppet stories?

ⓐ 60 minutes

ⓑ 50 minutes

ⓒ 15 minutes

ⓓ 5 minutes

20. How long is the path?

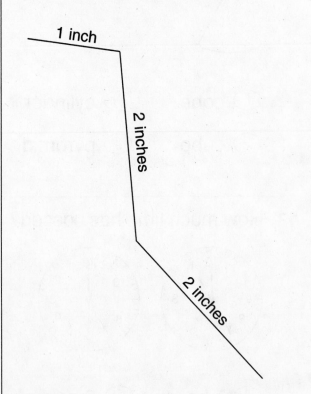

ⓕ 7 in.   ⓗ 5 in.

ⓖ 6 in.   ⓙ 3 in.

STOP

Chapter-11 Teacher Interview

Core Concept: *Fractions and Probability*

Student Activity: The student demonstrates an understanding of fractions as parts of a whole, fractional parts of a group, and likely, unlikely, or improbable events. Have a collection of small objects such as coins, beans, or colored counters available for the student.

Teacher Question 1:

What does the fraction "one fourth" mean?

Understanding Student Response	Practice and Improvement
Student says it stands for a part of a whole, but cannot say into how many parts the whole has been divided.	Review lesson 7. Lay out a group of 4 objects and ask the student to gather one fourth of the group together. Use items like those following lesson 7 for further practice.
Student knows that the whole is divided into four parts, but does not specify that the parts must be equal.	Use the procedure above, reinforcing the idea from lesson 7 that the fractional parts must be equal. Using collections of objects, have student show other fractions such as $\frac{1}{3}$ and $\frac{1}{6}$.

Teacher Question 2:

Which is greater: $\frac{1}{8}$ or $\frac{1}{4}$? How do you know?

Understanding Student Response	Practice and Improvement
Student says $\frac{1}{8}$, because 8 is greater than 4.	Review lesson 8. Lay out 8 objects and ask the student to gather one eighth of the group together and count how many. Repeat for $\frac{1}{4}$. Have the student compare the results and amend the answer with an explanation.
Student says $\frac{1}{8}$ is greater, but is unable to explain why.	Follow a procedure similar to the one above. Have student practice drawing and visualizing all of the fractions covered in lessons 7 and 8.

Teacher Question 3:

If you have 15 red beans and 5 black beans in a bag and you pick one bean without looking, what color are you most likely to pick?

Understanding Student Response	Practice and Improvement
Student says both colors are equally likely.	Review lesson 9 to emphasize that since there are more red beans, it is more likely that red will be picked. Do an experiment using beans or colored counters and record the results.
Student says that it depends on how many beans of each color have been picked before.	Point out that previous picks can't influence future picks, as long as the object is returned to the bag every time. Assign exercises in lesson 10, perhaps using a spinner to experiment.

Chapter-11 Journal Writing

Encourage students to generate their own journal entries related to math ideas in general or to concepts in this chapter. Present the following journal prompt and have students share their drawing/writing with a partner:

- ⊚ What does it mean to say that you have $\frac{3}{4}$ of something?

- ⊚ Draw a circle and color $\frac{3}{4}$ of it. Then draw a square and color $\frac{3}{4}$ of it. How much of each one is not colored?

  *(Responses should state that the fraction represents three of four **equal** parts. Students should see that the uncolored part is $\frac{1}{4}$ of the whole.)*

FOLLOW UP

At the end of the day, review the concept fractions. You do not have to use the terms numerator or denominator, but students should understand that the "bottom number" shows the number of equal parts into which the whole is divided and the "top number" tells how many of those equal parts one has. Ask students to think about what it might mean if the bottom number and the top number were the same.

Have students think of situations where they use fractions in ordinary conversation, like "quarter to three" or "half-pint of milk." They may draw representations of these and similar expressions in their journals and then share their work with a math partner.

Chapter-11 Monitoring Student Progress

☐ **Form A**   ☐ **Form B**

Student Name _____ Date _____

Directions: For each item that is answered incorrectly, cross out the item number. Then record the number of correct responses in the appropriate Student Score column. If the student has not met the Criterion Score for an objective, circle the student's score. Recommended assignments are listed in the Prescription Table on the next page.

Objective	Item Numbers	Criterion Score	Student Score
A. Identify fractional parts of a whole.	2, 4, 7, 10,11, 12	5/6	/6
B. Identify fractions as part of a group.	1, 3, 5, 6, 8, 9	5/6	/6
C. Identify whether events are most likely or least likely.	13, 14, 15, 16	3/4	/4
D. Solve problems, including those that involve drawing a picture.	17, 18, 19, 20	3/4	/4
Total Test Score		16/20	/20
Total Percent Correct			%

Chapter-11 Prescription Table

The following chart correlates the tested objectives for this chapter to supplementary materials that meet the individual needs of the students. The Practice and Reteach pages are designed for students who need further instruction in the math concepts taught in this chapter. The Enrich pages are designed for students who need advanced challenges.

Objective	Practice	Reteach	Enrich
A. Identify fractional parts of a whole.	319, 322, 325, 328	320, 323, 326, 329	321, 324, 327, 330
B. Identify fractions as part of a group.	337, 340	338, 341	339, 342
C. Identify whether events are most likely or least likely.	343, 346	344, 347	345, 348
D. Solve problems, including those that involve drawing a picture.	331–334	335–336	

Choose the correct answer.

What is the fraction for the shaded part?

1.

(A) $\frac{3}{4}$ (C) $\frac{1}{3}$

(B) $\frac{2}{4}$ (D) $\frac{1}{4}$

2.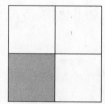

(F) $\frac{1}{2}$ (H) $\frac{1}{4}$

(G) $\frac{1}{3}$ (J) $\frac{1}{5}$

3.

(A) $\frac{9}{12}$ (C) $\frac{4}{12}$

(B) $\frac{5}{12}$ (D) $\frac{3}{12}$

4.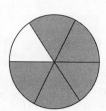

(F) $\frac{5}{6}$ (H) $\frac{2}{5}$

(G) $\frac{2}{4}$ (J) $\frac{1}{8}$

5.

(A) $\frac{5}{8}$ (C) $\frac{3}{8}$

(B) $\frac{4}{8}$ (D) $\frac{2}{8}$

GO ON

6.

(F) $\frac{7}{8}$ (H) $\frac{1}{2}$

(G) $\frac{2}{3}$ (J) $\frac{1}{3}$

7.

(A) $\frac{1}{2}$ (C) $\frac{1}{4}$

(B) $\frac{1}{3}$ (D) $\frac{1}{5}$

8.

(F) $\frac{2}{3}$ (H) $\frac{1}{3}$

(G) $\frac{1}{2}$ (J) $\frac{1}{4}$

9.

(A) $\frac{5}{5}$ (C) $\frac{3}{6}$

(B) $\frac{5}{6}$ (D) $\frac{1}{2}$

10. Which shows $\frac{1}{3}$ shaded?

(F)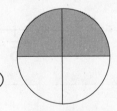

(G)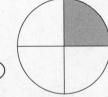

(H)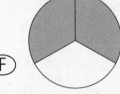

(J)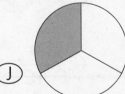

GO ON

11. Which shows $\frac{5}{8}$ shaded?

(A)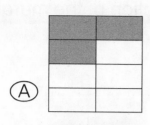

(B)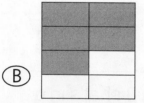

(C)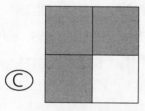

(D)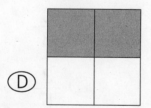

12. Which shows $\frac{3}{12}$ shaded?

(F)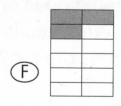

(H)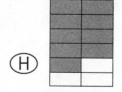

(G)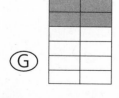

(J)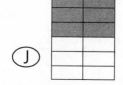

Mrs. Burke's class plays a game using this spinner. Use the spinner to answer items 13 and 14.

13. What is the most likely spin?

(A) red   (C) blue

(B) yellow   (D) green

14. What is the least likely spin?

(F) red   (H) blue

(G) yellow   (J) green

GO ON

Use the picture for items 15–16.

15. Which shape is the most likely to be picked?

Ⓐ triangle Ⓒ square

Ⓑ circle Ⓓ rectangle

16. Which shape is the least likely to be picked?

Ⓕ triangle Ⓗ square

Ⓖ circle Ⓙ rectangle

Solve.

17. Mark folds a piece of paper into 4 equal parts. He colors 3 of the parts. What fraction of the paper does he color?

Ⓐ $\dfrac{3}{4}$ Ⓒ $\dfrac{1}{3}$

Ⓑ $\dfrac{2}{3}$ Ⓓ $\dfrac{1}{4}$

18. Amy's mural has 6 sections. She colors 1 section purple. What fraction of the mural is purple?

Ⓕ $\dfrac{4}{6}$ Ⓗ $\dfrac{1}{4}$

Ⓖ $\dfrac{3}{6}$ Ⓙ $\dfrac{1}{6}$

19. Zach has 8 shells in a basket. There are 5 pink shells and 3 gray ones. What fraction of the shells are pink?

Ⓐ $\dfrac{6}{8}$ Ⓒ $\dfrac{3}{8}$

Ⓑ $\dfrac{5}{8}$ Ⓓ $\dfrac{3}{5}$

20. Erika has 6 grapes in a cup. There are 5 red grapes and 1 green one. What fraction of Erika's grapes are red?

Ⓕ $\dfrac{7}{8}$ Ⓗ $\dfrac{1}{5}$

Ⓖ $\dfrac{5}{6}$ Ⓙ $\dfrac{1}{6}$

STOP

Name _____

Write the answer.
What is the fraction for the shaded part?

1.

_____

2.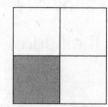

_____

3.

_____

4.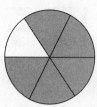

_____

5.

_____

GO ON

6.

_____

7.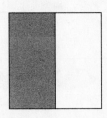

_____

8.

_____

9.

_____

10. Which shows $\frac{1}{3}$ shaded?
Circle the figure.

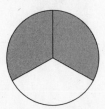

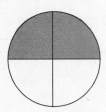

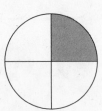

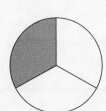

GO ON ➡

11. Which shows $\frac{5}{8}$ shaded? Circle the figure.

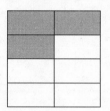 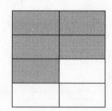

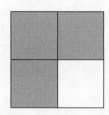 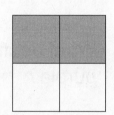

12. Which shows $\frac{3}{12}$ shaded? Circle the figure.

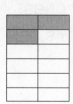 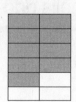

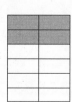 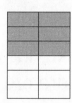

Mrs. Burke's class plays a game using this spinner. Use the spinner to answer items 13 and 14.

13. What is the most likely spin?

_____

_____

14. What is the least likely spin?

_____

GO ON

Use the picture for items 15–16.

15. Which shape is the most likely to be picked?

_____

_____

16. Which shape is the least likely to be picked?

_____

Solve.

17. Mark folds a piece of paper into 4 equal parts. He colors 3 of the parts. What fraction of the paper does he color?

_____

18. Amy's mural has 6 sections. She colors 1 section purple. What fraction of the mural is purple?

_____

19. Zach has 8 shells in a basket. There are 5 pink shells and 3 gray ones. What fraction of the shells are pink?

_____

20. Erika has 6 grapes in a cup. There are 5 red grapes and 1 green one. What fraction of Erika's grapes are red?

_____

STOP

Choose the correct answer.

What is the fraction for the shaded area?

1.

Ⓐ $\frac{3}{4}$ Ⓒ $\frac{1}{4}$

Ⓑ $\frac{2}{4}$ Ⓓ $\frac{1}{6}$

2.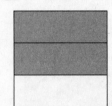

Ⓕ $\frac{2}{3}$ Ⓗ $\frac{1}{3}$

Ⓖ $\frac{2}{5}$ Ⓙ $\frac{1}{4}$

3.

Ⓐ $\frac{9}{12}$ Ⓒ $\frac{5}{12}$

Ⓑ $\frac{7}{12}$ Ⓓ $\frac{1}{12}$

4.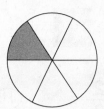

Ⓕ $\frac{3}{6}$ Ⓗ $\frac{1}{3}$

Ⓖ $\frac{1}{5}$ Ⓙ $\frac{1}{6}$

5.

Ⓐ $\frac{5}{8}$ Ⓒ $\frac{1}{2}$

Ⓑ $\frac{3}{5}$ Ⓓ $\frac{3}{8}$

GO ON

6.

(F) $\frac{2}{3}$ (H) $\frac{2}{5}$

(G) $\frac{1}{2}$ (J) $\frac{1}{3}$

7.

(A) $\frac{1}{5}$ (C) $\frac{1}{3}$

(B) $\frac{1}{4}$ (D) $\frac{1}{2}$

8.

(F) $\frac{1}{2}$ (H) $\frac{1}{5}$

(G) $\frac{1}{3}$ (J) $\frac{1}{4}$

9.

(A) $\frac{2}{6}$ (C) $\frac{1}{6}$

(B) $\frac{5}{6}$ (D) $\frac{1}{5}$

10. Which shows $\frac{1}{4}$ shaded?

(F)

(G)

(H)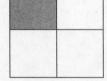

(J)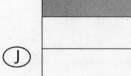

GO ON

11. Which shows $\frac{5}{6}$ shaded?

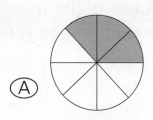

Ⓐ

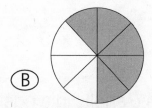

Ⓑ

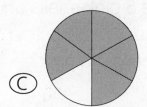

Ⓒ

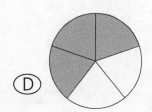

Ⓓ

12. Which shows $\frac{9}{12}$ shaded?

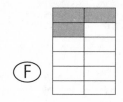

Ⓕ

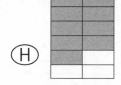

Ⓗ

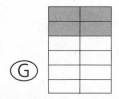

Ⓖ

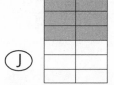

Ⓙ

Mr. Lee's class plays a game using this spinner. Use the spinner to answer items 13 and 14.

13. What is the most likely spin?

Ⓐ red   Ⓒ blue

Ⓑ yellow   Ⓓ green

14. What is the least likely spin?

Ⓕ red   Ⓗ blue

Ⓖ yellow   Ⓙ green

GO ON

Use the picture for exercises 15–16.

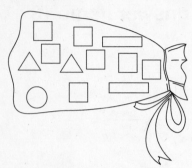

15. Which is the most likely to be picked?

Ⓐ circle Ⓒ triangle

Ⓑ square Ⓓ rectangle

16. Which is the least likely to be picked?

Ⓕ circle Ⓗ triangle

Ⓖ square Ⓙ rectangle

Solve.

17. Mark folds a paper into 3 equal parts. He colors 2 of the parts. What fraction of the paper does he color?

Ⓐ $\frac{1}{3}$ Ⓒ $\frac{2}{3}$

Ⓑ $\frac{1}{4}$ Ⓓ $\frac{3}{4}$

18. Amy's mural has 4 sections. She colors 1 section orange. What fraction of the mural does Amy color orange?

Ⓕ $\frac{4}{5}$ Ⓗ $\frac{1}{4}$

Ⓖ $\frac{3}{4}$ Ⓙ $\frac{1}{5}$

19. Zach has 6 shells in a basket. There are 5 pink shells and 1 gray one. What fraction of Zach's shells are pink?

Ⓐ $\frac{5}{6}$ Ⓒ $\frac{1}{3}$

Ⓑ $\frac{2}{3}$ Ⓓ $\frac{1}{6}$

20. Erika has 8 grapes in a cup. There are 3 red grapes and 5 green ones. What fraction of Erika's grapes are red?

Ⓕ $\frac{7}{8}$ Ⓗ $\frac{5}{8}$

Ⓖ $\frac{6}{8}$ Ⓙ $\frac{3}{8}$

STOP

Name _____

6.

_____

7.

_____

8.

_____

9.

_____

10. Which shows $\frac{1}{4}$ shaded?

Circle the figure.

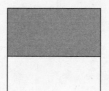 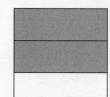

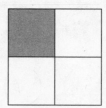 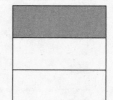

GO ON

11. Which shows $\frac{5}{6}$ shaded?
Circle the figure.

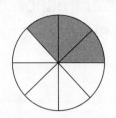 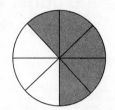

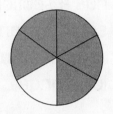 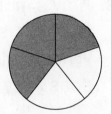

12. Which shows $\frac{9}{12}$ shaded?
Circle the figure.

 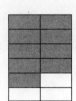

 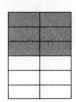

Mr. Lee's class plays a game using this spinner. Use the spinner to answer items 13 and 14.

13. What is the most likely spin?

_____

_____

14. What is the least likely spin?

_____

GO ON

Use the picture for exercises 15–16.

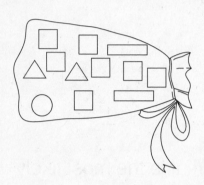

15. Which is the most likely to be picked?

_____

16. Which is the least likely to be picked?

_____

Solve.

17. Mark folds a paper into 3 equal parts. He colors 2 of the parts. What fraction of the paper does he color?

_____

18. Amy's mural has 4 sections. She colors 1 section orange. What fraction of the mural does Amy color orange?

_____

19. Zach has 6 shells in a basket. There are 5 pink shells and 1 gray one. What fraction of Zach's shells are pink?

_____

20. Erika has 8 grapes in a cup. There are 3 red grapes and 5 green ones. What fraction of Erika's grapes are red?

_____

STOP

Chapter-12 Teacher Interview

Core Concept: *Place Value to 1,000*

Student Activity: The student demonstrates an understanding of reading, writing, comparing, and ordering numbers to 1,000, as well as identifying number patterns to 1,000. Have plenty of beans or counters, some hundreds models, tens models, and ones models, and plenty of graph paper for the student. Ask the student questions such as, "What is the biggest number you can write using the digits 1, 3, and 9?"

Teacher Question 1:
◎ Write the number that is 8 more than 798.

Understanding Student Response	Practice and Improvement
Student regroups in the ones place but not in the tens place, obtaining a result like 796.	Review appropriate parts of Chapter 5. Put the 10 tens models together to make a hundred square, and move it to the hundreds place. Point out that no tens are left.
Student does not regroup in the hundreds place, obtaining a result like 706.	Use the same procedure as above, with the place-value models. Point out because 8 and 798 are being added, the sum must be greater than 798.

Teacher Question 2:
◎ What is the greatest number you can write using the digits 1, 3, and 9?

Understanding Student Response	Practice and Improvement
Student says 139, perhaps because that is the order in which the digits are given.	Review lesson 6 to reinforce that we write and read numbers from left to right, with the greatest value to the left or in the hundreds place. Therefore, the greatest digit must be in the hundreds place, the next greatest in the tens, and finally the least in the ones. Use items in lesson 6 for practice.
Student says 913.	Use lesson 6 to have the student put 913 and 931 in expanded form and then compare the numbers to see which is greater.

Teacher Question 3:
◎ Listen to these numbers, and tell me if I am counting by ones, tens, or hundreds: 129, 229, 329, (etc.).

Understanding Student Response	Practice and Improvement
Student cannot detect any pattern.	Review lesson 11 thoroughly. Use Practice items following lesson 11 to have student read the numbers out loud and tell the patterns.
Student says you are counting by ones or by tens.	Review lesson 11 prior to repeating the sequence. Ask the student to tell what was said differently each time (the hundreds). Give more items like those following lesson 11 for practice.

Chapter-12 Journal Writing

Encourage students to generate their own journal entries related to math ideas in general or to concepts in this chapter. Present the following journal prompt and have students share their drawing/writing with a partner:

⊚ How is it helpful to show a number in expanded form? Make up some 3-digit numbers, and write them in expanded form. Write the name of each number. Ask your math partner to check your work, while you check your partner's work.

(Responses should state expanded form makes it easier to see what each digit in the number stands for—hundreds, tens, or ones.)

FOLLOW UP

At the end of the day, ask students to read several three-digit numbers. Ask for responses to what the number would be if a number of ones or tens or hundreds were added. Students should grasp the concept that when a number is written in expanded form, the separate parts are added to get the number in its common form.

Have students practice going to expanded form and back with numbers having zeros in the ones or tens place, and blank in the hundreds place. Students should write these equations in their journal and share their work with a math partner.

Chapter-12 Monitoring Student Progress

☐ **Form A**　　　☐ **Form B**

Student Name _____ Date _____

Directions: For each item that is answered incorrectly, cross out the item number. Then record the number of correct responses in the appropriate Student Score column. If the student has not met the Criterion Score for an objective, circle the student's score. Recommended assignments are listed in the Prescription Table on the next page.

Objective	Item Numbers	Criterion Score	Student Score
A. Count, read, write and represent numbers to 1,000.	1, 4, 7, 10	3/4	/4
B. Identify the place value for each digit for numbers to 1,000.	2, 5, 8, 11	3/4	/4
C. Compare and order numbers to 1,000 by using the symbols.	3, 6, 9, 12	3/4	/4
D. Identify, describe, and extend patterns.	13, 14, 15, 16	3/4	/4
E. Solve problems, including those that involve finding a pattern.	17, 18, 19, 20	3/4	/4
Total Test Score		15/20	/20
Total Percent Correct			%

Chapter-12 Prescription Table

The following chart correlates the tested objectives for this chapter to supplementary materials that meet the individual needs of the students. The Practice and Reteach pages are designed for students who need further instruction in the math concepts taught in this chapter. The Enrich pages are designed for students who need advanced challenges.

Objective	Practice	Reteach	Enrich
A. Count, read, write and represent numbers to 1,000.	352, 364	353, 365	354, 366
B. Identify the place value for each digit for numbers to 1,000.	355, 358, 361, 367	356, 359, 362, 368	357, 360, 363, 369
C. Compare and order numbers to 1,000 by using the symbols.	376, 379	377, 380	378, 381
D. Identify, describe, and extend patterns.	382	383	384
E. Solve problems, including those that involve finding a pattern.	370–373	374–375	

Name _____

Choose the correct answer.

1. What number is shown?

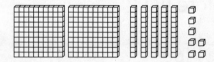

A 752   C 275

B 572   D 257

---

2. How many tens are in 879?

F 90   H 9

G 70   J 7

---

3. Which is true?

A 935 > 940

B 962 > 753

C 412 > 420

D 424 > 447

4. What number is shown?

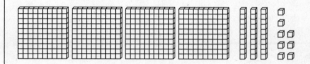

F 843

G 834

H 438

J 384

---

5. How many ones are in 491?

A 10

B 9

C 4

D 1

GO ON ➤

6. Which is true?

   Ⓕ 675 < 890

   Ⓖ 622 < 611

   Ⓗ 889 < 879

   Ⓙ 850 < 848

7. What is the word name for 651?

   Ⓐ six hundred fifty-one

   Ⓑ six hundred fifteen

   Ⓒ five hundred sixty-one

   Ⓓ one hundred fifty-six

8. What is the value of the 2 in 284?

   Ⓕ 2 hundreds

   Ⓖ 2 tens

   Ⓗ 2 ones

   Ⓙ 28 ones

9. Which number comes just before 469?

   Ⓐ 460   Ⓒ 470

   Ⓑ 468   Ⓓ 467

10. How do you write 7 hundreds 1 ten 3 ones as a number?

   Ⓕ 731

   Ⓖ 730

   Ⓗ 713

   Ⓙ 703

11. What is the value of the 5 in the number 152?

   Ⓐ 5 hundreds

   Ⓑ 5 tens

   Ⓒ 5 ones

   Ⓓ 15 ones

GO ON ▶

12. Which number comes between 830 and 832?

   (F) 381

   (G) 820

   (H) 829

   (J) 831

Find the missing number in each pattern.

13. 145, 245, 345,

   (A) 346   (C) 440

   (B) 355   (D) 445

14. 420, 430, 440, ▨

   (F) 450

   (G) 444

   (H) 441

   (J) 410

15. 432, ▨, 434, 435

   (A) 431

   (B) 433

   (C) 436

   (D) 439

16. 757, 758, ▨, 760

   (F) 759

   (G) 756

   (H) 755

   (J) 750

GO ON

Solve.

17. There are 257 people in line to buy tickets to the football game. Sam is the last person in line. How many people are in front of Sam?

Ⓐ 256   Ⓒ 258

Ⓑ 257   Ⓓ 260

18. Maria is making a necklace. Continue her pattern. Which two beads could come next?

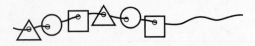

Ⓕ △ ○

Ⓖ ○ □

Ⓗ □ ○

Ⓙ □ △

19. The grocery store orders 100 boxes of tissues each week. How many boxes of tissues does the store order in 4 weeks?

Week 1	100
Week 2	100
Week 3	100
Week 4	100

Ⓐ 600   Ⓒ 400

Ⓑ 500   Ⓓ 300

20. How many pennies does Alex have?

Ⓕ 600   Ⓗ 800

Ⓖ 700   Ⓙ 900

STOP

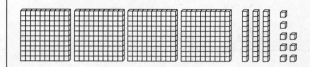
Write the answer.

1. What number is shown?

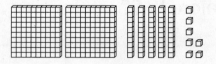

_____

2. How many tens are in 879?

_____ tens

3. Use >, <, or = to compare.

962 〇 753

4. What number is shown?

_____

5. How many ones are in 491?

_____ ones

GO ON

6. Use >, <, or = to compare.

675 ◯ 890

_____

7. Write the word name for 651.

_____

8. What is the value of the 2 in 284?

_____

9. Which number comes just before 469?

_____

10. How do you write 7 hundreds 1 ten 3 ones as a number?

_____

11. What is the value of the 5 in the number 152?

_____

GO ON →

12. Which number comes between 830 and 832?

_____

Find the missing number in each pattern.

13. 145, 245, 345, _____

_____

14. 420, 430, 440, _____

15. 432, _____, 434, 435

_____

16. 757, 758, _____, 760

Solve.

17. There are 257 people in line to buy tickets to the football game. Sam is the last person in line. How many people are in front of Sam?

_____ people

18. Maria is making a necklace. Continue her pattern. Which could come next?

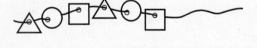

_____ △°_____

19. The grocery store orders 100 boxes of tissues each week. How many boxes of tissues does the store order in 4 weeks?

Week 1	100
Week 2	100
Week 3	100
Week 4	100

_____ boxes

20. How many pennies does Alex have?

_____ pennies

STOP

Choose the correct answer.

1. What number is shown?

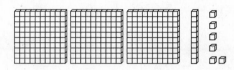

   Ⓐ 361   Ⓒ 163

   Ⓑ 316   Ⓓ 136

---

2. How many hundreds are in 293?

   Ⓕ 20   Ⓗ 3

   Ⓖ 9   Ⓙ 2

---

3. Which is true?

   Ⓐ 501 > 531

   Ⓑ 522 > 557

   Ⓒ 542 > 513

   Ⓓ 660 > 668

4. What number is shown?

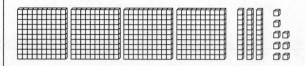

   Ⓕ 843

   Ⓖ 834

   Ⓗ 438

   Ⓙ 384

---

5. How many ones are in 519?

   Ⓐ 50

   Ⓑ 9

   Ⓒ 5

   Ⓓ 1

GO ON

6. Which is true?

(F) 710 < 701

(G) 762 < 785

(H) 843 < 813

(J) 886 < 854

7. What is the word name for 745?

(A) seven hundred fifty-four

(B) seven hundred forty-five

(C) four hundred fifty-seven

(D) five hundred forty-seven

8. What is the value of the 7 in 371?

(F) 7 hundreds

(G) 7 tens

(H) 7 ones

(J) 37 ones

9. Which number comes just after 333?

(A) 233   (C) 334

(B) 332   (D) 343

10. How do you write 4 hundreds 1 ten 6 ones as a number?

(F) 461

(G) 460

(H) 416

(J) 406

11. What is the value of the 6 in the number 618?

(A) 6 hundreds

(B) 6 tens

(C) 6 ones

(D) 61 ones

GO ON

12. Which number comes between 634 and 636?

    (F) 345

    (G) 635

    (H) 639

    (J) 643

Find the missing number in each pattern.

13. 235, 335, 435,

    (A) 436   (C) 535

    (B) 445   (D) 545

14. 510, 520, 530,

    (F) 580

    (G) 540

    (H) 535

    (J) 525

15. 234, ▢, 236, 237

    (A) 239

    (B) 338

    (C) 235

    (D) 233

16. 577, 578, ▢, 580

    (F) 581

    (G) 579

    (H) 576

    (J) 570

GO ON

Solve.

17. There are 324 people in line to buy tickets to the football game. How many people are in front of the last person in line?

Ⓐ 350   Ⓒ 324

Ⓑ 325   Ⓓ 323

---

18. Maria is making a necklace. Continue her pattern. Which two beads could come next?

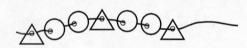

Ⓕ △ △

Ⓖ □ ◯

Ⓗ △ □

Ⓙ ◯ ◯

19. The grocery store orders 200 boxes of tissues each week. How many boxes of tissues does the store order in 4 weeks?

Week 1	200
Week 2	200
Week 3	200
Week 4	200

Ⓐ 800   Ⓒ 200

Ⓑ 600   Ⓓ 100

---

20. How many pennies does Amanda have?

Ⓕ 400   Ⓗ 600

Ⓖ 500   Ⓙ 700

STOP

Write the answer

1. What number is shown?

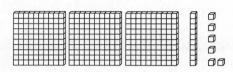

_____

_____

2. How many hundreds are in 293?

_____ hundreds

3. Use >, <, or = to compare.

542 ◯ 513

4. What number is shown?

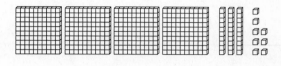

_____

5. How many ones are in 519?

_____ ones

GO ON

6. Use >, <, or = to compare.

762 ◯ 785

_____

7. What is the word name for 745?

_____

8. What is the value of the 7 in 371?

_____

9. Which number comes just after 333?

_____

10. How do you write 4 hundreds 1 ten 6 ones as a number?

_____

11. What is the value of the 6 in the number 618?

_____

GO ON ➡

12. Which number comes between 634 and 636?

_____

Find the missing number in each pattern.

13. 235, 335, 435, _____

14. 510, 520, 530, _____

15. 234, _____, 236, 237

_____

16. 577, 578, _____, 580

Solve.

17. There are 324 people in line to buy tickets to the football game. How many people are in front of the last person in line?

_____ people

18. Maria is making a necklace. Continue her pattern. Draw the bead that could come next.

_____

19. The grocery store orders 200 boxes of tissues each week. How many boxes of tissues does the store order in 4 weeks?

Week 1	200
Week 2	200
Week 3	200
Week 4	200

_____ boxes

20. How many pennies does Amanda have?

_____ pennies

STOP

Chapter-13 Teacher Interview

Core Concept: *Adding and Subtracting 3-digit Numbers*

Student Activity: The student will demonstrate an understanding of adding and subtracting 3-digit numbers with and without regrouping, including money amounts. Have manipulative materials such as place-value models and place-value mats available for the student. You may also have beans or counters and cups available. Ask the student questions such as, "Find the difference between 728 and 300 by counting back by hundreds."

Teacher Question 1:

Marcus got autographs from two pro football players. One of the football players weighed 268 pound, and the other weighed 325 pounds. Estimate how much the players weighed together.

Understanding Student Response	Practice and Improvement
Student adds the weights to get an exact amount.	Review estimating from lesson 5 and remind the student that they were asked to estimate the weight. Observe whether they find the nearest hundreds correctly, and review using a number line if needed.
Student does not know how to find the nearest hundreds.	Review estimating sums from lesson 5. Point out that this is a good way to check for reasonableness.

Teacher Question 2:

Find the difference between 728 – 300 by counting back by hundreds.

Understanding Student Response	Practice and Improvement
Student does not know how to count back by hundreds.	Practice counting back by hundreds using items like **Try It** in lesson 8. Use a number line to help student understand.
Student drops the tens and ones while counting back.	Review lesson 8 and then ask the student to put 728 in expanded form. Then count back by hundreds, and finally combine the tens and ones to make 428.

Teacher Question 3:

Abby spent $5.85 on a CD and $3.50 on food. How much did she spend all together?

Understanding Student Response	Practice and Improvement
Student does not know whether to add or to subtract.	Review lesson 2. Remind the student that addition is required because of the, "altogether." Assign **Facts Practice** if needed.
Student does not line up numbers on the decimal point.	Review that to the left of the decimal is the dollar amount and to the right is the change. Assign money items from **Concepts and Skills** in Chapter Review for practice.

Chapter-13 Journal Writing

Encourage students to generate their own journal entries related to math ideas in general or to concepts in this chapter. Present the following journal prompt and have students share their drawing/writing with a partner:

◉ The city library received a donation of 736 books. Of those, 347 were children's books. How many of the books were not children's books? In your journal, tell how to solve this problem, solve it, and check your work by addition. Explain why this process checks your work. Then explain how you could also check by estimating.

(Responses should indicate that subtraction is the process to use in solving the problem. The correct result is 389. This difference is added back to 347 to check—if you add back what you first took away, you should come back to the same starting point. If one found the nearest hundreds, one could subtract 700 − 300 = 400, which is reasonably close to 389.)

FOLLOW UP

Ask students to reflect on the process of checking subtraction by addition. Have them make up a few subtraction problems that they will solve, and then check by addition, in their journals. These should be 3-digit numbers, and should include some with zeros in the ones and tens place.

Have students write two word problems using 3 digit numbers. One should use addition and the other should use subtraction. Trade with a partner and solve each other's word problems. Remind students to use addition or estimation to check their work. When they are done, they should share their work with a math partner.

Chapter-13 Monitoring Student Progress

☐ Form A   ☐ Form B

Student Name _____ Date _____

Directions: For each item that is answered incorrectly, cross out the item number. Then record the number of correct responses in the appropriate Student Score column. If the student has not met the Criterion Score for an objective, circle the student's score. Recommended assignments are listed in the Prescription Table on the next page.

Objective	Item Numbers	Criterion Score	Student Score
A. Add three-digit numbers.	1, 2, 3, 4, 5, 6	5/6	/6
B. Subtract three-digit numbers.	7, 8, 9, 10, 11, 12	5/6	/6
C. add and subtract money amounts.	13, 14, 15, 16	3/4	/4
D. Solve problems, including those that involve making a graph.	17, 18, 19, 20	3/4	/4
Total Test Score		16/20	/20
Total Percent Correct			%

Chapter-13 Prescription Table

The following chart correlates the tested objectives for this chapter to supplementary materials that meet the individual needs of the students. The Practice and Reteach pages are designed for students who need further instruction in the math concepts taught in this chapter. The Enrich pages are designed for students who need advanced challenges.

Objective	Practice	Reteach	Enrich
A. Add three-digit numbers.	388, 391, 394, 397	389, 392, 395, 398	390, 393, 396, 399
B. Subtract three-digit numbers.	409, 412, 415, 418	410, 413, 416, 419	411, 414, 417, 420
C. Add and subtract money amounts.	424	425	426
D. Solve problems, including those that involve making a graph.	403–406	407–408	

Pages 400-402 involve estimating sums.
Pages 421-423 involve estimating differences.

Choose the correct answer.

1.   400
       + 300

    (A) 800   (C) 600

    (B) 700   (D) 100

---

2.   326
       + 243

    (F) 669

    (G) 579

    (H) 569

    (J) 529

---

3.   648
       + 137

    (A) 785   (C) 771

    (B) 775   (D) 512

---

4.   275
       + 63

    (F) 348

    (G) 338

    (H) 248

    (J) 238

---

5.   535
       + 386

    (A) 931   (C) 831

    (B) 921   (D) 821

---

6.   724
       + 192

    (F) 926   (H) 876

    (G) 916   (J) 816

GO ON

7.   600
      − 300

(A) 500   (C) 300

(B) 400   (D) 200

8.   457
      − 234

(F) 283

(G) 223

(H) 124

(J) 123

9.   816
      − 205

(A) 621   (C) 521

(B) 611   (D) 511

10.   738
       − 46

(F) 582

(G) 592

(H) 682

(J) 692

11.   642
       − 137

(A) 579   (C) 506

(B) 519   (D) 505

12.   324
       − 256

(F) 580   (H) 68

(G) 132   (J) 58

GO ON

13. $9.37
     − 6.54

   Ⓐ $15.91

   Ⓑ $3.23

   Ⓒ $2.84

   Ⓓ $2.83

14. $7.25
     − 1.17

   Ⓕ $8.42

   Ⓖ $6.18

   Ⓗ $6.08

   Ⓙ $6.07

15. $5.00
     + 2.86

   Ⓐ $8.86

   Ⓑ $7.86

   Ⓒ $3.14

   Ⓓ $2.14

16. $7.81
     + 1.59

   Ⓕ $9.50

   Ⓖ $9.40

   Ⓗ $8.40

   Ⓙ $6.40

GO ON

Solve.

17. This graph shows how many minutes three friends walked in the Walkathon.

WALKATHON

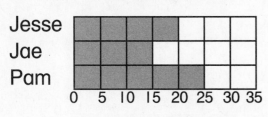

Number of Minutes

Jae walked for 5 more minutes. Which bar shows how much time Jae walked altogether?

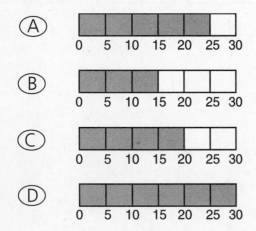

18. Brad's class collects 294 cans of dog food. Theo's class collects 127 cans of dog food for dogs at the animal shelter. How many cans do they collect in all?

(F) 421 cans   (H) 321 cans

(G) 412 cans   (J) 312 cans

19. Kathy has $7.50. She spends $6.68 on a present for her mom. How much change will she have left?

(A) $0.58   (C) $0.82

(B) $0.62   (D) $0.88

20. Andy's scout troop has 354 phone books. If they hand out 272 phone books, how many will they have left?

(F) 524 phone books

(G) 182 phone books

(H) 82 phone books

(J) 62 phone books

STOP

Write the answer.

1. 400
    + 300

4. 275
    + 63

2. 326
    + 243

5. 535
    + 386

3. 648
    + 137

6. 724
    + 192

GO ON

7.   600
   − 300
   _____

10.   738
    − 46
    _____

8.   457
   − 234
   _____

11.   642
    − 137
    _____

9.   816
   − 205
   _____

12.   324
    − 256
    _____

GO ON

13. $\begin{array}{r} \$9.37 \\ -\ 6.54 \\ \hline \$ \end{array}$

15. $\begin{array}{r} \$5.00 \\ +\ 2.86 \\ \hline \$ \end{array}$

14. $\begin{array}{r} \$7.25 \\ -\ 1.17 \\ \hline \$ \end{array}$

16. $\begin{array}{r} \$7.81 \\ +\ 1.59 \\ \hline \$ \end{array}$

GO ON

Solve.

17. This graph shows how many minutes three friends walked in the Walkathon.

WALKATHON

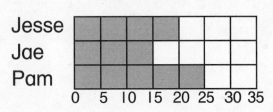

Number of Minutes

Jae walked for 5 more minutes. Circle the bar that shows how much time Jae walked altogether.

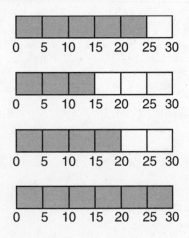

18. Brad's class collects 294 cans of dog food. Theo's class collects 127 cans of dog food for dogs at the animal shelter. How many cans do they collect in all?

_____ cans

19. Kathy has $7.50. She spends $6.68 on a present for her mom. How much change will she have left?

$ _____

20. Andy's scout troop has 354 phone books. If they hand out 272 phone books, how many will they have left?

_____ phone books

STOP

Choose the correct answer.

1.   300
       + 200

　　Ⓐ 600　　Ⓒ 400

　　Ⓑ 500　　Ⓓ 100

2.   435
       + 254

　　Ⓕ 689

　　Ⓖ 688

　　Ⓗ 621

　　Ⓙ 221

3.   627
       + 149

　　Ⓐ 785　　Ⓒ 775

　　Ⓑ 776　　Ⓓ 522

4.   385
       + 61

　　Ⓕ 396

　　Ⓖ 426

　　Ⓗ 446

　　Ⓙ 456

5.   577
       + 259

　　Ⓐ 936　　Ⓒ 836

　　Ⓑ 846　　Ⓓ 726

6.   635
       + 174

　　Ⓕ 909　　Ⓗ 809

　　Ⓖ 819　　Ⓙ 709

GO ON

7.   700
       − 300

Ⓐ 500   © 300

Ⓑ 400   Ⓓ 200

8.   347
       − 124

Ⓕ 283

Ⓖ 223

Ⓗ 124

Ⓙ 123

9.   926
       − 314

Ⓐ 640   © 612

Ⓑ 632   Ⓓ 512

10.   626
        − 57

Ⓕ 683

Ⓖ 603

Ⓗ 569

Ⓙ 553

11.   451
        − 246

Ⓐ 605   © 214

Ⓑ 215   Ⓓ 205

12.   437
        − 288

Ⓕ 651   Ⓗ 149

Ⓖ 251   Ⓙ 141

GO ON

13. $8.29
  − 6.47

  Ⓐ $14.76

  Ⓑ $3.23

  Ⓒ $2.22

  Ⓓ $1.82

15. $4.00
  + 2.59

  Ⓐ $6.39

  Ⓑ $6.59

  Ⓒ $7.59

  Ⓓ $7.09

14. $5.26
  − 2.18

  Ⓕ $7.42

  Ⓖ $3.32

  Ⓗ $3.08

  Ⓙ $3.02

16. $4.72
  + 3.68

  Ⓕ $9.40

  Ⓖ $8.50

  Ⓗ $8.40

  Ⓙ $7.40

Solve.

17. This graph shows how many minutes three friends walked in the Walkathon.

WALKATHON

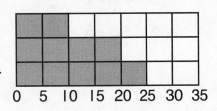

Number of Minutes

Sara walked for 10 more minutes. Which bar shows how much time Sara walked altogether?

Ⓐ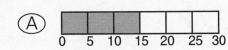

Ⓑ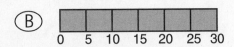

Ⓒ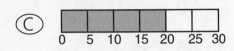

Ⓓ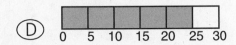

18. Theo's class collects 283 cans of dog food for the dogs at the animal shelter. Brad's class collects 325 cans of dog food. How many cans do they collect in all?

Ⓕ 609 cans Ⓗ 508 cans

Ⓖ 608 cans Ⓙ 42 cans

19. Jina has $8.50. She spends $7.15 on a birthday present for her dad. How much change will she have left?

Ⓐ $0.85 Ⓒ $1.05

Ⓑ $0.95 Ⓓ $1.35

20. Andy's scout troop has 286 phone books. If they hand out 167 phone books, how many will they have left?

Ⓕ 453 phone books

Ⓖ 451 phone books

Ⓗ 121 phone books

Ⓙ 119 phone books

STOP

Write the answer.

1.   300
   + 200

4.   385
   + 61

2.   435
   + 254

5.   577
   + 259

3.   627
   + 149

6.   635
   + 174

7.
$$\begin{array}{r} 700 \\ -\ 300 \\ \hline \end{array}$$

10.
$$\begin{array}{r} 626 \\ -\ 57 \\ \hline \end{array}$$

8.
$$\begin{array}{r} 347 \\ -\ 124 \\ \hline \end{array}$$

11.
$$\begin{array}{r} 451 \\ -\ 246 \\ \hline \end{array}$$

9.
$$\begin{array}{r} 926 \\ -\ 314 \\ \hline \end{array}$$

12.
$$\begin{array}{r} 437 \\ -\ 288 \\ \hline \end{array}$$

GO ON ➡

13. $8.29
    − 6.47
    $

15. $4.00
    + 2.59
    $

14. $5.26
    − 2.18
    $

16. $4.72
    + 3.68
    $

Solve.

17. This graph shows how many minutes three friends walked in the Walkathon.

WALKATHON

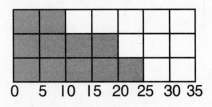

Number of Minutes

Sara walked for 10 more minutes. Circle the bar that shows how much time Sara walked altogether.

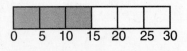

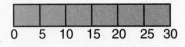

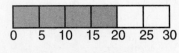

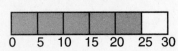

18. Theo's class collects 283 cans of dog food for the dogs at the animal shelter. Brad's class collects 325 cans of dog food. How many cans do they collect in all?

_____ cans

19. Judy has $8.50. She spends $7.15 on a birthday present for her dad. How much change will she have left?

$ _____

20. Andy's scout troop has 286 phone books. If they hand out 167 phone books, how many will they have left?

_____ phone books

STOP

Chapter-14 Teacher Interview

Core Concept: *Multiplication and Division*

Student Activity: The student demonstrates an understanding of multiplying and dividing, with and without remainders. Have manipulative materials, such as place-value models, available for the student. You may also have beans or counters and cups available.

Teacher Question 1:

◎ What is a multiplication sentence that means the same as 2 + 2 + 2 + 2 = 8?

Understanding Student Response	Practice and Improvement
Student is confused by the term 'multiplication sentence.'	Review lesson 2 for terminology and practice; review lesson 3 on arrays. Help student see the problem as an array.
Student writes a multiplication sentence using factors other than 4 and 2, such as 8 × 1 = 8, or an addition sentence like 6 + 2 = 8.	Point out that these are ways to get a "correct" answer, but they do not address the question. Use procedure above and assign **Facts Practice** following lesson 5.

Teacher Question 2:

◎ Twelve people are going to town in 4 cars. How many will ride in each car, if each car is to carry an equal number of people?

Understanding Student Response	Practice and Improvement
Student says you should put 4 or 5 people in each car.	Review lessons 10 and 11 to remind the student that each car has an equal number of people. Have them sketch 12 people and 4 cars, then group people by 3s and assign to cars. Assign **Extra Practice** items.
Student does not place all 12 people in a car or does not divide them evenly.	Review lessons 10 and 11. Have the student use 4 cups for cars and 12 beans for people. Put a bean in each cup until all are grouped.

Teacher Question 3:

◎ What is the remainder when you divide 15 by 6?

Understanding Student Response	Practice and Improvement
Student is confused by the term 'remainder.'	Review lesson 11 to explain that items cannot always be grouped equally. When the equal groups have been created, the remainder is what is left ungrouped.
Student calculates a remainder other than 3.	Have student redo calculation after reviewing remainders from lesson 11. Put 15 beans in 6 cups until no more equal groups can be formed – the remainder is 3. Use **Extra Practice** items.

Chapter-14 Journal Writing

Encourage students to generate their own journal entries related to math ideas in general or to concepts in this chapter. Present the following journal prompt and have students share their drawing/writing with a partner:

◎ Multiplication is like repeated addition. Division is like repeated subtraction. Draw diagrams to show that 4 × 6 = 24, and that 35 ÷ 7 = 5. Then draw a diagram to show the result and the remainder in 37 ÷ 7 = 5 R2.

(Responses to the multiplication prompt may show groups of 4 (or 6) added together or aligned for counting. If students show other groups, ask for clarification. Responses to the division prompt may show a group of 35 objects with 5 groups of 7 (or 7 groups of 5) circled. Responses to the last prompt should be like the previous example, with 2 objects ungrouped.)

FOLLOW UP

At the end of the day, review ways to multiply and divide through graphic means, relating this to repetitive addition and subtraction. Ask students to make up and solve problems involving multiplication and division.

Have the students figure out how many students would be in each group if they divided the class into groups of 3, 4, 5, and 6. Have the students discuss the process that they followed. Also, have the students discuss why they may want to divide the class into groups. Have the students share their work with a math partner.

Chapter-14 Monitoring Student Progress

☐ **Form A**   ☐ **Form B**

Student Name _____ Date _____

Directions: For each item that is answered incorrectly, cross out the item number. Then record the number of correct responses in the appropriate Student Score column. If the student has not met the Criterion Score for an objective, circle the student's score. Recommended assignments are listed in the Prescription Table on the next page.

Objective	Item Numbers	Criterion Score	Student Score
A. Find the product given groups of equal numbers.	1, 4, 7, 10, 13, 15	5/6	/6
B. Find how many groups and how many in each group.	2, 5, 8, 11, 14, 16	5/6	/6
C. Find how many in each group with remainders.	3, 6, 9, 12	3/4	/4
D. Solve problems, including those those that involve drawing a picture.	17, 18, 19, 20	3/4	/4
Total Test Score		16/20	
Total Percent Correct			%

Chapter-14 Prescription Table

The following chart correlates the tested objectives for this chapter to supplementary materials that meet the individual needs of the students. The Practice and Reteach pages are designed for students who need further instruction in the math concepts taught in this chapter. The Enrich pages are designed for students who need advanced challenges.

Objective	Practice	Reteach	Enrich
A. Find the product given groups of equal numbers.	430, 433, 436, 439, 442	431, 434, 437, 440, 443	432, 435, 438, 441, 444
B. Find how many groups and how many in each group.	451, 457	452, 458	453, 459
C. Find how many in each group with remainders.	454, 460	455, 461	456, 462
D. Solve problems, including those that involve drawing a picture.	445–448	449–450	

Choose the correct answer.

1.
$$\begin{array}{r} 2 \\ \times\, 5 \\ \hline \end{array}$$

Ⓐ 10   Ⓒ 5

Ⓑ 7   Ⓓ 2

2. Make equal groups.
You have 8 seeds.
You can put 2 seeds in each pot.
How many pots do you need?

Ⓕ 2   Ⓗ 6

Ⓖ 4   Ⓙ 10

3. Divide.
17 into 3 equal groups is

Ⓐ 6 in each group, 0 left over

Ⓑ 5 in each group, 2 left over

Ⓒ 5 in each group, 1 left over

Ⓓ 4 in each group, 2 left over

4. $5 \times 3 =$

Ⓕ 16   Ⓗ 10

Ⓖ 15   Ⓙ 8

5. Make equal groups.
You have 12 jars.
You can put 4 jars in each box.
How many boxes do you need?

Ⓐ 16   Ⓒ 6

Ⓑ 8   Ⓓ 3

6. Divide.
15 into 6 equal groups is

Ⓕ 3 in each group, 0 left over

Ⓖ 3 in each group, 3 left over

Ⓗ 2 in each group, 1 left over

Ⓙ 2 in each group, 3 left over

7.   6
     × 2

Ⓐ 12   Ⓒ 6

Ⓑ 8   Ⓓ 2

8. Make equal groups.
There are 2 baskets.
There are 10 apples.
How many apples in each
basket?

Ⓕ 4   Ⓗ 6

Ⓖ 5   Ⓙ 12

9. Divide.
15 into 5 equal groups is

Ⓐ 4 in each group, 0 left over

Ⓑ 4 in each group, 1 left over

Ⓒ 3 in each group, 2 left over

Ⓓ 3 in each group, 0 left over

10. 10 × 2 =

Ⓕ 20

Ⓖ 16

Ⓗ 12

Ⓙ 10

11. Make equal groups.
There are 2 children.
There are 18 grapes.
How many grapes for each
child?

Ⓐ 18   Ⓒ 9

Ⓑ 12   Ⓓ 3

GO ON →

12. Divide.

13 into 5 equal groups is

(F) 3 in each group, 1 left over

(G) 3 in each group, 0 left over

(H) 2 in each group, 3 left over

(J) 2 in each group, 1 left over

13. $4 \times 5 =$

(A) 25   (C) 9

(B) 20   (D) 7

14. Make equal groups.
There are 5 shelves.
There are 15 books.
How many books for each shelf?

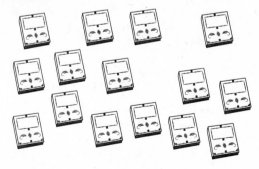

(F) 3   (H) 5

(G) 4   (J) 6

15.
$$\begin{array}{r} 2 \\ \times 9 \\ \hline \end{array}$$

(A) 20   (C) 11

(B) 18   (D) 9

16. Make equal groups.
You have 20 eggs.
You can put 5 eggs in each carton.
How many cartons do you need?

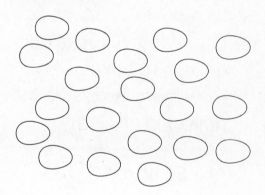

(F) 20

(G) 10

(H) 5

(J) 4

GO ON

Solve.

17. Lisa plants 3 rows of flowers with 10 flowers in each row. How many flowers does she plant in all?

(A) 35 flowers

(B) 30 flowers

(C) 13 flowers

(D) 10 flowers

19. In the morning, 7 scouts each sell 2 boxes of cookies. How many boxes do they sell in all?

(A) 21 boxes

(B) 14 boxes

(C) 7 boxes

(D) 2 boxes

18. On Friday, 5 trucks each deliver 10 boxes. How many boxes do they deliver in all?

(F) 50 boxes

(G) 40 boxes

(H) 15 boxes

(J) 10 boxes

20. There are 5 balloons in each bag. Terry buys 3 bags of balloons. How many balloons does Terry buy in all?

(F) 20 balloons

(G) 15 balloons

(H) 10 balloons

(J) 5 balloons

STOP

Write the answer.

1. $\begin{array}{r} 2 \\ \times\ 5 \\ \hline \end{array}$

4. $4 \times 3 = $ _____

5. Make equal groups.
   You have 12 jars.
   You can put 4 jars in each box.
   How many boxes do you need?

_____ boxes

2. Make equal groups.
   You have 8 seeds.
   You can put 2 seeds in
   each pot.
   How many pots do you need?

_____ pots

6. Divide.
   15 into 6 equal groups is

   _____ in each group,

   _____ left over

3. Divide.
   17 into 3 equal groups is

   _____ in each group,

   _____ left over

GO ON

7.   6
    × 2

10. $10 \times 2 =$ _____

8. Make equal groups.
There are 2 baskets.
There are 10 apples.
How many apples in each
basket?

_____ apples

11. Make equal groups.
There are 2 children.
There are 18 grapes.
How many grapes for each
child?

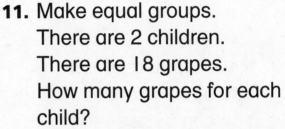

_____ grapes

9. Divide.
12 into 4 equal groups is

_____ in each group,

_____ left over

GO ON

12. Divide.

13 into 5 equal groups is

_____ in each group,

_____ left over

15.   2
         × 9

13. $4 \times 5 =$ _____

14. Make equal groups.
There are 5 shelves.
There are 15 books.
How many books for each shelf?

_____ books

16. Make equal groups.
You have 18 eggs.
You can put 6 eggs in each carton.
How many cartons do you need?

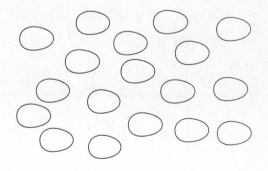

_____ cartons

GO ON

Solve.

17. Lisa plants 3 rows of flowers with 6 flowers in each row. How many flowers does she plant in all?

_____ flowers

18. On Friday, 5 trucks each deliver 10 boxes. How many boxes do they deliver in all?

_____ boxes

19. In the morning, 7 scouts each sell 4 boxes of cookies. How many boxes do they sell in all?

_____ boxes

20. There are 5 balloons in each bag. Terry buys 3 bags of balloons. How many balloons does Terry buy in all?

_____ balloons

STOP

Choose the correct answer.

1.
$$\begin{array}{r} 2 \\ \times\ 4 \\ \hline \end{array}$$

Ⓐ 8   Ⓒ 7

Ⓑ 10   Ⓓ 4

2. Make equal groups.
You have 10 flowers.
You can plant 5 flowers in each pot.
How many pots do you need?

Ⓕ 2   Ⓗ 6

Ⓖ 4   Ⓙ 12

3. Divide.
9 into 2 equal groups is

Ⓐ 4 in each group, 2 left over

Ⓑ 4 in each group, 1 left over

Ⓒ 3 in each group, 2 left over

Ⓓ 3 in each group, 1 left over

4. $6 \times 2 =$

Ⓕ 16   Ⓗ 10

Ⓖ 12   Ⓙ 7

5. Make equal groups.
You have 8 boxes.
You can put 2 boxes in each wagon.
How many wagons do you need?

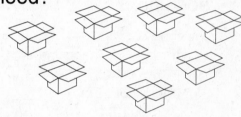

Ⓐ 8   Ⓒ 4

Ⓑ 6   Ⓓ 2

6. Divide.
22 into 5 equal groups is

Ⓕ 5 in each group, 0 left over

Ⓖ 5 in each group, 4 left over

Ⓗ 4 in each group, 3 left over

Ⓙ 4 in each group, 2 left over

7. $\begin{array}{r} 5 \\ \times\ 2 \\ \hline \end{array}$

(A) 12   (C) 7

(B) 10   (D) 2

8. Make equal groups.
There are 14 crayons.
There are 2 boxes.
How many crayons in
each box?

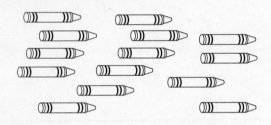

(F) 14   (H) 5

(G) 7   (J) 2

9. Divide.
15 into 3 equal groups is

(A) 5 in each group, 2 left over

(B) 5 in each group, 0 left over

(C) 4 in each group, 1 left over

(D) 4 in each group, 0 left over

10. $7 \times 5 =$

(F) 40

(G) 35

(H) 25

(J) 20

11. Make equal groups.
There are 3 students.
There are 15 markers.
How many markers for
each student?

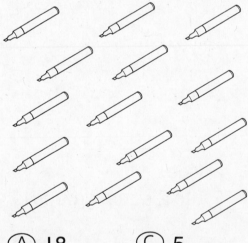

(A) 18   (C) 5

(B) 9   (D) 3

GO ON

12. Divide.
   11 into 2 equal groups is

   Ⓕ 6 in each group, 0 left over

   Ⓖ 5 in each group, 2 left over

   Ⓗ 5 in each group, 1 left over

   Ⓙ 4 in each group, 3 left over

13. $10 \times 3 =$

   Ⓐ 13   Ⓒ 33

   Ⓑ 30   Ⓓ 103

14. Make equal groups.
   There are 3 plates.
   There are 12 muffins.
   How many muffins on each
   plate?

   Ⓕ 15   Ⓗ 4

   Ⓖ 6   Ⓙ 3

15. $\begin{array}{r} 3 \\ \times 5 \\ \hline \end{array}$

   Ⓐ 15   Ⓒ 10

   Ⓑ 12   Ⓓ 9

16. Make equal groups.
   You have 25 eggs.
   You can put 5 eggs in
   each basket.
   How many baskets do
   you need?

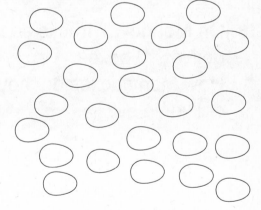

   Ⓕ 25

   Ⓖ 10

   Ⓗ 8

   Ⓙ 5

GO ON

Solve.

17. Janna plants 5 rows of flowers with 6 flowers in each row.
How many flowers does she plant in all?

   Ⓐ 30 flowers

   Ⓑ 18 flowers

   Ⓒ 11 flowers

   Ⓓ 6 flowers

18. On Monday, 7 trucks each deliver 10 boxes.
How many boxes do they deliver in all?

   Ⓕ 70 boxes

   Ⓖ 60 boxes

   Ⓗ 17 boxes

   Ⓙ 10 boxes

19. After school, 10 scouts each sell 4 boxes of cookies.
How many boxes do they sell in all?

   Ⓐ 40 boxes

   Ⓑ 30 boxes

   Ⓒ 24 boxes

   Ⓓ 14 boxes

20. There are 7 balloons in each bag.
Derrick buys 5 bags of balloons.
How many balloons does Derrick buy in all?

   Ⓕ 35 balloons

   Ⓖ 25 balloons

   Ⓗ 20 balloons

   Ⓙ 15 balloons

STOP

Write the answer.

1.
$$\begin{array}{r} 2 \\ \times\ 4 \\ \hline \end{array}$$

_____

2. Make equal groups.
You have 9 flowers.
You can plant 3 flowers in each pot.
How many pots do you need?

_____ pots

_____

3. Divide.
9 into 2 equal groups is

_____ in each group,

_____ left over

4. $6 \times 2 =$ _____

_____

5. Make equal groups.
You have 8 boxes.
You can put 2 boxes in each wagon.
How many wagons do you need?

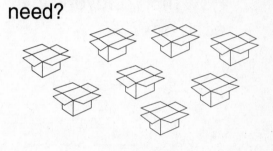

_____ wagons

_____

6. Divide.
18 into 4 equal groups is

_____ in each group,

_____ left over

GO ON

7. $\begin{array}{r} 5 \\ \times\ 2 \\ \hline \end{array}$

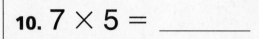

10. $7 \times 5 =$ _____

8. Make equal groups.
There are 14 crayons.
There are 2 boxes.
How many crayons in
each box?

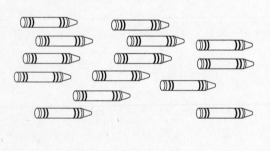

_____ crayons

11. Make equal groups.
There are 3 students.
There are 15 markers.
How many markers for
each student?

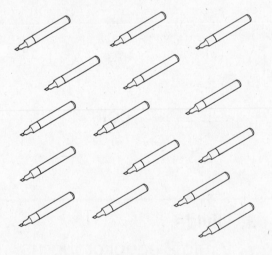

_____ markers

9. Divide.
15 into 3 equal groups is

_____ in each group,

_____ left over

© McGraw-Hill School Division

GO ON

12. Divide.
I I into 2 equal groups is

_____ in each group,

_____ left over

_____

13. I0 × 3 = _____

14. Make equal groups.
There are 3 plates.
There are I2 muffins.
How many muffins on each
plate?

_____ muffins

15. $\begin{array}{r} 3 \\ \times\, 5 \\ \hline \end{array}$

_____

16. Make equal groups.
You have 24 eggs.
You can put 6 eggs in
each basket.
How many baskets do
you need?

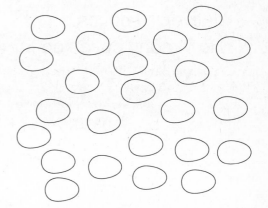

_____ baskets

GO ON

Solve.

17. Janna plants 5 rows of flowers with 6 flowers in each row.
How many flowers does she plant in all?

_____ flowers

18. On Monday, 7 trucks each deliver 10 boxes.
How many boxes do they deliver in all?

_____ boxes

19. After school, 10 scouts each sell 4 boxes of cookies.
How many boxes do they sell in all?

_____ boxes

20. There are 7 balloons in each bag.
Derrick buys 5 bags of balloons.
How many balloons does Derrick buy in all?

_____ balloons

STOP

Monitoring Student Progress
Final Test

Student Name _____ Date _____

Directions: This test targets selected objectives. For each item that is answered incorrectly, cross out the item number. Then record the number of correct responses for each strand in the column labeled **Number of Correct Responses**. Add to find the **Total Number of Correct Responses** and record the total. Use this total to determine the **Total Test Score** and the **Total Percent Correct.**

Strand • Objective(s)	Item Numbers	Number of Correct Responses
Number Sense		
◉ Subtract, facts to 20.	1	
◉ Identify the place value for each digit for numbers to 100.	2	
◉ Give the value of a set of coins or a set of bills and coins.	3	
◉ Identify fractional parts of a whole.	5	
◉ Identify fractions as part of a group.	6	
◉ Find the product given groups of equal numbers.	14	
◉ Compare and order numbers to 1,000 by using the symbols.	7	
◉ Add and subtract three-digit numbers.	9, 10, 12	
◉ Find how many in each group with remainders.	11	
◉ Find how many groups and how many in each group.	13	
◉ Identify the place value for each digit for numbers to 1,000.	8, 15	
Measurement and Geometry		
◉ Tell and write time to 5-minute intervals.	4	
◉ Read temperatures.	16	
Statistics, Data, and Probability		
◉ Read numerical data in systematic ways.	17	
Mathematical Reasoning		
◉ Solve problems, including those that involve acting it out.	18	
◉ Solve problems, including those that involve finding a pattern.	19	
◉ Solve problems, including those that involve drawing a picture.	20	
Total Number of Correct Responses		
Total Test Score		/20
Total Percent Correct		%

Choose the correct answer.

1.
$$14 - 5$$
□

□ + 5 = 14

   (A) 9   (C) 7

   (B) 8   (D) 6

2. How many tens are in 83?

   (F) 80   (H) 8

   (G) 30   (J) 3

3. How much money is shown?

   (A) 53¢

   (B) 48¢

   (C) 38¢

   (D) 33¢

4. What time does the clock show?

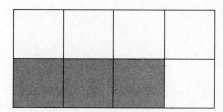

   (F) 2:20   (H) 3:25

   (G) 2:25   (J) 5:10

5. What part is shaded?

   (A) $\dfrac{5}{8}$

   (B) $\dfrac{3}{5}$

   (C) $\dfrac{4}{8}$

   (D) $\dfrac{3}{8}$

GO ON

6. What part is shaded?

Ⓕ $\frac{1}{4}$ 　　Ⓗ $\frac{1}{2}$

Ⓖ $\frac{1}{3}$ 　　Ⓙ $\frac{3}{4}$

7. Choose the correct sign.

470 ⬤ 407

Ⓐ < 　　Ⓒ =

Ⓑ > 　　Ⓓ +

8. What number does the picture show?

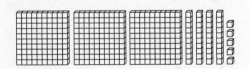

Ⓕ 543

Ⓖ 534

Ⓗ 453

Ⓙ 345

9.
$$\begin{array}{r} 128 \\ + 311 \\ \hline \blacksquare \end{array}$$

Ⓐ 439 　　Ⓒ 349

Ⓑ 417 　　Ⓓ 217

10.
$$\begin{array}{r} 824 \\ - 303 \\ \hline \blacksquare \end{array}$$

Ⓕ 627 　　Ⓗ 503

Ⓖ 521 　　Ⓙ 421

11. 15 into equal groups of 2 is

Ⓐ 7 groups, 2 leftover

Ⓑ 7 groups, 1 leftover

Ⓒ 7 groups, 0 leftover

Ⓓ 6 groups, 1 leftover

GO ON

12.

$$468 \\ -\ \blacksquare \\ \overline{253}$$

Ⓕ 222

Ⓖ 215

Ⓗ 121

Ⓙ 111

13. Make equal groups.
You have 15 boxes.
You can put 5 boxes in
each wagon.
How many wagons do you
need?

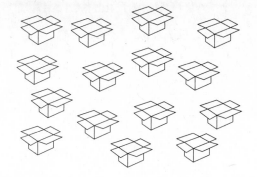

Ⓐ 15   Ⓒ 3

Ⓑ 5   Ⓓ 2

14. $5 \times 4 = \blacksquare$

Ⓕ 25

Ⓖ 20

Ⓗ 9

Ⓙ 1

15. Which digit is in the tens
place?

326

Ⓐ 6

Ⓑ 4

Ⓒ 3

Ⓓ 2

16. What is the temperature?

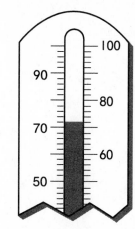

Ⓕ 74°F

Ⓖ 72°F

Ⓗ 70°F

Ⓙ 68°F

Solve.

Anna's class collected pet food for the animal shelter. Use the pictograph to answer exercise 17.

Pet Food Pictograph

Week 1

Week 2

Week 3

Week 4

◻ = 2 cans

17. How many more cans were collected in week 2 than in week 1?

Ⓐ 8 cans   Ⓒ 4 cans

Ⓑ 6 cans   Ⓓ 1 can

18. I have 4 sides and 4 vertices. What plane figure am I?

Ⓕ circle   Ⓗ rectangle

Ⓖ triangle   Ⓙ pentagon

19. There are 318 people in line to buy tickets for a concert. How many people are in front of the last person?

Ⓐ 320

Ⓑ 318

Ⓒ 317

Ⓓ 310

20. Andrew buys 4 packs of markers.
There are 5 markers in each pack.
How many markers does he buy in all?

Ⓕ 25 markers

Ⓖ 20 markers

Ⓗ 9 markers

Ⓙ 5 markers

STOP

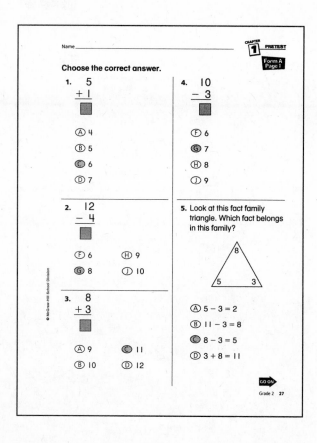

Choose the correct answer.

1.
$$5$$
$$+1$$

- Ⓐ 4
- Ⓑ 5
- Ⓒ 6
- Ⓓ 7

2.
$$12$$
$$-4$$

- Ⓕ 6
- Ⓖ 8
- Ⓗ 9
- Ⓙ 10

3.
$$8$$
$$+3$$

- Ⓐ 9
- Ⓑ 10
- Ⓒ 11
- Ⓓ 12

4.
$$10$$
$$-3$$

- Ⓕ 6
- Ⓖ 7
- Ⓗ 8
- Ⓙ 9

5. Look at this fact family triangle. Which fact belongs in this family?

(triangle with 8 at top, 5 and 3 at bottom)

- Ⓐ $5 - 3 = 2$
- Ⓑ $11 - 3 = 8$
- Ⓒ $8 - 3 = 5$
- Ⓓ $3 + 8 = 11$

GO ON
Grade 2 **27**

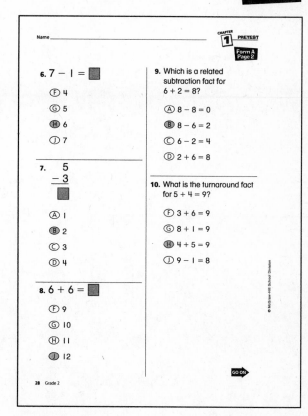

6. $7 - 1 = $ ▮

- Ⓕ 4
- Ⓖ 5
- Ⓗ 6
- Ⓙ 7

7.
$$5$$
$$-3$$

- Ⓐ 1
- Ⓑ 2
- Ⓒ 3
- Ⓓ 4

8. $6 + 6 = $ ▮

- Ⓕ 9
- Ⓖ 10
- Ⓗ 11
- Ⓙ 12

9. Which is a related subtraction fact for $6 + 2 = 8$?

- Ⓐ $8 - 8 = 0$
- Ⓑ $8 - 6 = 2$
- Ⓒ $6 - 2 = 4$
- Ⓓ $2 + 6 = 8$

10. What is the turnaround fact for $5 + 4 = 9$?

- Ⓕ $3 + 6 = 9$
- Ⓖ $8 + 1 = 9$
- Ⓗ $4 + 5 = 9$
- Ⓙ $9 - 1 = 8$

GO ON
28 Grade 2

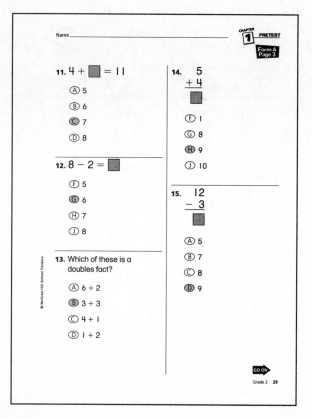

11. $4 + $ ▮ $= 11$

- Ⓐ 5
- Ⓑ 6
- Ⓒ 7
- Ⓓ 8

12. $8 - 2 = $ ▮

- Ⓕ 5
- Ⓖ 6
- Ⓗ 7
- Ⓙ 8

13. Which of these is a doubles fact?

- Ⓐ $6 + 2$
- Ⓑ $3 + 3$
- Ⓒ $4 + 1$
- Ⓓ $1 + 2$

14.
$$5$$
$$+4$$

- Ⓕ 1
- Ⓖ 8
- Ⓗ 9
- Ⓙ 10

15.
$$12$$
$$-3$$

- Ⓐ 5
- Ⓑ 7
- Ⓒ 8
- Ⓓ 9

GO ON
Grade 2 **29**

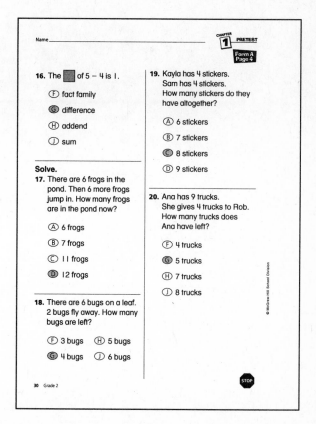

16. The ▮ of $5 - 4$ is 1.

- Ⓕ fact family
- Ⓖ difference
- Ⓗ addend
- Ⓙ sum

Solve.

17. There are 6 frogs in the pond. Then 6 more frogs jump in. How many frogs are in the pond now?

- Ⓐ 6 frogs
- Ⓑ 7 frogs
- Ⓒ 11 frogs
- Ⓓ 12 frogs

18. There are 6 bugs on a leaf. 2 bugs fly away. How many bugs are left?

- Ⓕ 3 bugs
- Ⓖ 4 bugs
- Ⓗ 5 bugs
- Ⓙ 6 bugs

19. Kayla has 4 stickers. Sam has 4 stickers. How many stickers do they have altogether?

- Ⓐ 6 stickers
- Ⓑ 7 stickers
- Ⓒ 8 stickers
- Ⓓ 9 stickers

20. Ana has 9 trucks. She gives 4 trucks to Rob. How many trucks does Ana have left?

- Ⓕ 4 trucks
- Ⓖ 5 trucks
- Ⓗ 7 trucks
- Ⓙ 8 trucks

STOP
30 Grade 2

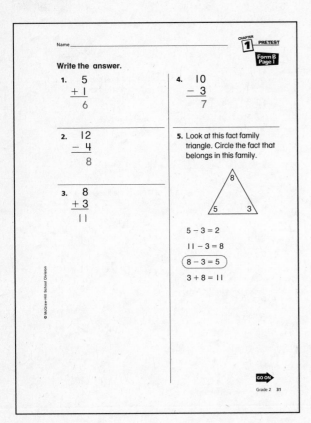

Name _____

CHAPTER 1 PRETEST
Form B Page 1

Write the answer.

1. $\begin{array}{r} 5 \\ +1 \\ \hline 6 \end{array}$

2. $\begin{array}{r} 12 \\ -4 \\ \hline 8 \end{array}$

3. $\begin{array}{r} 8 \\ +3 \\ \hline 11 \end{array}$

4. $\begin{array}{r} 10 \\ -3 \\ \hline 7 \end{array}$

5. Look at this fact family triangle. Circle the fact that belongs in this family.

(triangle: 8 top, 5 and 3 bottom)

$5 - 3 = 2$

$11 - 3 = 8$

$(8 - 3 = 5)$

$3 + 8 = 11$

GO ON
Grade 2 31

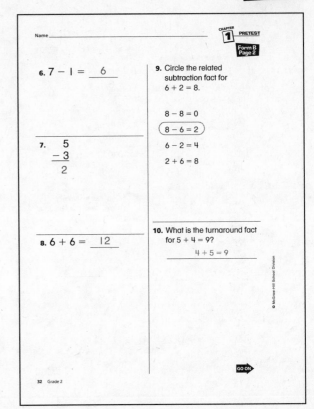

Name _____

CHAPTER 1 PRETEST
Form B Page 2

6. $7 - 1 = \underline{6}$

7. $\begin{array}{r} 5 \\ -3 \\ \hline 2 \end{array}$

8. $6 + 6 = \underline{12}$

9. Circle the related subtraction fact for $6 + 2 = 8$.

$8 - 8 = 0$

$(8 - 6 = 2)$

$6 - 2 = 4$

$2 + 6 = 8$

10. What is the turnaround fact for $5 + 4 = 9$?

$4 + 5 = 9$

32 Grade 2
GO ON

Name _____

CHAPTER 1 PRETEST
Form B Page 3

11. $4 + \underline{7} = 11$

12. $8 - 2 = \underline{6}$

13. Which of these is a doubles fact? Circle the answer.

$6 + 2$

$(3 + 3)$

$4 + 1$

$1 + 2$

14. $\begin{array}{r} 5 \\ +4 \\ \hline 9 \end{array}$

15. $\begin{array}{r} 12 \\ -3 \\ \hline 9 \end{array}$

GO ON
Grade 2 33

Name _____

CHAPTER 1 PRETEST
Form B Page 4

16. Complete the sentence using one of the following: fact family, difference, addend, or sum.

The __difference__ of $5 - 4$ is 1.

Solve.

17. There are 6 frogs in the pond. Then 6 more frogs jump in. How many frogs are in the pond now?

_12_ frogs

18. There are 6 bugs on a leaf. 2 bugs fly away. How many bugs are left?

_4_ bugs

19. Kayla has 4 stickers. Sam has 4 stickers. How many stickers do they have altogether?

_8_ stickers

20. Ana has 9 trucks. She gives 4 trucks to Rob. How many trucks does Ana have left?

_5_ trucks

34 Grade 2
STOP

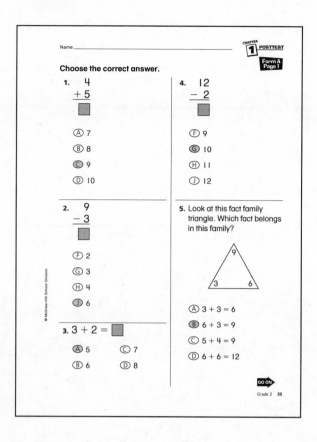

Choose the correct answer.

1.   4
       + 5
       ▪

  Ⓐ 7
  Ⓑ 8
  ⓒ 9
  Ⓓ 10

2.   9
       − 3
       ▪

  Ⓕ 2
  Ⓖ 3
  Ⓗ 4
  Ⓙ 6

3. 3 + 2 = ▪

  Ⓐ 5   ⓒ 7
  Ⓑ 6   Ⓓ 8

4.   12
       − 2
       ▪

  Ⓕ 9
  Ⓖ 10
  Ⓗ 11
  Ⓙ 12

5. Look at this fact family triangle. Which fact belongs in this family?

    9
  3   6

  Ⓐ 3 + 3 = 6
  Ⓑ 6 + 3 = 9
  ⓒ 5 + 4 = 9
  Ⓓ 6 + 6 = 12

GO ON
Grade 2 **35**

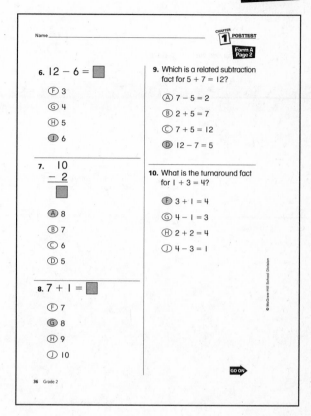

6. 12 − 6 = ▪

  Ⓕ 3
  Ⓖ 4
  Ⓗ 5
  Ⓙ 6

7.   10
       − 2
       ▪

  Ⓐ 8
  Ⓑ 7
  ⓒ 6
  Ⓓ 5

8. 7 + 1 = ▪

  Ⓕ 7
  Ⓖ 8
  Ⓗ 9
  Ⓙ 10

9. Which is a related subtraction fact for 5 + 7 = 12?

  Ⓐ 7 − 5 = 2
  Ⓑ 2 + 5 = 7
  ⓒ 7 + 5 = 12
  Ⓓ 12 − 7 = 5

10. What is the turnaround fact for 1 + 3 = 4?

  Ⓕ 3 + 1 = 4
  Ⓖ 4 − 1 = 3
  Ⓗ 2 + 2 = 4
  Ⓙ 4 − 3 = 1

36 Grade 2

GO ON

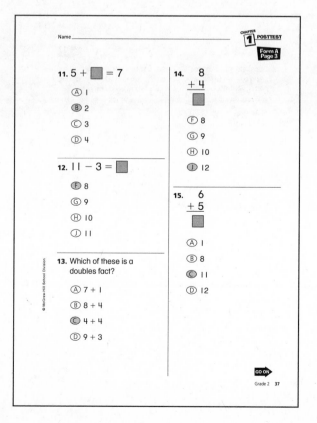

11. 5 + ▪ = 7

  Ⓐ 1
  Ⓑ 2
  ⓒ 3
  Ⓓ 4

12. 11 − 3 = ▪

  Ⓕ 8
  Ⓖ 9
  Ⓗ 10
  Ⓙ 11

13. Which of these is a doubles fact?

  Ⓐ 7 + 1
  Ⓑ 8 + 4
  ⓒ 4 + 4
  Ⓓ 9 + 3

14.   8
        + 4
        ▪

  Ⓕ 8
  Ⓖ 9
  Ⓗ 10
  Ⓙ 12

15.   6
        + 5
        ▪

  Ⓐ 1
  Ⓑ 8
  ⓒ 11
  Ⓓ 12

GO ON
Grade 2 **37**

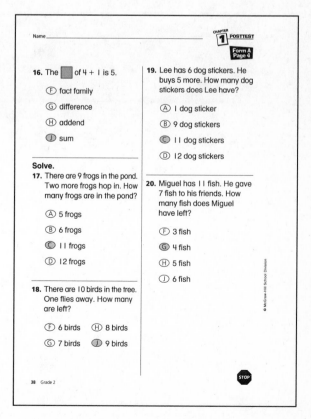

16. The ▪ of 4 + 1 is 5.

  Ⓕ fact family
  Ⓖ difference
  Ⓗ addend
  Ⓙ sum

Solve.

17. There are 9 frogs in the pond. Two more frogs hop in. How many frogs are in the pond?

  Ⓐ 5 frogs
  Ⓑ 6 frogs
  ⓒ 11 frogs
  Ⓓ 12 frogs

18. There are 10 birds in the tree. One flies away. How many are left?

  Ⓕ 6 birds   Ⓗ 8 birds
  Ⓖ 7 birds   Ⓙ 9 birds

19. Lee has 6 dog stickers. He buys 5 more. How many dog stickers does Lee have?

  Ⓐ 1 dog sticker
  Ⓑ 9 dog stickers
  ⓒ 11 dog stickers
  Ⓓ 12 dog stickers

20. Miguel has 11 fish. He gave 7 fish to his friends. How many fish does Miguel have left?

  Ⓕ 3 fish
  Ⓖ 4 fish
  Ⓗ 5 fish
  Ⓙ 6 fish

38 Grade 2

STOP

Write the answer.

1.   4
  + 5
  ___
    9

2.   9
  − 3
  ___
    6

3.   3
  + 2
  ___
    5

4.   12
  − 2
  ___
    10

5. Look at this fact family triangle. Circle the fact that belongs in this family.

3 + 3 = 6
(6 + 3 = 9)
5 + 4 = 9
6 + 6 = 12

6.   12
  − 6
  ___
    6

7.   10
  − 2
  ___
    8

8.   7
  + 1
  ___
    8

9. Circle the related subtraction fact for 5 + 7 = 12.

7 − 5 = 2
2 + 5 = 7
7 + 5 = 12
(12 − 7 = 5)

10. What is the turnaround fact for 1 + 3 = 4?

_____3 + 1 = 4_____

GO ON

11. 5 + __2__ = 7

12. 11 − 3 = __8__

13. Which of these is a doubles fact? Circle the answer.

7 + 1
8 + 4
(4 + 4)
9 + 3

14.   8
  + 4
  ___
    12

15.   6
  + 5
  ___
    11

16. Complete the sentence using one of the following: *fact family, difference, addend, sum.*

The ___sum___ of 4 + 1 is 5.

Solve.

17. There are 9 frogs in the pond. Two more frogs hop in. How many frogs are in the pond?

___11___ frogs

18. There are 10 birds in the tree. One flies away. How many are left?

___9___ birds

19. Lee has 6 dog stickers. He buys 5 more. How many dog stickers does Lee have?

___11___ dog stickers

20. Miguel has 11 fish. He gave 7 fish to his friends. How many fish does Miguel have left?

___4___ fish

STOP

Choose the correct answer.

1. $8 + 8 = \blacksquare$
   - A 15
   - B 16
   - C 17
   - D 18

2. $\begin{array}{r} 7 \\ + 6 \\ \hline \blacksquare \end{array}$
   - F 11 H 13
   - G 12 J 14

3. $\begin{array}{r} 9 \\ + 4 \\ \hline \blacksquare \end{array}$
   - A 5 C 13
   - B 12 D 14

4. $6 + \blacksquare = 15$
   - F 7
   - G 8
   - H 9
   - J 10

5. $\begin{array}{r} 16 \\ - 8 \\ \hline \blacksquare \end{array}$
   - A 6
   - B 7
   - C 8
   - D 9

GO ON
Grade 2 47

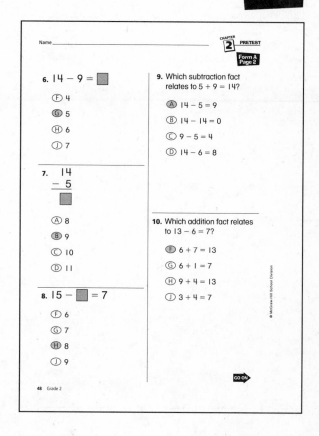

6. $14 - 9 = \blacksquare$
   - F 4
   - G 5
   - H 6
   - J 7

7. $\begin{array}{r} 14 \\ - 5 \\ \hline \blacksquare \end{array}$
   - A 8
   - B 9
   - C 10
   - D 11

8. $15 - \blacksquare = 7$
   - F 6
   - G 7
   - H 8
   - J 9

9. Which subtraction fact relates to $5 + 9 = 14$?
   - A $14 - 5 = 9$
   - B $14 - 14 = 0$
   - C $9 - 5 = 4$
   - D $14 - 6 = 8$

10. Which addition fact relates to $13 - 6 = 7$?
    - F $6 + 7 = 13$
    - G $6 + 1 = 7$
    - H $9 + 4 = 13$
    - J $3 + 4 = 7$

48 Grade 2
GO ON

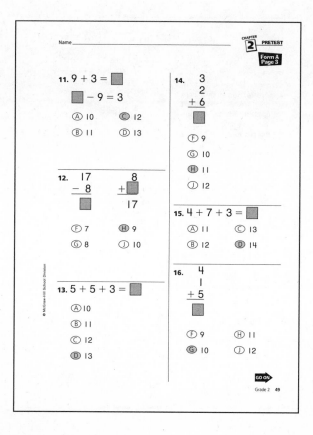

11. $9 + 3 = \blacksquare$
    $\blacksquare - 9 = 3$
    - A 10 C 12
    - B 11 D 13

12. $\begin{array}{r} 17 \\ - 8 \\ \hline \blacksquare \end{array}$ $\begin{array}{r} 8 \\ + \blacksquare \\ \hline 17 \end{array}$
    - F 7 H 9
    - G 8 J 10

13. $5 + 5 + 3 = \blacksquare$
    - A 10
    - B 11
    - C 12
    - D 13

14. $\begin{array}{r} 3 \\ 2 \\ + 6 \\ \hline \blacksquare \end{array}$
    - F 9
    - G 10
    - H 11
    - J 12

15. $4 + 7 + 3 = \blacksquare$
    - A 11 C 13
    - B 12 D 14

16. $\begin{array}{r} 4 \\ 1 \\ + 5 \\ \hline \blacksquare \end{array}$
    - F 9 H 11
    - G 10 J 12

GO ON
Grade 2 49

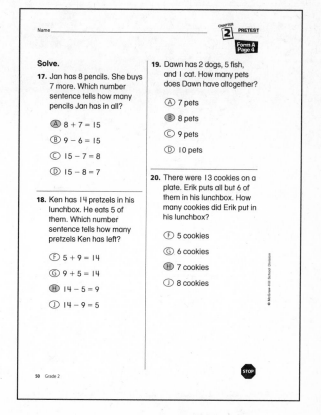

Solve.

17. Jan has 8 pencils. She buys 7 more. Which number sentence tells how many pencils Jan has in all?
    - A $8 + 7 = 15$
    - B $9 - 6 = 15$
    - C $15 - 7 = 8$
    - D $15 - 8 = 7$

18. Ken has 14 pretzels in his lunchbox. He eats 5 of them. Which number sentence tells how many pretzels Ken has left?
    - F $5 + 9 = 14$
    - G $9 + 5 = 14$
    - H $14 - 5 = 9$
    - J $14 - 9 = 5$

19. Dawn has 2 dogs, 5 fish, and 1 cat. How many pets does Dawn have altogether?
    - A 7 pets
    - B 8 pets
    - C 9 pets
    - D 10 pets

20. There were 13 cookies on a plate. Erik puts all but 6 of them in his lunchbox. How many cookies did Erik put in his lunchbox?
    - F 5 cookies
    - G 6 cookies
    - H 7 cookies
    - J 8 cookies

50 Grade 2
STOP

Page 1

Write the answer.

1. $8 + 8 = 16$

4. $6 + \underline{}9 = 15$

2. $\begin{array}{r} 7 \\ + 6 \\ \hline 13 \end{array}$

5. $\begin{array}{r} 16 \\ - 8 \\ \hline 8 \end{array}$

3. $\begin{array}{r} 9 \\ + 4 \\ \hline 13 \end{array}$

GO ON

Page 2

6. $14 - 9 = \underline{}5$

7. $\begin{array}{r} 14 \\ - 5 \\ \hline 9 \end{array}$

8. $15 - \underline{}8 = 7$

9. What is the subtraction fact that relates to $5 + 9 = 14$?

$14 - 5 = 9$

10. What is the addition fact that relates to $13 - 6 = 7$?

$6 + 7 = 13$

GO ON

Page 3

11. $9 + 3 = \underline{}12$

$\underline{}12 - 9 = 3$

12. $\begin{array}{r} 17 \\ - 8 \\ \hline 9 \end{array}$ $\begin{array}{r} 8 \\ + \boxed{9} \\ \hline 17 \end{array}$

13. $5 + 5 + 3 = \underline{}13$

14. $\begin{array}{r} 3 \\ 2 \\ + 6 \\ \hline 11 \end{array}$

15. $4 + 7 + 3 = \underline{}14$

16. $\begin{array}{r} 4 \\ 1 \\ + 5 \\ \hline 10 \end{array}$

GO ON

Page 4

Solve.

17. Jan has 8 pencils. She buys 7 more. How many pencils does she have altogether? Circle the number sentence that you would use to solve this problem.

(8 + 7 = 15)
9 − 6 = 15
15 − 7 = 8
15 − 8 = 7

18. Ken has 14 pretzels in his lunchbox. He eats 5 of them. How many pretzels does Ken have now? Circle the number sentence that you would use to solve this problem.

5 + 9 = 14
9 + 5 = 14
(14 − 5 = 9)
14 − 9 = 5

19. Dawn has 2 dogs, 5 fish, and 1 cat. How many pets does Dawn have altogether?

$\underline{}8$ pets

20. There were 13 cookies on a plate. Erik puts all but 6 of them in his lunchbox. How many cookies did Erik put in his lunchbox?

$\underline{}7$ cookies

STOP

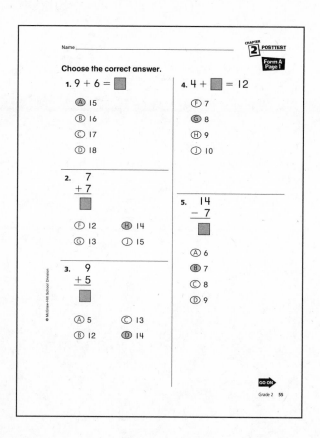

Choose the correct answer.

1. 9 + 6 = ▢
   - Ⓐ 15
   - Ⓑ 16
   - Ⓒ 17
   - Ⓓ 18

2. 7
   + 7
   ▢
   - Ⓕ 12   Ⓗ 14
   - Ⓖ 13   Ⓙ 15

3. 9
   + 5
   ▢
   - Ⓐ 5   Ⓒ 13
   - Ⓑ 12   Ⓓ 14

4. 4 + ▢ = 12
   - Ⓕ 7
   - Ⓖ 8
   - Ⓗ 9
   - Ⓙ 10

5. 14
   − 7
   ▢
   - Ⓐ 6
   - Ⓑ 7
   - Ⓒ 8
   - Ⓓ 9

GO ON

Grade 2 **55**

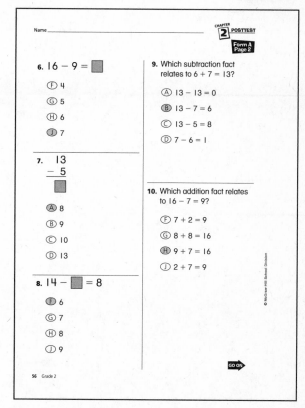

6. 16 − 9 = ▢
   - Ⓕ 4
   - Ⓖ 5
   - Ⓗ 6
   - Ⓙ 7

7. 13
   − 5
   ▢
   - Ⓐ 8
   - Ⓑ 9
   - Ⓒ 10
   - Ⓓ 13

8. 14 − ▢ = 8
   - Ⓕ 6
   - Ⓖ 7
   - Ⓗ 8
   - Ⓙ 9

9. Which subtraction fact relates to 6 + 7 = 13?
   - Ⓐ 13 − 13 = 0
   - Ⓑ 13 − 7 = 6
   - Ⓒ 13 − 5 = 8
   - Ⓓ 7 − 6 = 1

10. Which addition fact relates to 16 − 7 = 9?
   - Ⓕ 7 + 2 = 9
   - Ⓖ 8 + 8 = 16
   - Ⓗ 9 + 7 = 16
   - Ⓙ 2 + 7 = 9

GO ON

56 Grade 2

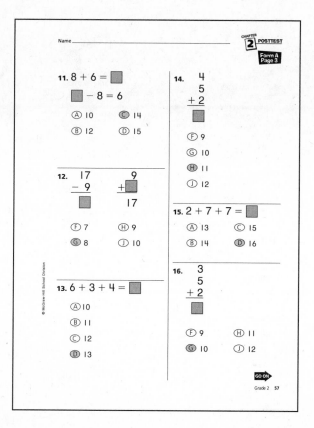

11. 8 + 6 = ▢
    ▢ − 8 = 6
    - Ⓐ 10   Ⓒ 14
    - Ⓑ 12   Ⓓ 15

12. 17   9
    − 9   + ▢
    ▢   17
    - Ⓕ 7   Ⓗ 9
    - Ⓖ 8   Ⓙ 10

13. 6 + 3 + 4 = ▢
    - Ⓐ 10
    - Ⓑ 11
    - Ⓒ 12
    - Ⓓ 13

14. 4
    5
    + 2
    ▢
    - Ⓕ 9
    - Ⓖ 10
    - Ⓗ 11
    - Ⓙ 12

15. 2 + 7 + 7 = ▢
    - Ⓐ 13   Ⓒ 15
    - Ⓑ 14   Ⓓ 16

16. 3
    5
    + 2
    ▢
    - Ⓕ 9   Ⓗ 11
    - Ⓖ 10   Ⓙ 12

GO ON

Grade 2 **57**

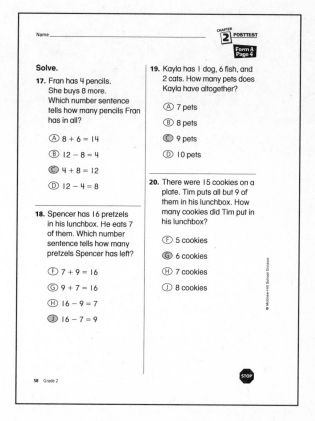

Solve.

17. Fran has 4 pencils. She buys 8 more. Which number sentence tells how many pencils Fran has in all?
   - Ⓐ 8 + 6 = 14
   - Ⓑ 12 − 8 = 4
   - Ⓒ 4 + 8 = 12
   - Ⓓ 12 − 4 = 8

18. Spencer has 16 pretzels in his lunchbox. He eats 7 of them. Which number sentence tells how many pretzels Spencer has left?
   - Ⓕ 7 + 9 = 16
   - Ⓖ 9 + 7 = 16
   - Ⓗ 16 − 9 = 7
   - Ⓙ 16 − 7 = 9

19. Kayla has 1 dog, 6 fish, and 2 cats. How many pets does Kayla have altogether?
   - Ⓐ 7 pets
   - Ⓑ 8 pets
   - Ⓒ 9 pets
   - Ⓓ 10 pets

20. There were 15 cookies on a plate. Tim puts all but 9 of them in his lunchbox. How many cookies did Tim put in his lunchbox?
   - Ⓕ 5 cookies
   - Ⓖ 6 cookies
   - Ⓗ 7 cookies
   - Ⓙ 8 cookies

STOP

58 Grade 2

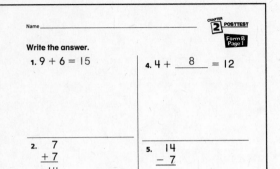

Name_____

Write the answer.

1. $9 + 6 = 15$

4. $4 + \underline{\quad 8 \quad} = 12$

2. $\begin{array}{r} 7 \\ + 7 \\ \hline 14 \end{array}$

5. $\begin{array}{r} 14 \\ - 7 \\ \hline 7 \end{array}$

3. $\begin{array}{r} 9 \\ + 5 \\ \hline 14 \end{array}$

© McGraw-Hill School Division

Name_____

6. $16 - 9 = \underline{\quad 7 \quad}$

9. What is the subtraction fact that relates to $6 + 7 = 13$?

$13 - 7 = 6$

7. $\begin{array}{r} 13 \\ - 5 \\ \hline 8 \end{array}$

10. What is the addition fact that relates to $16 - 7 = 9$?

$9 + 7 = 16$

8. $14 - \underline{\quad 6 \quad} = 8$

© McGraw-Hill School Division

Name_____

11. $8 + 6 = \underline{\quad 14 \quad}$

14. $\begin{array}{r} 4 \\ 5 \\ + 2 \\ \hline 11 \end{array}$

12. $\begin{array}{r} 17 \\ - 9 \\ \hline 8 \end{array}$

15. $2 + 7 + 7 = \underline{\quad 16 \quad}$

13. $6 + 3 + 4 = \underline{\quad 13 \quad}$

16. $\begin{array}{r} 3 \\ 5 \\ + 2 \\ \hline 10 \end{array}$

© McGraw-Hill School Division

Name_____

Solve.

17. Fran has 4 pencils. She buys 8 more. How many pencils does she have altogether? Circle the number sentence that you would use to solve this problem.

$8 + 6 = 15$

$12 - 8 = 4$

$\boxed{4 + 8 = 12}$

$12 - 4 = 8$

18. Spencer has 16 pretzels in his lunchbox. He eats 7 of them. How many pretzels does Spencer have now? Circle the number sentence that you would use to solve this problem.

$7 + 9 = 16$

$9 + 7 = 16$

$16 - 9 = 7$

$\boxed{16 - 7 = 9}$

19. Kayla has 1 dog, 6 fish, and 2 cats. How many pets does Kayla have altogether?

$\underline{\quad 9 \quad}$ pets

20. There were 15 cookies on a plate. Tim puts all but 9 of them in his lunchbox. How many cookies did Tim put in his lunchbox?

$\underline{\quad 6 \quad}$ cookies

© McGraw-Hill School Division

© McGraw-Hill School Division

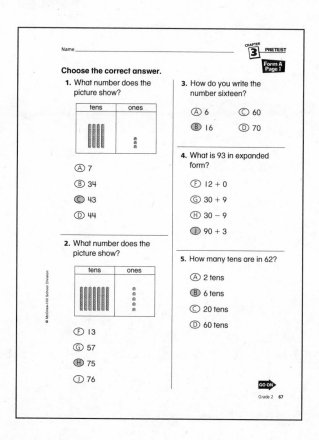

Page 1

Name _____

Choose the correct answer.

1. What number does the picture show?

| tens | ones |

(A) 7
(B) 34
(C) 43
(D) 44

2. What number does the picture show?

| tens | ones |

(F) 13
(G) 57
(H) 75
(J) 76

3. How do you write the number sixteen?

(A) 6   (C) 60
(B) 16   (D) 70

4. What is 93 in expanded form?

(F) 12 + 0
(G) 30 + 9
(H) 30 − 9
(J) 90 + 3

5. How many tens are in 62?

(A) 2 tens
(B) 6 tens
(C) 20 tens
(D) 60 tens

GO ON
Grade 2   67

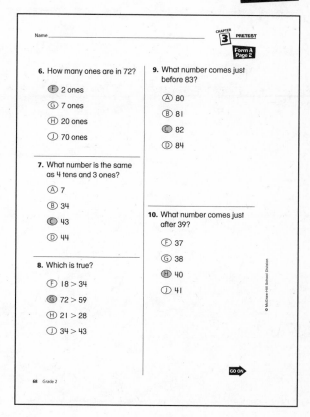

Page 2

Name _____

6. How many ones are in 72?

(F) 2 ones
(G) 7 ones
(H) 20 ones
(J) 70 ones

7. What number is the same as 4 tens and 3 ones?

(A) 7
(B) 34
(C) 43
(D) 44

8. Which is true?

(F) 18 > 34
(G) 72 > 59
(H) 21 > 28
(J) 34 > 43

9. What number comes just before 83?

(A) 80
(B) 81
(C) 82
(D) 84

10. What number comes just after 39?

(F) 37
(G) 38
(H) 40
(J) 41

GO ON
68   Grade 2

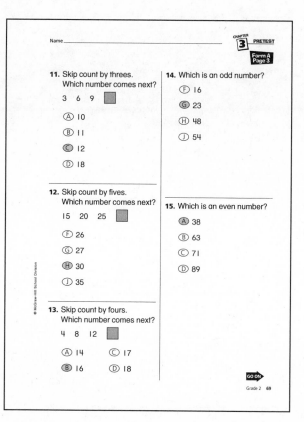

Page 3

Name _____

11. Skip count by threes. Which number comes next?

3 6 9 ☐

(A) 10
(B) 11
(C) 12
(D) 18

12. Skip count by fives. Which number comes next?

15 20 25 ☐

(F) 26
(G) 27
(H) 30
(J) 35

13. Skip count by fours. Which number comes next?

4 8 12 ☐

(A) 14   (C) 17
(B) 16   (D) 18

14. Which is an odd number?

(F) 16
(G) 23
(H) 48
(J) 54

15. Which is an even number?

(A) 38
(B) 63
(C) 71
(D) 89

GO ON
Grade 2   69

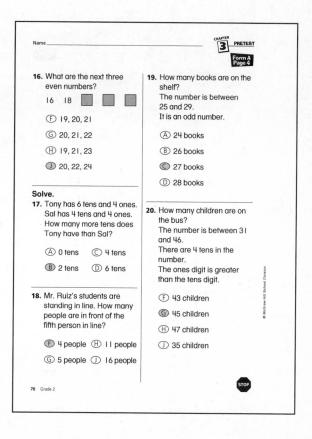

Page 4

Name _____

16. What are the next three even numbers?

16 18 ☐ ☐ ☐

(F) 19, 20, 21
(G) 20, 21, 22
(H) 19, 21, 23
(J) 20, 22, 24

Solve.

17. Tony has 6 tens and 4 ones. Sal has 4 tens and 4 ones. How many more tens does Tony have than Sal?

(A) 0 tens   (C) 4 tens
(B) 2 tens   (D) 6 tens

18. Mr. Ruiz's students are standing in line. How many people are in front of the fifth person in line?

(F) 4 people   (H) 11 people
(G) 5 people   (J) 16 people

19. How many books are on the shelf?
The number is between 25 and 29.
It is an odd number.

(A) 24 books
(B) 26 books
(C) 27 books
(D) 28 books

20. How many children are on the bus?
The number is between 31 and 46.
There are 4 tens in the number.
The ones digit is greater than the tens digit.

(F) 43 children
(G) 45 children
(H) 47 children
(J) 35 children

STOP
70   Grade 2

Grade 2   **347**

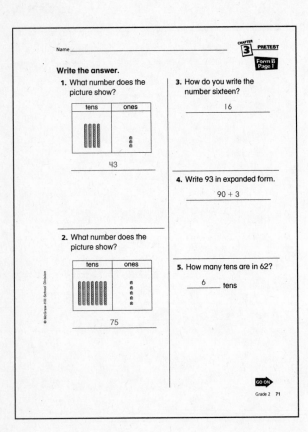

Name _____

Write the answer.

1. What number does the picture show?

tens	ones

43

2. What number does the picture show?

tens	ones

75

3. How do you write the number sixteen?

16

4. Write 93 in expanded form.

90 + 3

5. How many tens are in 62?

6 tens

GO ON

Grade 2 **71**

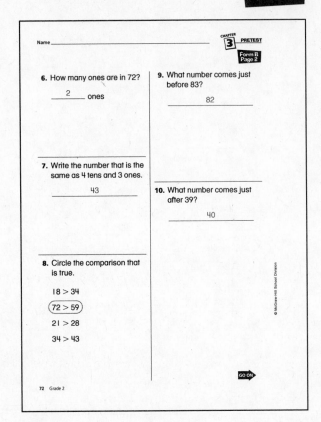

Name _____

6. How many ones are in 72?

2 ones

7. Write the number that is the same as 4 tens and 3 ones.

43

8. Circle the comparison that is true.

18 > 34

(72 > 59)

21 > 28

34 > 43

9. What number comes just before 83?

82

10. What number comes just after 39?

40

GO ON

72 Grade 2

Name _____

11. Skip count by threes. Which number comes next?

3 6 9 ___12___

12. Skip count by fives. Which number comes next?

15 20 25 ___30___

13. Skip count by fours. Which number comes next?

4 8 12 ___16___

14. Which is an odd number: 16, 23, 48, or 54?

23

15. Which is an even number: 38, 63, 71, or 89?

38

GO ON

Grade 2 **73**

Name _____

16. Write the next three even numbers.

16 18 _20_ _22_ _24_

Solve.

17. Tony has 6 tens and 4 ones. Sal has 4 tens and 4 ones. How many more tens does Tony have than Sal?

2 tens

18. Mr. Ruiz's students are standing in line. How many people are in front of the fifth person in line?

4 people

19. How many books are on the shelf?
The number is between 25 and 29.
It is an odd number.

27 books

20. How many children are on the bus?
The number is between 31 and 46.
There are 4 tens in the number.
The ones digit is greater than the tens digit.

45 children

STOP

74 Grade 2

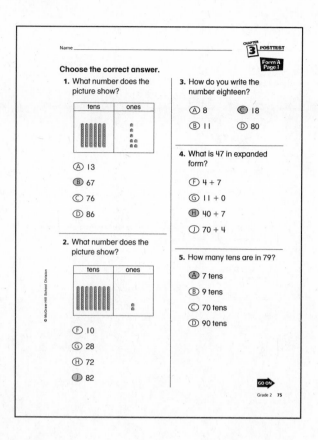

Name _____

Choose the correct answer.

1. What number does the picture show?

tens	ones

Ⓐ 13
Ⓑ 67
Ⓒ 76
Ⓓ 86

2. What number does the picture show?

tens	ones

Ⓕ 10
Ⓖ 28
Ⓗ 72
Ⓙ 82

3. How do you write the number eighteen?
Ⓐ 8   Ⓒ 18
Ⓑ 11   Ⓓ 80

4. What is 47 in expanded form?
Ⓕ 4 + 7
Ⓖ 11 + 0
Ⓗ 40 + 7
Ⓙ 70 + 4

5. How many tens are in 79?
Ⓐ 7 tens
Ⓑ 9 tens
Ⓒ 70 tens
Ⓓ 90 tens

Grade 2 75

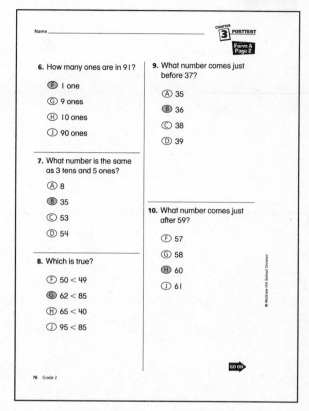

6. How many ones are in 91?
Ⓕ 1 one
Ⓖ 9 ones
Ⓗ 10 ones
Ⓙ 90 ones

7. What number is the same as 3 tens and 5 ones?
Ⓐ 8
Ⓑ 35
Ⓒ 53
Ⓓ 54

8. Which is true?
Ⓕ 50 < 49
Ⓖ 62 < 85
Ⓗ 65 < 40
Ⓙ 95 < 85

9. What number comes just before 37?
Ⓐ 35
Ⓑ 36
Ⓒ 38
Ⓓ 39

10. What number comes just after 59?
Ⓕ 57
Ⓖ 58
Ⓗ 60
Ⓙ 61

76 Grade 2

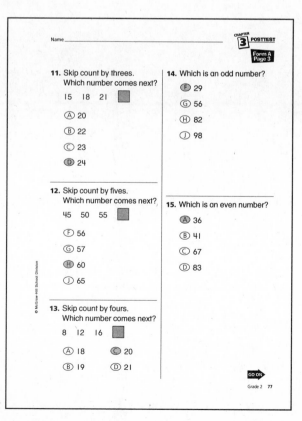

11. Skip count by threes. Which number comes next?
15 18 21 ▢
Ⓐ 20
Ⓑ 22
Ⓒ 23
Ⓓ 24

12. Skip count by fives. Which number comes next?
45 50 55 ▢
Ⓕ 56
Ⓖ 57
Ⓗ 60
Ⓙ 65

13. Skip count by fours. Which number comes next?
8 12 16 ▢
Ⓐ 18   Ⓒ 20
Ⓑ 19   Ⓓ 21

14. Which is an odd number?
Ⓕ 29
Ⓖ 56
Ⓗ 82
Ⓙ 98

15. Which is an even number?
Ⓐ 36
Ⓑ 41
Ⓒ 67
Ⓓ 83

Grade 2 77

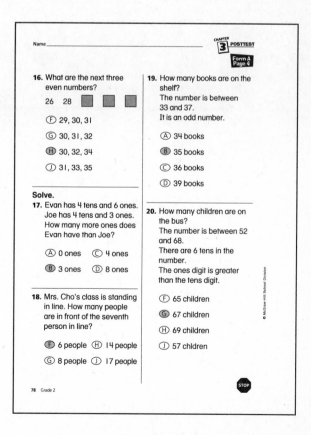

16. What are the next three even numbers?
26 28 ▢ ▢ ▢
Ⓕ 29, 30, 31
Ⓖ 30, 31, 32
Ⓗ 30, 32, 34
Ⓙ 31, 33, 35

Solve.

17. Evan has 4 tens and 6 ones. Joe has 4 tens and 3 ones. How many more ones does Evan have than Joe?
Ⓐ 0 ones   Ⓒ 4 ones
Ⓑ 3 ones   Ⓓ 8 ones

18. Mrs. Cho's class is standing in line. How many people are in front of the seventh person in line?
Ⓕ 6 people   Ⓗ 14 people
Ⓖ 8 people   Ⓙ 17 people

19. How many books are on the shelf?
The number is between 33 and 37.
It is an odd number.
Ⓐ 34 books
Ⓑ 35 books
Ⓒ 36 books
Ⓓ 39 books

20. How many children are on the bus?
The number is between 52 and 68.
There are 6 tens in the number.
The ones digit is greater than the tens digit.
Ⓕ 65 children
Ⓖ 67 children
Ⓗ 69 children
Ⓙ 57 children

78 Grade 2

Grade 2 **349**

Name _____

Write the answer.

1. What number does the picture show?

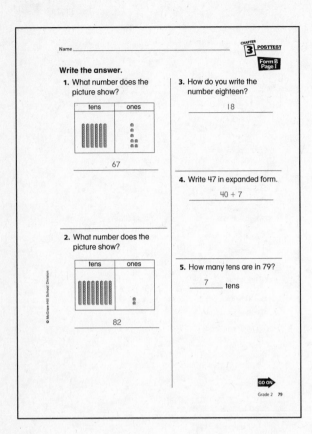

tens	ones

67

2. What number does the picture show?

tens	ones

82

3. How do you write the number eighteen?

18

4. Write 47 in expanded form.

40 + 7

5. How many tens are in 79?

7 tens

Name _____

6. How many ones are in 91?

1 ones

7. Write the number that is the same as 3 tens and 5 ones.

35

8. Circle the comparison that is true.

50 < 49

(62 < 85)

65 < 40

95 < 85

9. What number comes just before 37?

36

10. What number comes just after 59?

60

Name _____

11. Skip count by threes. Which number comes next?

15 18 21 24

12. Skip count by fives. Which number comes next?

45 50 55 60

13. Skip count by fours. Which number comes next?

8 12 16 20

14. Which is an odd number: 29, 56, 82, or 98?

29

15. Which is an even number: 36, 41, 67, or 83?

36

Name _____

16. Write the next three even numbers.

26 28 30 32 34

Solve.

17. Evan has 4 tens and 6 ones. Joe has 4 tens and 3 ones. How many more ones does Evan have than Joe?

3 ones

18. Mrs. Cho's class is standing in line. How many people are in front of the seventh person in line?

6 people

19. How many books are on the shelf?
The number is between 33 and 37.
It is an odd number.

35 books

20. How many children are on the bus?
The number is between 52 and 68.
There are 6 tens in the number.
The ones digit is greater than the tens digit.

67 children

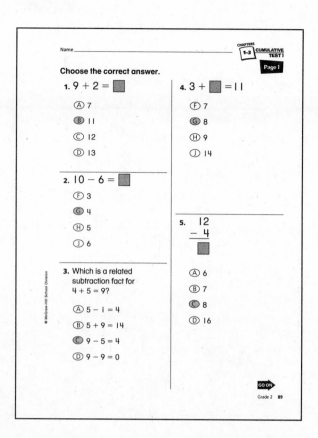

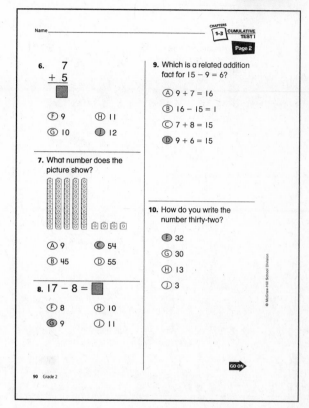

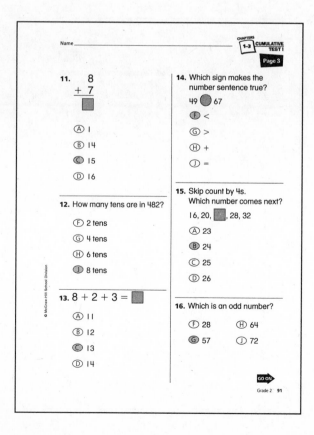

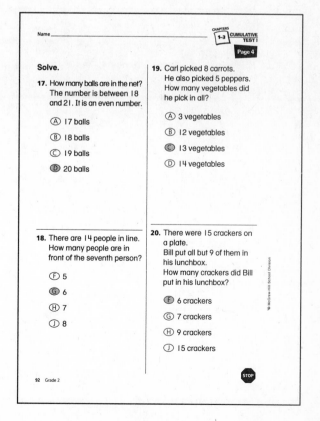

Page 1

Name _____

Choose the correct answer.

1. $9 + 2 =$ ▨
- Ⓐ 7
- Ⓑ 11
- Ⓒ 12
- Ⓓ 13

2. $10 - 6 =$ ▨
- Ⓕ 3
- Ⓖ 4
- Ⓗ 5
- Ⓙ 6

3. Which is a related subtraction fact for $4 + 5 = 9$?
- Ⓐ $5 - 1 = 4$
- Ⓑ $5 + 9 = 14$
- Ⓒ $9 - 5 = 4$
- Ⓓ $9 - 9 = 0$

4. $3 +$ ▨ $= 11$
- Ⓕ 7
- Ⓖ 8
- Ⓗ 9
- Ⓙ 14

5. $\begin{array}{r} 12 \\ -\ 4 \\ \hline \end{array}$ ▨
- Ⓐ 6
- Ⓑ 7
- Ⓒ 8
- Ⓓ 16

Grade 2 **89**

Page 2

6. $\begin{array}{r} 7 \\ +\ 5 \\ \hline \end{array}$ ▨
- Ⓕ 9 Ⓗ 11
- Ⓖ 10 Ⓙ 12

7. What number does the picture show?
- Ⓐ 9 Ⓒ 54
- Ⓑ 45 Ⓓ 55

8. $17 - 8 =$ ▨
- Ⓕ 8 Ⓗ 10
- Ⓖ 9 Ⓙ 11

9. Which is a related addition fact for $15 - 9 = 6$?
- Ⓐ $9 + 7 = 16$
- Ⓑ $16 - 15 = 1$
- Ⓒ $7 + 8 = 15$
- Ⓓ $9 + 6 = 15$

10. How do you write the number thirty-two?
- Ⓕ 32
- Ⓖ 30
- Ⓗ 13
- Ⓙ 3

90 Grade 2

Page 3

11. $\begin{array}{r} 8 \\ +\ 7 \\ \hline \end{array}$ ▨
- Ⓐ 1
- Ⓑ 14
- Ⓒ 15
- Ⓓ 16

12. How many tens are in 482?
- Ⓕ 2 tens
- Ⓖ 4 tens
- Ⓗ 6 tens
- Ⓙ 8 tens

13. $8 + 2 + 3 =$ ▨
- Ⓐ 11
- Ⓑ 12
- Ⓒ 13
- Ⓓ 14

14. Which sign makes the number sentence true?
49 ◯ 67
- Ⓕ $<$
- Ⓖ $>$
- Ⓗ $+$
- Ⓙ $=$

15. Skip count by 4s. Which number comes next?
16, 20, ▨, 28, 32
- Ⓐ 23
- Ⓑ 24
- Ⓒ 25
- Ⓓ 26

16. Which is an odd number?
- Ⓕ 28 Ⓗ 64
- Ⓖ 57 Ⓙ 72

Grade 2 **91**

Page 4

Solve.

17. How many balls are in the net? The number is between 18 and 21. It is an even number.
- Ⓐ 17 balls
- Ⓑ 18 balls
- Ⓒ 19 balls
- Ⓓ 20 balls

18. There are 14 people in line. How many people are in front of the seventh person?
- Ⓕ 5
- Ⓖ 6
- Ⓗ 7
- Ⓙ 8

19. Carl picked 8 carrots. He also picked 5 peppers. How many vegetables did he pick in all?
- Ⓐ 3 vegetables
- Ⓑ 12 vegetables
- Ⓒ 13 vegetables
- Ⓓ 14 vegetables

20. There were 15 crackers on a plate. Bill put all but 9 of them in his lunchbox. How many crackers did Bill put in his lunchbox?
- Ⓕ 6 crackers
- Ⓖ 7 crackers
- Ⓗ 9 crackers
- Ⓙ 15 crackers

92 Grade 2

Grade 2 **351**

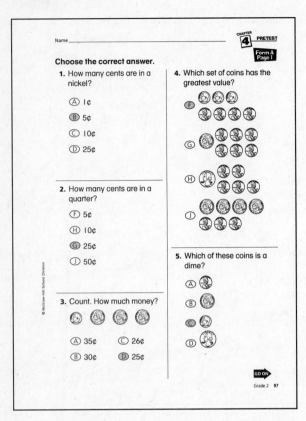

Name _____

Choose the correct answer.

1. How many cents are in a nickel?

Ⓐ 1¢
Ⓑ 5¢
Ⓒ 10¢
Ⓓ 25¢

2. How many cents are in a quarter?

Ⓕ 5¢
Ⓗ 10¢
Ⓖ 25¢
Ⓙ 50¢

3. Count. How much money?

Ⓐ 35¢   Ⓒ 26¢
Ⓑ 30¢   Ⓓ 25¢

4. Which set of coins has the greatest value?

Ⓕ
Ⓖ
Ⓗ
Ⓙ

5. Which of these coins is a dime?

Ⓐ
Ⓑ
Ⓒ
Ⓓ

GO ON

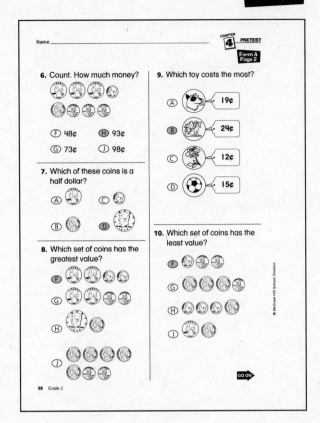

Name _____

6. Count. How much money?

Ⓕ 48¢   Ⓗ 93¢
Ⓖ 73¢   Ⓙ 98¢

7. Which of these coins is a half dollar?

Ⓐ   Ⓒ
Ⓑ   Ⓓ

8. Which set of coins has the greatest value?

Ⓕ
Ⓖ
Ⓗ
Ⓙ

9. Which toy costs the most?

Ⓐ — 19¢
Ⓑ — 24¢
Ⓒ — 12¢
Ⓓ — 15¢

10. Which set of coins has the least value?

Ⓕ
Ⓖ
Ⓗ
Ⓙ

GO ON

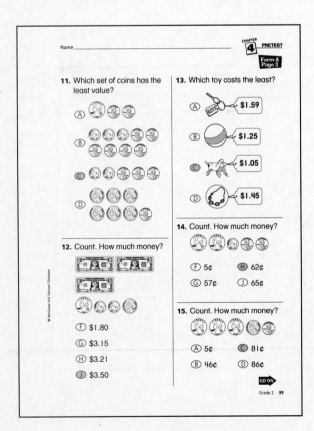

Name _____

11. Which set of coins has the least value?

Ⓐ
Ⓑ
Ⓒ
Ⓓ

12. Count. How much money?

Ⓕ $1.80
Ⓖ $3.15
Ⓗ $3.21
Ⓙ $3.50

13. Which toy costs the least?

Ⓐ — $1.59
Ⓑ — $1.25
Ⓒ — $1.05
Ⓓ — $1.45

14. Count. How much money?

Ⓕ 5¢   Ⓗ 62¢
Ⓖ 57¢   Ⓙ 65¢

15. Count. How much money?

Ⓐ 5¢   Ⓒ 81¢
Ⓑ 46¢   Ⓓ 86¢

GO ON

Name _____

16. Count. How much money?

Ⓕ $1.05
Ⓖ $1.17
Ⓗ $1.32
Ⓙ $1.50

Solve.

17. Kyle has 6 dimes. He buys a drink for 55¢. How much change should he get back?

Ⓐ 1¢   Ⓒ 10¢
Ⓑ 5¢   Ⓓ 50¢

18. Denise has dimes and nickels. How many ways can she buy a cookie for 25¢?

Ⓕ 1 way   Ⓗ 3 ways
Ⓖ 2 ways   Ⓙ 4 ways

19. Ted buys some candy for 65¢. He only has nickels. How many nickels does he need?

Ⓐ 5
Ⓑ 6
Ⓒ 11
Ⓓ 13

20. Evan wants to buy a glass of juice for 20¢. How many nickels does he need?

Ⓕ 2
Ⓖ 3
Ⓗ 4
Ⓙ 5

STOP

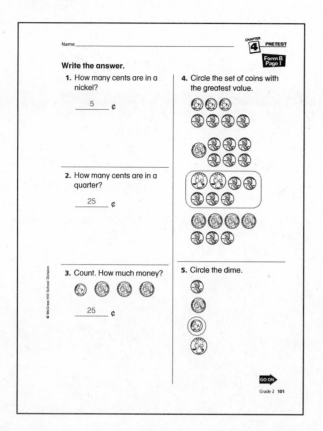

Name _____

Write the answer.

1. How many cents are in a nickel?

_____5_____ ¢

2. How many cents are in a quarter?

_____25_____ ¢

3. Count. How much money?

_____25_____ ¢

4. Circle the set of coins with the greatest value.

5. Circle the dime.

Name _____

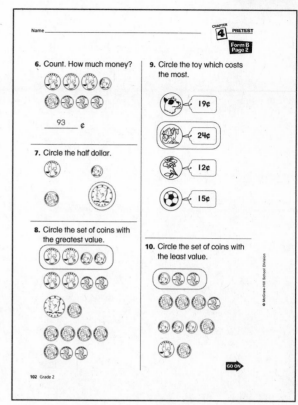

6. Count. How much money?

_____93_____ ¢

7. Circle the half dollar.

8. Circle the set of coins with the greatest value.

9. Circle the toy which costs the most.

19¢

24¢

12¢

15¢

10. Circle the set of coins with the least value.

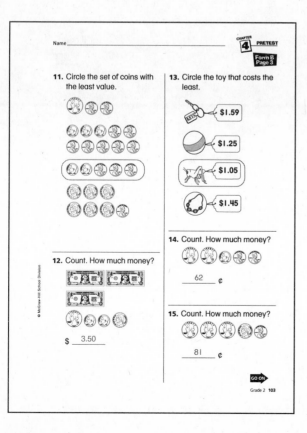

Name _____

11. Circle the set of coins with the least value.

12. Count. How much money?

$ _____3.50_____

13. Circle the toy that costs the least.

$1.59

$1.25

$1.05

$1.45

14. Count. How much money?

_____62_____ ¢

15. Count. How much money?

_____81_____ ¢

Name _____

16. Count. How much money?

$ _____1.32_____

Solve.

17. Kyle has 6 dimes. He buys a drink for 55¢. How much change should he get back?

_____5_____ ¢

18. Denise has dimes and nickels. How many ways can she buy a cookie for 25¢?

_____3_____ ways

19. Ted buys some candy for 65¢. He only has nickels. How many nickels does he need?

_____13_____ nickels

20. Evan wants to buy a glass of juice for 20¢. How many nickels does he need?

_____4_____ nickels

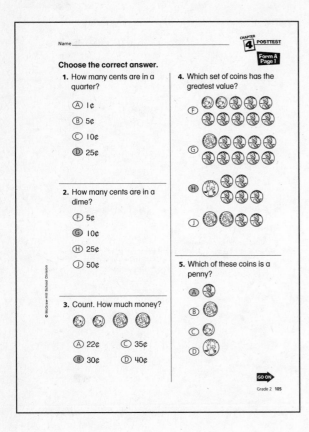

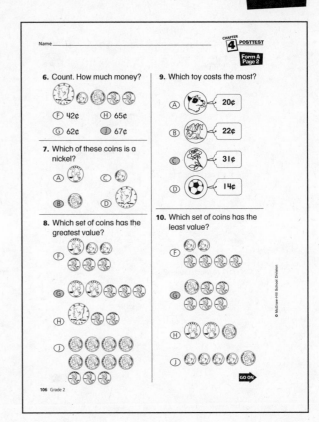

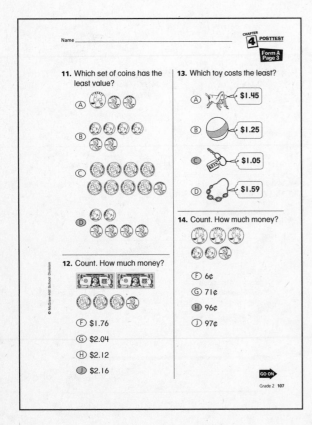

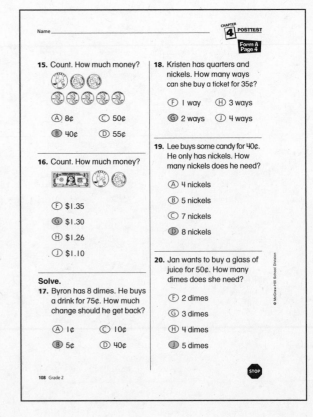

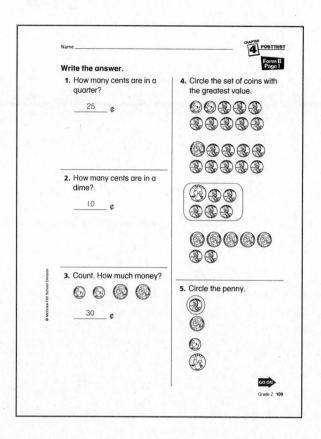

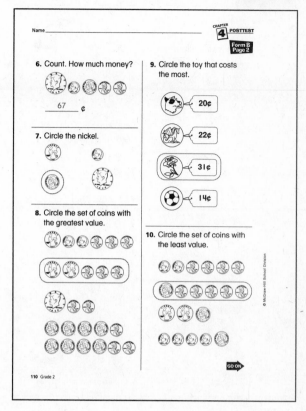

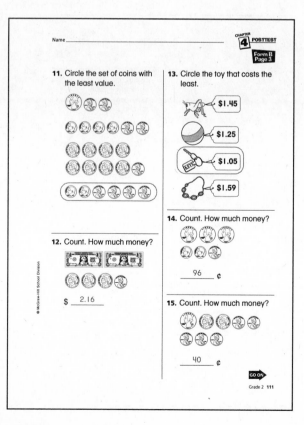

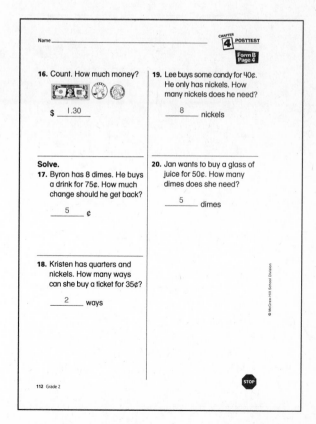

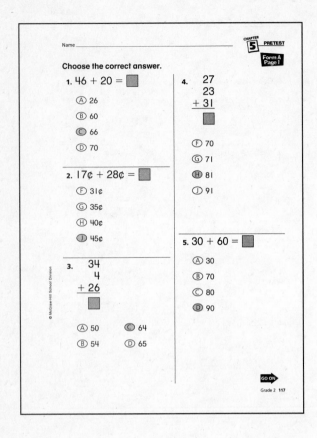

Choose the correct answer.

1. 46 + 20 = ☐
A 26
B 60
C 66
D 70

2. 17¢ + 28¢ = ☐
F 31¢
G 35¢
H 40¢
J 45¢

3.
$$\begin{array}{r} 34 \\ 4 \\ + 26 \\ \hline \square \end{array}$$
A 50   C 64
B 54   D 65

4.
$$\begin{array}{r} 27 \\ 23 \\ + 31 \\ \hline \square \end{array}$$
F 70
G 71
H 81
J 91

5. 30 + 60 = ☐
A 30
B 70
C 80
D 90

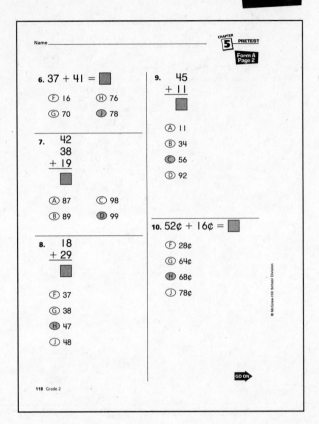

6. 37 + 41 = ☐
F 16   H 76
G 70   J 78

7.
$$\begin{array}{r} 42 \\ 38 \\ + 19 \\ \hline \square \end{array}$$
A 87   C 98
B 89   D 99

8.
$$\begin{array}{r} 18 \\ + 29 \\ \hline \square \end{array}$$
F 37
G 38
H 47
J 48

9.
$$\begin{array}{r} 45 \\ + 11 \\ \hline \square \end{array}$$
A 11
B 34
C 56
D 92

10. 52¢ + 16¢ = ☐
F 28¢
G 64¢
H 68¢
J 78¢

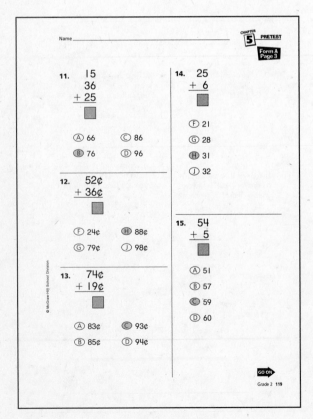

11.
$$\begin{array}{r} 15 \\ 36 \\ + 25 \\ \hline \square \end{array}$$
A 66   C 86
B 76   D 96

12.
$$\begin{array}{r} 52¢ \\ + 36¢ \\ \hline \square \end{array}$$
F 24¢   H 88¢
G 79¢   J 98¢

13.
$$\begin{array}{r} 74¢ \\ + 19¢ \\ \hline \square \end{array}$$
A 83¢   C 93¢
B 85¢   D 94¢

14.
$$\begin{array}{r} 25 \\ + 6 \\ \hline \square \end{array}$$
F 21
G 28
H 31
J 32

15.
$$\begin{array}{r} 54 \\ + 5 \\ \hline \square \end{array}$$
A 51
B 57
C 59
D 60

16.
$$\begin{array}{r} 47 \\ + 33 \\ \hline \square \end{array}$$
F 70   H 80
G 74   J 84

Solve.

17. On Tuesday, 18 boys and 16 girls visit the library. How many children visit the library in all?
A 22 children
B 27 children
C 34 children
D 40 children

18. There are 15 books about dogs and 12 books about cats on the shelf. How many books are on the shelf?
F 3 books   H 27 books
G 13 books   J 28 books

19. There are 10 children playing at the park. Then 18 more children join them. How many children are at the park in all?
A 12 children
B 28 children
C 30 children
D 38 children

20. Mr. Smith is at the store. He buys 12 red apples and 19 green apples. How many apples does he buy in all?
F 20 apples
G 21 apples
H 27 apples
J 31 apples

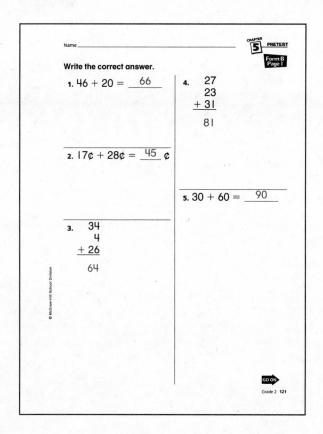

Write the correct answer.

1. 46 + 20 = __66__

2. 17¢ + 28¢ = __45__ ¢

3.
```
  34
   4
+ 26
  64
```

4.
```
  27
  23
+ 31
  81
```

5. 30 + 60 = __90__

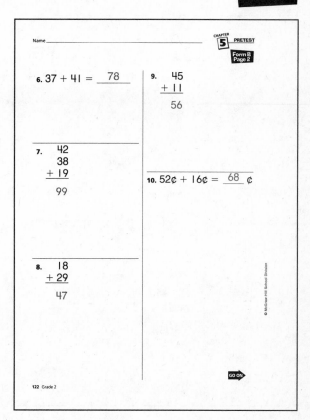

6. 37 + 41 = __78__

7.
```
  42
  38
+ 19
  99
```

8.
```
  18
+ 29
  47
```

9.
```
  45
+ 11
  56
```

10. 52¢ + 16¢ = __68__ ¢

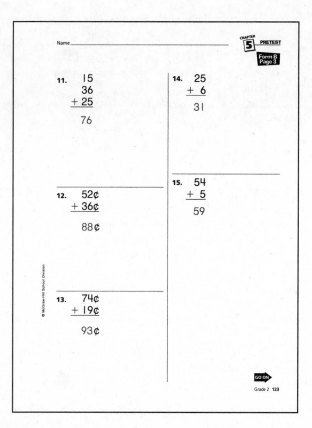

11.
```
  15
  36
+ 25
  76
```

12.
```
  52¢
+ 36¢
  88¢
```

13.
```
  74¢
+ 19¢
  93¢
```

14.
```
  25
+  6
  31
```

15.
```
  54
+  5
  59
```

16.
```
  47
+ 33
  80
```

Solve.

17. On Tuesday, 18 boys and 16 girls visit the library. How many children are at the library?

__34__ children

18. There are 15 books about dogs and 12 books about cats on the shelf. How many books are on the shelf?

__27__ books

19. There are 10 children playing at the park. Then 18 more children join them. How many children are at the park in all?

__28__ children

20. Mr. Smith is at the store. He buys 12 red apples and 19 green apples. How many apples does he buy in all?

__31__ apples

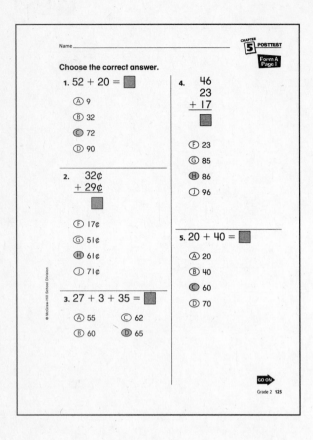

Choose the correct answer.

1. 52 + 20 = ☐

   Ⓐ 9
   Ⓑ 32
   Ⓒ 72
   Ⓓ 90

2. 32¢
   + 29¢
   ☐

   Ⓕ 17¢
   Ⓖ 51¢
   Ⓗ 61¢
   Ⓙ 71¢

3. 27 + 3 + 35 = ☐

   Ⓐ 55   Ⓒ 62
   Ⓑ 60   Ⓓ 65

4. 46
   23
   + 17
   ☐

   Ⓕ 23
   Ⓖ 85
   Ⓗ 86
   Ⓙ 96

5. 20 + 40 = ☐

   Ⓐ 20
   Ⓑ 40
   Ⓒ 60
   Ⓓ 70

GO ON

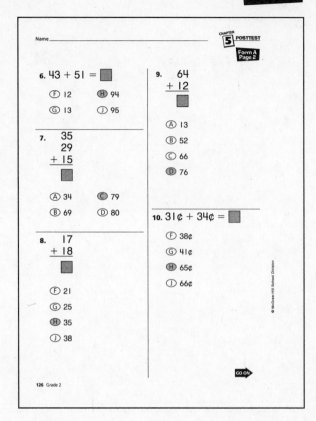

6. 43 + 51 = ☐

   Ⓕ 12   Ⓗ 94
   Ⓖ 13   Ⓙ 95

7. 35
   29
   + 15
   ☐

   Ⓐ 34   Ⓒ 79
   Ⓑ 69   Ⓓ 80

8. 17
   + 18
   ☐

   Ⓕ 21
   Ⓖ 25
   Ⓗ 35
   Ⓙ 38

9. 64
   + 12
   ☐

   Ⓐ 13
   Ⓑ 52
   Ⓒ 66
   Ⓓ 76

10. 31¢ + 34¢ = ☐

    Ⓕ 38¢
    Ⓖ 41¢
    Ⓗ 65¢
    Ⓙ 66¢

GO ON

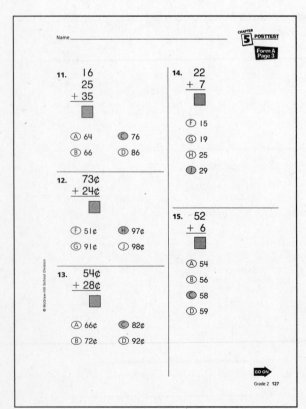

11. 16
    25
    + 35
    ☐

    Ⓐ 64   Ⓒ 76
    Ⓑ 66   Ⓓ 86

12. 73¢
    + 24¢
    ☐

    Ⓕ 51¢   Ⓗ 97¢
    Ⓖ 91¢   Ⓙ 98¢

13. 54¢
    + 28¢
    ☐

    Ⓐ 66¢   Ⓒ 82¢
    Ⓑ 72¢   Ⓓ 92¢

14. 22
    + 7
    ☐

    Ⓕ 15
    Ⓖ 19
    Ⓗ 25
    Ⓙ 29

15. 52
    + 6
    ☐

    Ⓐ 54
    Ⓑ 56
    Ⓒ 58
    Ⓓ 59

GO ON

16. 64
    + 19
    ☐

    Ⓕ 75   Ⓗ 83
    Ⓖ 78   Ⓙ 84

Solve.

17. On Friday, 19 boys and 15 girls visit the library. How many children visit the library in all?

    Ⓐ 16 children
    Ⓑ 24 children
    Ⓒ 34 children
    Ⓓ 40 children

18. There are 14 books about dogs and 15 books about cats on the shelf. How many books are on the shelf?

    Ⓕ 28 books   Ⓗ 30 books
    Ⓖ 29 books   Ⓙ 39 books

19. There are 17 children playing at the park. Then 11 more children join them. How many children are at the park in all?

    Ⓐ 14 children
    Ⓑ 28 children
    Ⓒ 30 children
    Ⓓ 36 children

20. Mr. Smith is at the store. He buys 15 red apples and 28 green apples. How many apples does he buy in all?

    Ⓕ 34 apples
    Ⓖ 42 apples
    Ⓗ 43 apples
    Ⓙ 44 apples

STOP

Name _____

Write the correct answer.

1. 52 + 20 = __72__

2.
```
   32¢
 + 29¢
 ─────
   61¢
```

3. 27 + 3 + 35 = __65__

4.
```
   46
   23
 + 17
 ────
   86
```

5. 20 + 40 = __60__

Name _____

6. 43 + 51 = __94__

7.
```
   35
   29
 + 15
 ────
   79
```

8.
```
   17
 + 18
 ────
   35
```

9.
```
   64
 + 12
 ────
   76
```

10. 31¢ + 34¢ = __65__ ¢

Name _____

11.
```
   16
   25
 + 35
 ────
   76
```

12.
```
   73¢
 + 24¢
 ─────
   97¢
```

13.
```
   54¢
 + 28¢
 ─────
   82¢
```

14.
```
   22
 +  7
 ────
   29
```

15.
```
   52
 +  6
 ────
   58
```

Name _____

16.
```
   64
 + 19
 ────
   83
```

Solve.

17. On Friday, 19 boys and 15 girls visit the library. How many children are at the library?
   __34__ children

18. There are 14 books about dogs and 15 books about cats on the shelf. How many books are on the shelf?
   __29__ books

19. There are 17 children playing at the park. Then 11 more children join them. How many children are at the park in all?
   __28__ children

20. Mr. Smith is at the store. He buys 15 red apples and 28 green apples. How many apples does he buy in all?
   __43__ apples

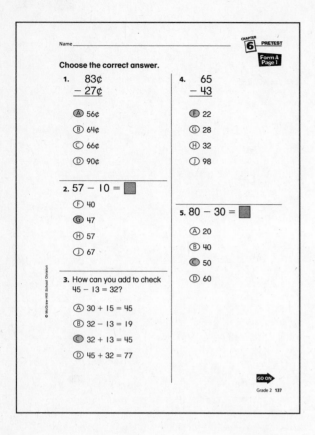

Choose the correct answer.

1. 83¢
   − 27¢

   (A) 56¢
   (B) 64¢
   (C) 66¢
   (D) 90¢

2. 57 − 10 = ▮

   (F) 40
   (G) 47
   (H) 57
   (J) 67

3. How can you add to check
   45 − 13 = 32?

   (A) 30 + 15 = 45
   (B) 32 − 13 = 19
   (C) 32 + 13 = 45
   (D) 45 + 32 = 77

4. 65
   − 43

   (F) 22
   (G) 28
   (H) 32
   (J) 98

5. 80 − 30 = ▮

   (A) 20
   (B) 40
   (C) 50
   (D) 60

GO ON

Grade 2 **137**

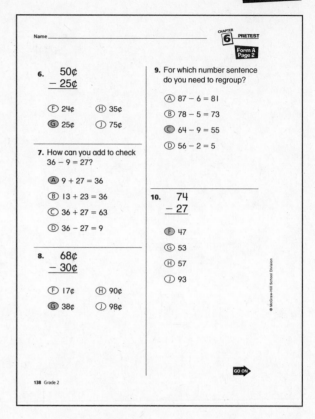

6. 50¢
   − 25¢

   (F) 24¢   (H) 35¢
   (G) 25¢   (J) 75¢

7. How can you add to check
   36 − 9 = 27?

   (A) 9 + 27 = 36
   (B) 13 + 23 = 36
   (C) 36 + 27 = 63
   (D) 36 − 27 = 9

8. 68¢
   − 30¢

   (F) 17¢   (H) 90¢
   (G) 38¢   (J) 98¢

9. For which number sentence
   do you need to regroup?

   (A) 87 − 6 = 81
   (B) 78 − 5 = 73
   (C) 64 − 9 = 55
   (D) 56 − 2 = 5

10. 74
    − 27

   (F) 47
   (G) 53
   (H) 57
   (J) 93

GO ON

138 Grade 2

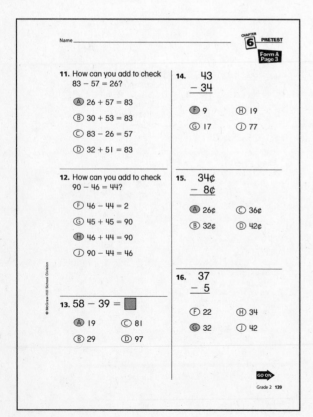

11. How can you add to check
    83 − 57 = 26?

    (A) 26 + 57 = 83
    (B) 30 + 53 = 83
    (C) 83 − 26 = 57
    (D) 32 + 51 = 83

12. How can you add to check
    90 − 46 = 44?

    (F) 46 − 44 = 2
    (G) 45 + 45 = 90
    (H) 46 + 44 = 90
    (J) 90 − 44 = 46

13. 58 − 39 = ▮

    (A) 19   (C) 81
    (B) 29   (D) 97

14. 43
    − 34

    (F) 9   (H) 19
    (G) 17   (J) 77

15. 34¢
    − 8¢

    (A) 26¢   (C) 36¢
    (B) 32¢   (D) 42¢

16. 37
    − 5

    (F) 22   (H) 34
    (G) 32   (J) 42

GO ON

Grade 2 **139**

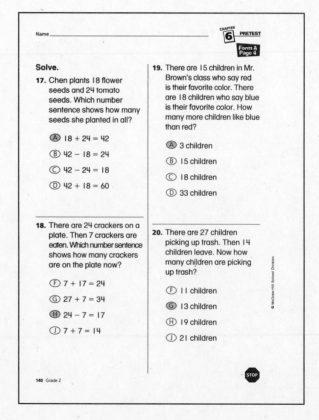

Solve.

17. Chen plants 18 flower
    seeds and 24 tomato
    seeds. Which number
    sentence shows how many
    seeds she planted in all?

    (A) 18 + 24 = 42
    (B) 42 − 18 = 24
    (C) 42 − 24 = 18
    (D) 42 + 18 = 60

18. There are 24 crackers on a
    plate. Then 7 crackers are
    eaten. Which number sentence
    shows how many crackers
    are on the plate now?

    (F) 7 + 17 = 24
    (G) 27 + 7 = 34
    (H) 24 − 7 = 17
    (J) 7 + 7 = 14

19. There are 15 children in Mr.
    Brown's class who say red
    is their favorite color. There
    are 18 children who say blue
    is their favorite color. How
    many more children like blue
    than red?

    (A) 3 children
    (B) 15 children
    (C) 18 children
    (D) 33 children

20. There are 27 children
    picking up trash. Then 14
    children leave. Now how
    many children are picking
    up trash?

    (F) 11 children
    (G) 13 children
    (H) 19 children
    (J) 21 children

STOP

140 Grade 2

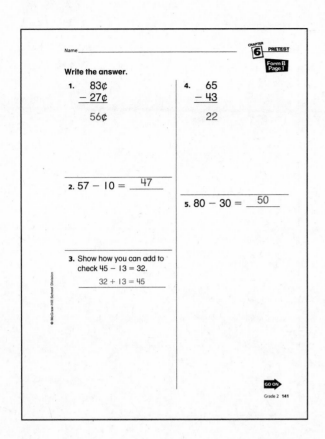

Name _____

Write the answer.

1. 83¢
    − 27¢
    ――――
    56¢

2. 57 − 10 = __47__

3. Show how you can add to check 45 − 13 = 32.

    32 + 13 = 45

4. 65
    − 43
    ――――
    22

5. 80 − 30 = __50__

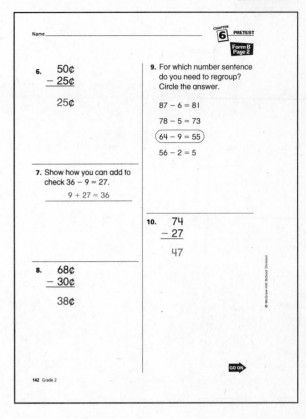

Name _____

6. 50¢
    − 25¢
    ――――
    25¢

7. Show how you can add to check 36 − 9 = 27.

    9 + 27 = 36

8. 68¢
    − 30¢
    ――――
    38¢

9. For which number sentence do you need to regroup? Circle the answer.

    87 − 6 = 81

    78 − 5 = 73

    (64 − 9 = 55)

    56 − 2 = 5

10. 74
    − 27
    ――――
    47

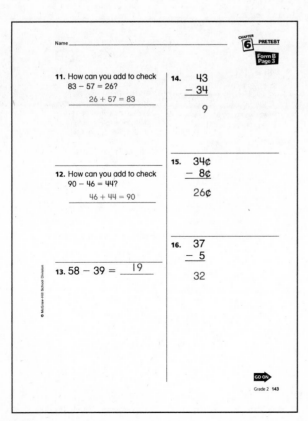

Name _____

11. How can you add to check 83 − 57 = 26?

    26 + 57 = 83

12. How can you add to check 90 − 46 = 44?

    46 + 44 = 90

13. 58 − 39 = __19__

14. 43
    − 34
    ――――
    9

15. 34¢
    − 8¢
    ――――
    26¢

16. 37
    − 5
    ――――
    32

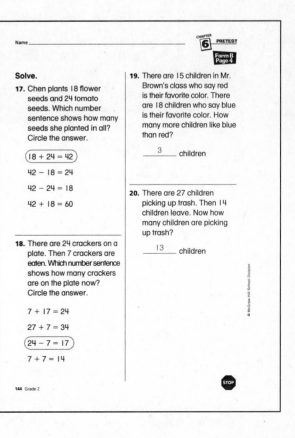

Name _____

Solve.

17. Chen plants 18 flower seeds and 24 tomato seeds. Which number sentence shows how many seeds she planted in all? Circle the answer.

    (18 + 24 = 42)

    42 − 18 = 24

    42 − 24 = 18

    42 + 18 = 60

18. There are 24 crackers on a plate. Then 7 crackers are eaten. Which number sentence shows how many crackers are on the plate now? Circle the answer.

    7 + 17 = 24

    27 + 7 = 34

    (24 − 7 = 17)

    7 + 7 = 14

19. There are 15 children in Mr. Brown's class who say red is their favorite color. There are 18 children who say blue is their favorite color. How many more children like blue than red?

    ___3___ children

20. There are 27 children picking up trash. Then 14 children leave. Now how many children are picking up trash?

    ___13___ children

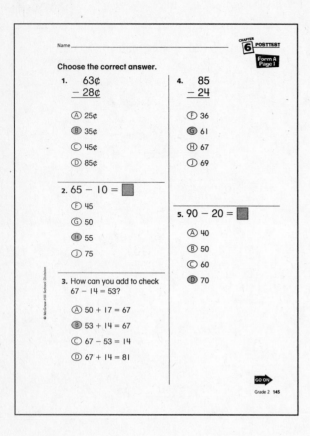

Name_____

Choose the correct answer.

1. 63¢
    − 28¢

    Ⓐ 25¢
    Ⓑ 35¢
    Ⓒ 45¢
    Ⓓ 85¢

2. 65 − 10 = ▓

    Ⓕ 45
    Ⓖ 50
    Ⓗ 55
    Ⓙ 75

3. How can you add to check
   67 − 14 = 53?

    Ⓐ 50 + 17 = 67
    Ⓑ 53 + 14 = 67
    Ⓒ 67 − 53 = 14
    Ⓓ 67 + 14 = 81

4. 85
    − 24

    Ⓕ 36
    Ⓖ 61
    Ⓗ 67
    Ⓙ 69

5. 90 − 20 = ▓

    Ⓐ 40
    Ⓑ 50
    Ⓒ 60
    Ⓓ 70

© McGraw-Hill School Division

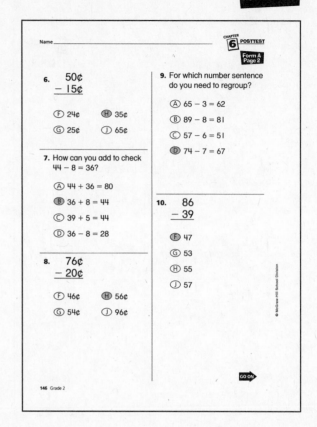

Name_____

6. 50¢
    − 15¢

    Ⓕ 24¢   Ⓗ 35¢
    Ⓖ 25¢   Ⓙ 65¢

7. How can you add to check
   44 − 8 = 36?

    Ⓐ 44 + 36 = 80
    Ⓑ 36 + 8 = 44
    Ⓒ 39 + 5 = 44
    Ⓓ 36 − 8 = 28

8. 76¢
    − 20¢

    Ⓕ 46¢   Ⓗ 56¢
    Ⓖ 54¢   Ⓙ 96¢

9. For which number sentence
   do you need to regroup?

    Ⓐ 65 − 3 = 62
    Ⓑ 89 − 8 = 81
    Ⓒ 57 − 6 = 51
    Ⓓ 74 − 7 = 67

10. 86
     − 39

    Ⓕ 47
    Ⓖ 53
    Ⓗ 55
    Ⓙ 57

© McGraw-Hill School Division

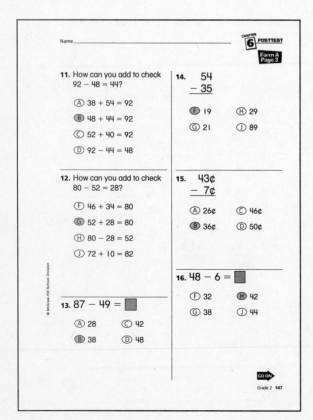

Name_____

11. How can you add to check
    92 − 48 = 44?

    Ⓐ 38 + 54 = 92
    Ⓑ 48 + 44 = 92
    Ⓒ 52 + 40 = 92
    Ⓓ 92 − 44 = 48

12. How can you add to check
    80 − 52 = 28?

    Ⓕ 46 + 34 = 80
    Ⓖ 52 + 28 = 80
    Ⓗ 80 − 28 = 52
    Ⓙ 72 + 10 = 82

13. 87 − 49 = ▓

    Ⓐ 28   Ⓒ 42
    Ⓑ 38   Ⓓ 48

14. 54
     − 35

    Ⓕ 19   Ⓗ 29
    Ⓖ 21   Ⓙ 89

15. 43¢
     − 7¢

    Ⓐ 26¢   Ⓒ 46¢
    Ⓑ 36¢   Ⓓ 50¢

16. 48 − 6 = ▓

    Ⓕ 32   Ⓗ 42
    Ⓖ 38   Ⓙ 44

© McGraw-Hill School Division

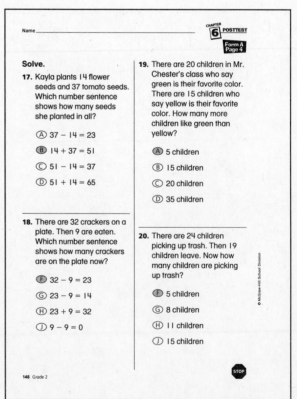

Name_____

Solve.

17. Kayla plants 14 flower
    seeds and 37 tomato seeds.
    Which number sentence
    shows how many seeds
    she planted in all?

    Ⓐ 37 − 14 = 23
    Ⓑ 14 + 37 = 51
    Ⓒ 51 − 14 = 37
    Ⓓ 51 + 14 = 65

18. There are 32 crackers on a
    plate. Then 9 are eaten.
    Which number sentence
    shows how many crackers
    are on the plate now?

    Ⓕ 32 − 9 = 23
    Ⓖ 23 − 9 = 14
    Ⓗ 23 + 9 = 32
    Ⓙ 9 − 9 = 0

19. There are 20 children in Mr.
    Chester's class who say
    green is their favorite color.
    There are 15 children who
    say yellow is their favorite
    color. How many more
    children like green than
    yellow?

    Ⓐ 5 children
    Ⓑ 15 children
    Ⓒ 20 children
    Ⓓ 35 children

20. There are 24 children
    picking up trash. Then 19
    children leave. Now how
    many children are picking
    up trash?

    Ⓕ 5 children
    Ⓖ 8 children
    Ⓗ 11 children
    Ⓙ 15 children

© McGraw-Hill School Division

STOP

© McGraw-Hill School Division

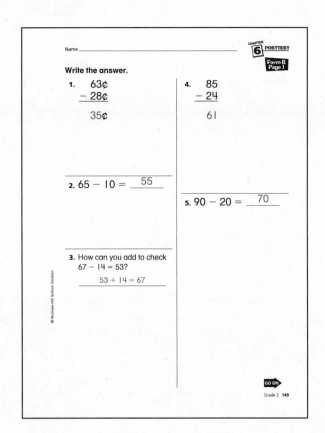

Write the answer.

1. 63¢
    − 28¢
    35¢

4. 85
    − 24
    61

2. 65 − 10 = __55__

5. 90 − 20 = __70__

3. How can you add to check
67 − 14 = 53?
    53 + 14 = 67

GO ON
Grade 2 **149**

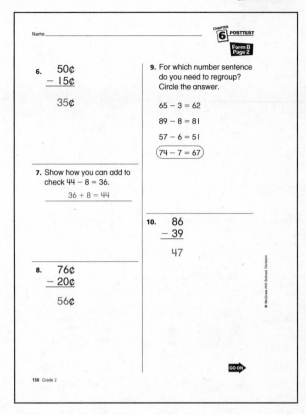

6. 50¢
    − 15¢
    35¢

7. Show how you can add to
check 44 − 8 = 36.
    36 + 8 = 44

8. 76¢
    − 20¢
    56¢

9. For which number sentence
do you need to regroup?
Circle the answer.

65 − 3 = 62

89 − 8 = 81

57 − 6 = 51

(74 − 7 = 67)

10. 86
    − 39
    47

GO ON
150 Grade 2

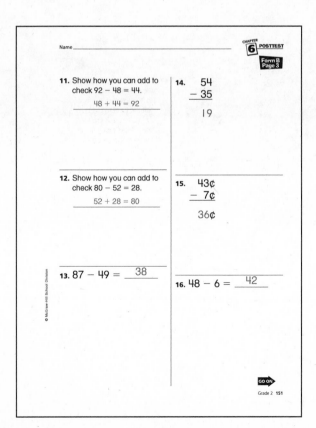

11. Show how you can add to
check 92 − 48 = 44.
    48 + 44 = 92

12. Show how you can add to
check 80 − 52 = 28.
    52 + 28 = 80

13. 87 − 49 = __38__

14. 54
    − 35
    19

15. 43¢
    − 7¢
    36¢

16. 48 − 6 = __42__

GO ON
Grade 2 **151**

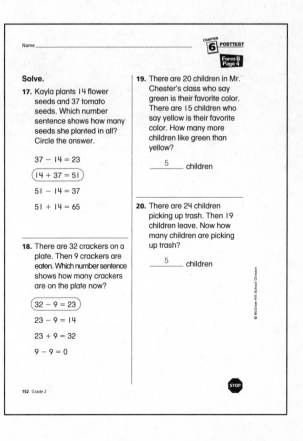

Solve.

17. Kayla plants 14 flower
seeds and 37 tomato
seeds. Which number
sentence shows how many
seeds she planted in all?
Circle the answer.

37 − 14 = 23

(14 + 37 = 51)

51 − 14 = 37

51 + 14 = 65

18. There are 32 crackers on a
plate. Then 9 crackers are
eaten. Which number sentence
shows how many crackers
are on the plate now?

(32 − 9 = 23)

23 − 9 = 14

23 + 9 = 32

9 − 9 = 0

19. There are 20 children in Mr.
Chester's class who say
green is their favorite color.
There are 15 children who
say yellow is their favorite
color. How many more
children like green than
yellow?

__5__ children

20. There are 24 children
picking up trash. Then 19
children leave. Now how
many children are picking
up trash?

__5__ children

STOP
152 Grade 2

Grade 2 **363**

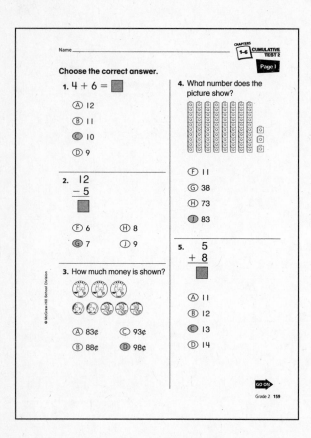

Name_____

CHAPTERS 1–6 CUMULATIVE TEST 2
Page 1

Choose the correct answer.

1. $4 + 6 = \blacksquare$

- Ⓐ 12
- Ⓑ 11
- Ⓒ 10
- Ⓓ 9

2.
$$\begin{array}{r} 12 \\ -\ 5 \\ \hline \blacksquare \end{array}$$

- Ⓕ 6   Ⓗ 8
- Ⓖ 7   Ⓙ 9

3. How much money is shown?

- Ⓐ 83¢   Ⓒ 93¢
- Ⓑ 88¢   Ⓓ 98¢

4. What number does the picture show?

- Ⓕ 11
- Ⓖ 38
- Ⓗ 73
- Ⓙ 83

5.
$$\begin{array}{r} 5 \\ +\ 8 \\ \hline \blacksquare \end{array}$$

- Ⓐ 11
- Ⓑ 12
- Ⓒ 13
- Ⓓ 14

GO ON

Grade 2 **159**

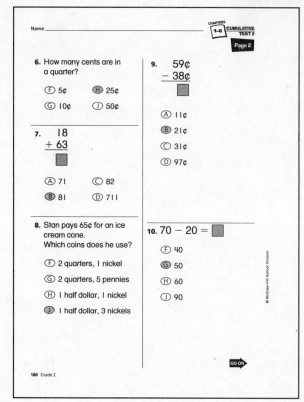

Name_____

CHAPTERS 1–6 CUMULATIVE TEST 2
Page 2

6. How many cents are in a quarter?

- Ⓕ 5¢   Ⓗ 25¢
- Ⓖ 10¢   Ⓙ 50¢

7.
$$\begin{array}{r} 18 \\ +\ 63 \\ \hline \blacksquare \end{array}$$

- Ⓐ 71   Ⓒ 82
- Ⓑ 81   Ⓓ 711

8. Stan pays 65¢ for an ice cream cone.
Which coins does he use?

- Ⓕ 2 quarters, 1 nickel
- Ⓖ 2 quarters, 5 pennies
- Ⓗ 1 half dollar, 1 nickel
- Ⓙ 1 half dollar, 3 nickels

9.
$$\begin{array}{r} 59¢ \\ -\ 38¢ \\ \hline \blacksquare \end{array}$$

- Ⓐ 11¢
- Ⓑ 21¢
- Ⓒ 31¢
- Ⓓ 97¢

10. $70 - 20 = \blacksquare$

- Ⓕ 40
- Ⓖ 50
- Ⓗ 60
- Ⓙ 90

GO ON

160 Grade 2

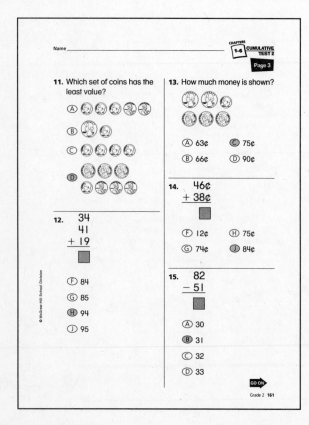

Name_____

CHAPTERS 1–6 CUMULATIVE TEST 2
Page 3

11. Which set of coins has the least value?

- Ⓐ
- Ⓑ
- Ⓒ
- Ⓓ

12.
$$\begin{array}{r} 34 \\ 41 \\ +\ 19 \\ \hline \blacksquare \end{array}$$

- Ⓕ 84
- Ⓖ 85
- Ⓗ 94
- Ⓙ 95

13. How much money is shown?

- Ⓐ 63¢   Ⓒ 75¢
- Ⓑ 66¢   Ⓓ 90¢

14.
$$\begin{array}{r} 46¢ \\ +\ 38¢ \\ \hline \blacksquare \end{array}$$

- Ⓕ 12¢   Ⓗ 75¢
- Ⓖ 74¢   Ⓙ 84¢

15.
$$\begin{array}{r} 82 \\ -\ 51 \\ \hline \blacksquare \end{array}$$

- Ⓐ 30
- Ⓑ 31
- Ⓒ 32
- Ⓓ 33

GO ON

Grade 2 **161**

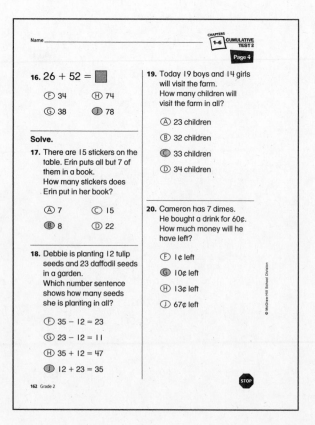

Name_____

CHAPTERS 1–6 CUMULATIVE TEST 2
Page 4

16. $26 + 52 = \blacksquare$

- Ⓕ 34   Ⓗ 74
- Ⓖ 38   Ⓙ 78

Solve.

17. There are 15 stickers on the table. Erin puts all but 7 of them in a book.
How many stickers does Erin put in her book?

- Ⓐ 7   Ⓒ 15
- Ⓑ 8   Ⓓ 22

18. Debbie is planting 12 tulip seeds and 23 daffodil seeds in a garden.
Which number sentence shows how many seeds she is planting in all?

- Ⓕ 35 − 12 = 23
- Ⓖ 23 − 12 = 11
- Ⓗ 35 + 12 = 47
- Ⓙ 12 + 23 = 35

19. Today 19 boys and 14 girls will visit the farm.
How many children will visit the farm in all?

- Ⓐ 23 children
- Ⓑ 32 children
- Ⓒ 33 children
- Ⓓ 34 children

20. Cameron has 7 dimes.
He bought a drink for 60¢.
How much money will he have left?

- Ⓕ 1¢ left
- Ⓖ 10¢ left
- Ⓗ 13¢ left
- Ⓙ 67¢ left

STOP

162 Grade 2

Name _____

Choose the correct answer.

1. What time does the clock show?

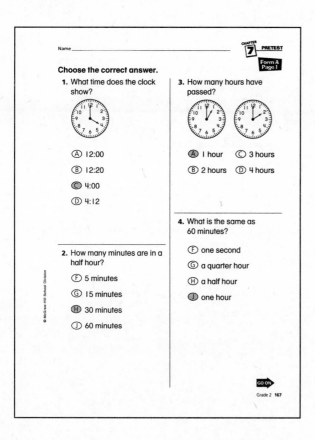

Ⓐ 12:00

Ⓑ 12:20

Ⓒ 4:00

Ⓓ 4:12

2. How many minutes are in a half hour?

Ⓕ 5 minutes

Ⓖ 15 minutes

Ⓗ 30 minutes

Ⓙ 60 minutes

3. How many hours have passed?

Ⓐ 1 hour   Ⓒ 3 hours

Ⓑ 2 hours   Ⓓ 4 hours

4. What is the same as 60 minutes?

Ⓕ one second

Ⓖ a quarter hour

Ⓗ a half hour

Ⓙ one hour

Name _____

Use the calendar to answer exercises 5–8.

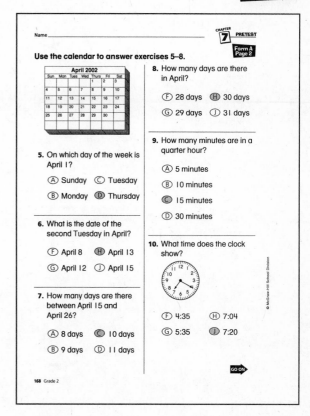

5. On which day of the week is April 1?

Ⓐ Sunday   Ⓒ Tuesday

Ⓑ Monday   Ⓓ Thursday

6. What is the date of the second Tuesday in April?

Ⓕ April 8   Ⓗ April 13

Ⓖ April 12   Ⓙ April 15

7. How many days are there between April 15 and April 26?

Ⓐ 8 days   Ⓒ 10 days

Ⓑ 9 days   Ⓓ 11 days

8. How many days are there in April?

Ⓕ 28 days   Ⓗ 30 days

Ⓖ 29 days   Ⓙ 31 days

9. How many minutes are in a quarter hour?

Ⓐ 5 minutes

Ⓑ 10 minutes

Ⓒ 15 minutes

Ⓓ 30 minutes

10. What time does the clock show?

Ⓕ 4:35   Ⓗ 7:04

Ⓖ 5:35   Ⓙ 7:20

Name _____

11. What is the same as 60 seconds?

Ⓐ one minute

Ⓑ a quarter hour

Ⓒ a half hour

Ⓓ one hour

12. What time does the clock show?

Ⓕ 3:55

Ⓖ 10:15

Ⓗ 11:15

Ⓙ 12:15

13. How many hours have passed?

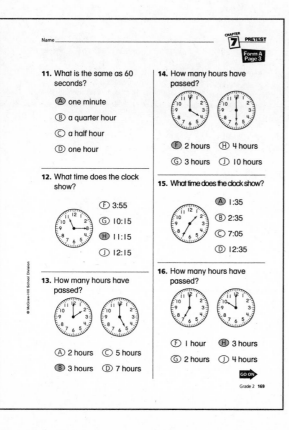

Ⓐ 2 hours   Ⓒ 5 hours

Ⓑ 3 hours   Ⓓ 7 hours

14. How many hours have passed?

Ⓕ 2 hours   Ⓗ 4 hours

Ⓖ 3 hours   Ⓙ 10 hours

15. What time does the clock show?

Ⓐ 1:35

Ⓑ 2:35

Ⓒ 7:05

Ⓓ 12:35

16. How many hours have passed?

Ⓕ 1 hour   Ⓗ 3 hours

Ⓖ 2 hours   Ⓙ 4 hours

Name _____

Solve.

17. Mrs. Ahart's class puts on puppet shows. Each show is 30 minutes long. How many minutes does it take to put on 2 puppet shows?

Ⓐ 30 minutes

Ⓑ 40 minutes

Ⓒ 50 minutes

Ⓓ 60 minutes

18. It takes 10 minutes to tell one puppet story. How long does it take to tell 3 puppet stories?

Ⓕ 10 minutes

Ⓖ 20 minutes

Ⓗ 30 minutes

Ⓙ 40 minutes

19. The puppets sing in the puppet show. It takes 4 minutes to sing each song. How long does it take to sing 5 puppet songs?

Ⓐ 5 minutes

Ⓑ 10 minutes

Ⓒ 20 minutes

Ⓓ 25 minutes

20. The students eat lunch at 12:30. They finish 30 minutes later. At what time do they finish?

Ⓕ 12:00

Ⓖ 12:30

Ⓗ 1:00

Ⓙ 1:30

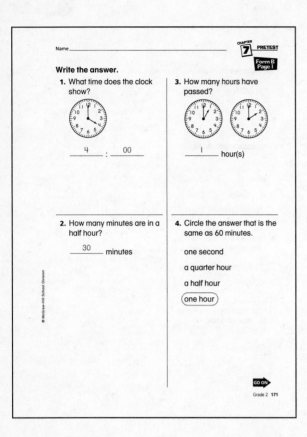

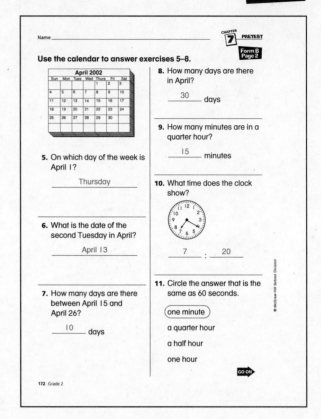

Name _____

Write the answer.

1. What time does the clock show?

___4___ : __00__

2. How many minutes are in a half hour?

___30___ minutes

3. How many hours have passed?

___I___ hour(s)

4. Circle the answer that is the same as 60 minutes.

one second

a quarter hour

a half hour

(one hour)

Name _____

Use the calendar to answer exercises 5–8.

April 2002						
Sun	Mon	Tues	Wed	Thurs	Fri	Sat
					1	2	3
4	5	6	7	8	9	10
11	12	13	14	15	16	17
18	19	20	21	22	23	24
25	26	27	28	29	30	

5. On which day of the week is April 1?

___Thursday___

6. What is the date of the second Tuesday in April?

___April 13___

7. How many days are there between April 15 and April 26?

___10___ days

8. How many days are there in April?

___30___ days

9. How many minutes are in a quarter hour?

___15___ minutes

10. What time does the clock show?

___7___ : __20__

11. Circle the answer that is the same as 60 seconds.

(one minute)

a quarter hour

a half hour

one hour

Name _____

12. What time does the clock show?

___11___ : __15__

13. How many hours have passed?

___3___ hours

14. How many hours have passed?

___2___ hours

15. What time does the clock show?

___I___ : __35__

16. How many hours have passed?

___3___ hours

Name _____

Solve.

17. Mrs. Ahart's class puts on puppet shows. Each show is 30 minutes long. How many minutes does it take to put on 2 puppet shows?

___60___ minutes

18. It takes 10 minutes to tell one puppet story. How long does it take to tell 3 puppet stories?

___30___ minutes

19. The puppets sing in the puppet show. It takes 4 minutes to sing each song. How long does it take to sing 5 puppet songs?

___20___ minutes

20. The students eat lunch at 12:30. They finish 30 minutes later. At what time do they finish?

___I___ : __00__

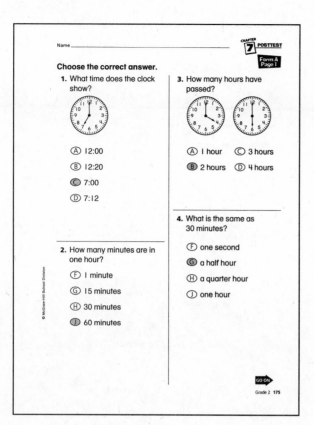

Name_____

Choose the correct answer.

1. What time does the clock show?

Ⓐ 12:00
Ⓑ 12:20
Ⓒ 7:00
Ⓓ 7:12

2. How many minutes are in one hour?

Ⓕ 1 minute
Ⓖ 15 minutes
Ⓗ 30 minutes
Ⓙ 60 minutes

3. How many hours have passed?

Ⓐ 1 hour   Ⓒ 3 hours
Ⓑ 2 hours   Ⓓ 4 hours

4. What is the same as 30 minutes?

Ⓕ one second
Ⓖ a half hour
Ⓗ a quarter hour
Ⓙ one hour

GO ON

Grade 2 **175**

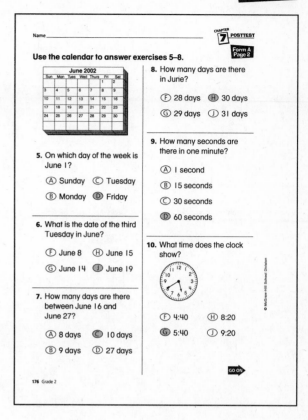

Name_____

Use the calendar to answer exercises 5–8.

June 2002

Sun	Mon	Tues	Wed	Thurs	Fri	Sat
					1	2
3	4	5	6	7	8	9
10	11	12	13	14	15	16
17	18	19	20	21	22	23
24	25	26	27	28	29	30

5. On which day of the week is June 1?

Ⓐ Sunday   Ⓒ Tuesday
Ⓑ Monday   Ⓓ Friday

6. What is the date of the third Tuesday in June?

Ⓕ June 8   Ⓗ June 15
Ⓖ June 14   Ⓙ June 19

7. How many days are there between June 16 and June 27?

Ⓐ 8 days   Ⓒ 10 days
Ⓑ 9 days   Ⓓ 27 days

8. How many days are there in June?

Ⓕ 28 days   Ⓗ 30 days
Ⓖ 29 days   Ⓙ 31 days

9. How many seconds are there in one minute?

Ⓐ 1 second
Ⓑ 15 seconds
Ⓒ 30 seconds
Ⓓ 60 seconds

10. What time does the clock show?

Ⓕ 4:40   Ⓗ 8:20
Ⓖ 5:40   Ⓙ 9:20

GO ON

176 Grade 2

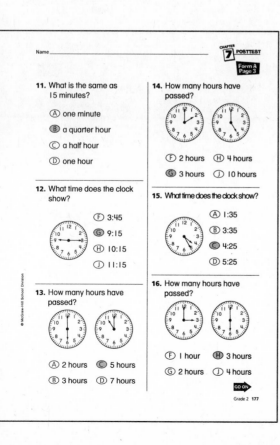

Name_____

11. What is the same as 15 minutes?

Ⓐ one minute
Ⓑ a quarter hour
Ⓒ a half hour
Ⓓ one hour

12. What time does the clock show?

Ⓕ 3:45
Ⓖ 9:15
Ⓗ 10:15
Ⓙ 11:15

13. How many hours have passed?

Ⓐ 2 hours   Ⓒ 5 hours
Ⓑ 3 hours   Ⓓ 7 hours

14. How many hours have passed?

Ⓕ 2 hours   Ⓗ 4 hours
Ⓖ 3 hours   Ⓙ 10 hours

15. What time does the clock show?

Ⓐ 1:35
Ⓑ 3:35
Ⓒ 4:25
Ⓓ 5:25

16. How many hours have passed?

Ⓕ 1 hour   Ⓗ 3 hours
Ⓖ 2 hours   Ⓙ 4 hours

GO ON

Grade 2 **177**

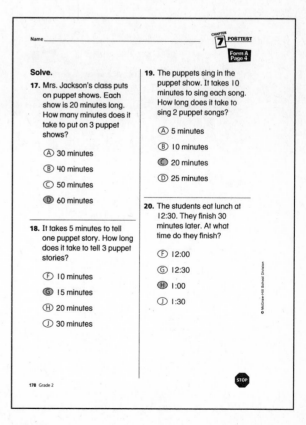

Name_____

Solve.

17. Mrs. Jackson's class puts on puppet shows. Each show is 20 minutes long. How many minutes does it take to put on 3 puppet shows?

Ⓐ 30 minutes
Ⓑ 40 minutes
Ⓒ 50 minutes
Ⓓ 60 minutes

18. It takes 5 minutes to tell one puppet story. How long does it take to tell 3 puppet stories?

Ⓕ 10 minutes
Ⓖ 15 minutes
Ⓗ 20 minutes
Ⓙ 30 minutes

19. The puppets sing in the puppet show. It takes 10 minutes to sing each song. How long does it take to sing 2 puppet songs?

Ⓐ 5 minutes
Ⓑ 10 minutes
Ⓒ 20 minutes
Ⓓ 25 minutes

20. The students eat lunch at 12:30. They finish 30 minutes later. At what time do they finish?

Ⓕ 12:00
Ⓖ 12:30
Ⓗ 1:00
Ⓙ 1:30

STOP

178 Grade 2

Name _____

7 POSTTEST
Form B
Page 1

Write the answer.

1. What time does the clock show?

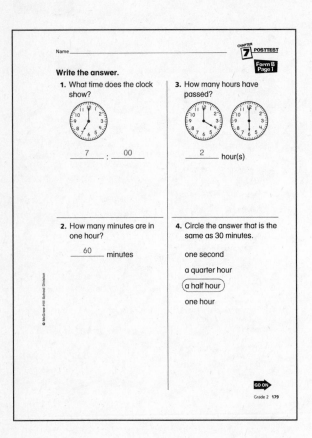

7 : 00

3. How many hours have passed?

2 hour(s)

2. How many minutes are in one hour?

60 minutes

4. Circle the answer that is the same as 30 minutes.

one second

a quarter hour

(a half hour)

one hour

GO ON
Grade 2 **179**

Name _____

7 POSTTEST
Form B
Page 2

Use the calendar to answer exercises 5–8.

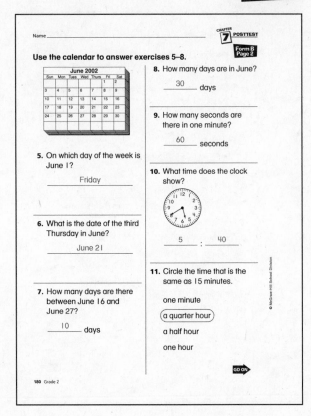

| June 2002 |
Sun	Mon	Tues	Wed	Thurs	Fri	Sat
					1	2
3	4	5	6	7	8	9
10	11	12	13	14	15	16
17	18	19	20	21	22	23
24	25	26	27	28	29	30

5. On which day of the week is June 1?

Friday

6. What is the date of the third Thursday in June?

June 21

7. How many days are there between June 16 and June 27?

10 days

8. How many days are in June?

30 days

9. How many seconds are there in one minute?

60 seconds

10. What time does the clock show?

5 : 40

11. Circle the time that is the same as 15 minutes.

one minute

(a quarter hour)

a half hour

one hour

GO ON
180 Grade 2

Name _____

7 POSTTEST
Form B
Page 3

12. What time does the clock show?

9 : 15

13. How many hours have passed?

5 hours

14. How many hours have passed?

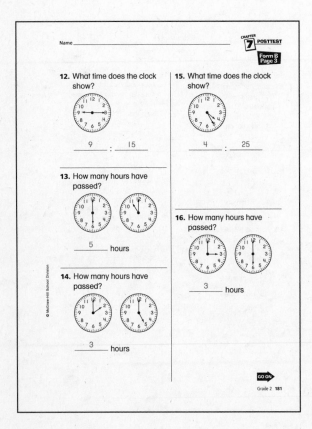

3 hours

15. What time does the clock show?

4 : 25

16. How many hours have passed?

3 hours

GO ON
Grade 2 **181**

Name _____

7 POSTTEST
Form B
Page 4

Solve.

17. Mrs. Jackson's class puts on puppet shows. Each show is 20 minutes long. How many minutes does it take to put on 3 puppet shows?

60 minutes

18. It takes 5 minutes to tell one puppet story. How long does it take to tell 3 puppet stories?

15 minutes

19. The puppets sing in the puppet show. It takes 10 minutes to sing each song. How long does it take to sing 2 puppet songs?

20 minutes

20. The students eat lunch at 12:30. They finish 30 minutes later. At what time do they finish?

1 : 00

STOP
182 Grade 2

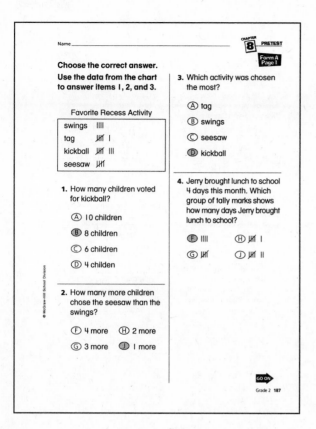

Choose the correct answer.
Use the data from the chart to answer items 1, 2, and 3.

Favorite Recess Activity

swings	IIII
tag	JHT I
kickball	JHT III
seesaw	JHT

1. How many children voted for kickball?

Ⓐ 10 children

Ⓑ 8 children

Ⓒ 6 children

Ⓓ 4 childen

2. How many more children chose the seesaw than the swings?

Ⓕ 4 more   Ⓗ 2 more

Ⓖ 3 more   Ⓙ 1 more

3. Which activity was chosen the most?

Ⓐ tag

Ⓑ swings

Ⓒ seesaw

Ⓓ kickball

4. Jerry brought lunch to school 4 days this month. Which group of tally marks shows how many days Jerry brought lunch to school?

Ⓕ IIII   Ⓗ JHT I

Ⓖ JHT   Ⓙ JHT II

GO ON

Grade 2 **187**

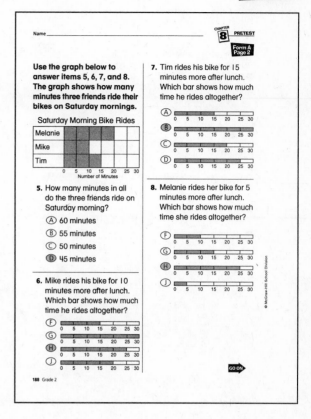

Use the graph below to answer items 5, 6, 7, and 8. The graph shows how many minutes three friends ride their bikes on Saturday mornings.

Saturday Morning Bike Rides

Melanie	
Mike	
Tim	

Number of Minutes

5. How many minutes in all do the three friends ride on Saturday morning?

Ⓐ 60 minutes

Ⓑ 55 minutes

Ⓒ 50 minutes

Ⓓ 45 minutes

6. Mike rides his bike for 10 minutes more after lunch. Which bar shows how much time he rides altogether?

Ⓕ

Ⓖ

Ⓗ

Ⓙ

7. Tim rides his bike for 15 minutes more after lunch. Which bar shows how much time he rides altogether?

Ⓐ

Ⓑ

Ⓒ

Ⓓ

8. Melanie rides her bike for 5 minutes more after lunch. Which bar shows how much time she rides altogether?

Ⓕ

Ⓖ

Ⓗ

Ⓙ

GO ON

188 Grade 2

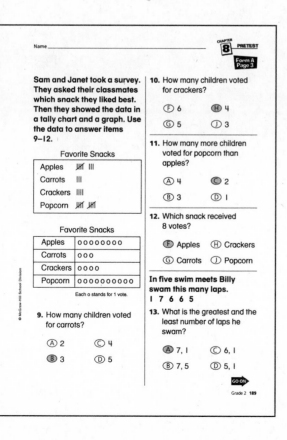

Sam and Janet took a survey. They asked their classmates which snack they liked best. Then they showed the data in a tally chart and a graph. Use the data to answer items 9–12.

Favorite Snacks

Apples	JHT III
Carrots	III
Crackers	IIII
Popcorn	JHT JHT

Favorite Snacks

Apples	o o o o o o o o
Carrots	o o o
Crackers	o o o o
Popcorn	o o o o o o o o o o

Each o stands for 1 vote.

9. How many children voted for carrots?

Ⓐ 2   Ⓒ 4

Ⓑ 3   Ⓓ 5

10. How many children voted for crackers?

Ⓕ 6   Ⓗ 4

Ⓖ 5   Ⓙ 3

11. How many more children voted for popcorn than apples?

Ⓐ 4   Ⓒ 2

Ⓑ 3   Ⓓ 1

12. Which snack received 8 votes?

Ⓕ Apples   Ⓗ Crackers

Ⓖ Carrots   Ⓙ Popcorn

In five swim meets Billy swam this many laps.
1 7 6 6 5

13. What is the greatest and the least number of laps he swam?

Ⓐ 7, 1   Ⓒ 6, 1

Ⓑ 7, 5   Ⓓ 5, 1

GO ON

Grade 2 **189**

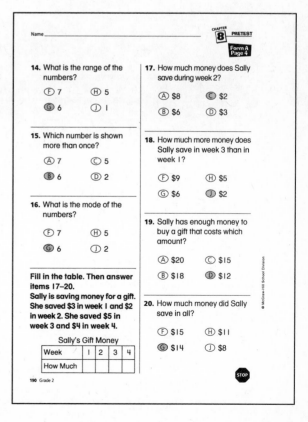

14. What is the range of the numbers?

Ⓕ 7   Ⓗ 5

Ⓖ 6   Ⓙ 1

15. Which number is shown more than once?

Ⓐ 7   Ⓒ 5

Ⓑ 6   Ⓓ 2

16. What is the mode of the numbers?

Ⓕ 7   Ⓗ 5

Ⓖ 6   Ⓙ 2

Fill in the table. Then answer items 17–20.
Sally is saving money for a gift. She saved $3 in week 1 and $2 in week 2. She saved $5 in week 3 and $4 in week 4.

Sally's Gift Money

Week	1	2	3	4
How Much				

17. How much money does Sally save during week 2?

Ⓐ $8   Ⓒ $2

Ⓑ $6   Ⓓ $3

18. How much more money does Sally save in week 3 than in week 1?

Ⓕ $9   Ⓗ $5

Ⓖ $6   Ⓙ $2

19. Sally has enough money to buy a gift that costs which amount?

Ⓐ $20   Ⓒ $15

Ⓑ $18   Ⓓ $12

20. How much money did Sally save in all?

Ⓕ $15   Ⓗ $11

Ⓖ $14   Ⓙ $8

STOP

190 Grade 2

Page 1

Write the correct answer.

Use the data from the chart to answer items 1, 2, and 3.

Favorite Recess Activity

swings	IIII
tag	I#I I
kickball	I#I III
seesaw	I#I

1. How many children voted for kickball?

_____8_____ children

2. How many more children chose the seesaw than the swings?

_____I_____ more

3. Which activity was chosen the most?

_____kickball_____

4. Jerry brought lunch to school 4 days this month. Draw tally marks to show how many days Jerry brought lunch to school.

_____IIII_____

GO ON

Page 2

Use the graph below to answer items 5, 6, 7, and 8. The graph shows how many minutes three friends ride their bikes on Saturday mornings.

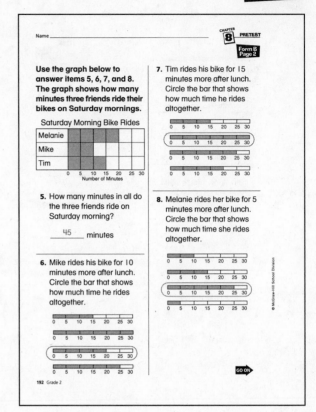

Saturday Morning Bike Rides

5. How many minutes in all do the three friends ride on Saturday morning?

_____45_____ minutes

6. Mike rides his bike for 10 minutes more after lunch. Circle the bar that shows how much time he rides altogether.

7. Tim rides his bike for 15 minutes more after lunch. Circle the bar that shows how much time he rides altogether.

8. Melanie rides her bike for 5 minutes more after lunch. Circle the bar that shows how much time she rides altogether.

GO ON

Page 3

Sam and Janet took a survey. They asked their classmates which snack they liked best. Then they showed the data in a tally chart and a graph. Use the data to answer items 9–12.

Favorite Snacks

Apples	I#I III
Carrots	III
Crackers	IIII
Popcorn	I#I I#I

Favorite Snacks

Apples	OOOOOOOO
Carrots	OOO
Crackers	OOOO
Popcorn	OOOOOOOOOO

Each o stands for 1 vote.

9. How many children voted for carrots?

_____3_____ children

10. How many children voted for crackers?

_____4_____ children

11. How many more children voted for popcorn than apples?

_____2_____ more children

12. Which snack received 8 votes?

_____apples_____

In five swim meets Billy swam this many laps.
I 7 6 6 5

13. What is the greatest and the least number of laps he swam?

Greatest number of laps: _____7_____

Least number of laps: _____I_____

GO ON

Page 4

14. What is the range of the numbers?

_____6_____

15. Which number is shown more than once?

_____6_____

16. What is the mode of the numbers?

_____6_____

Fill in the table. Then answer items 17–20.
Sally is saving money for a gift. She saved $3 in week 1 and $2 in week 2. She saved $5 in week 3 and $4 in week 4.

Sally's Gift Money

| Week | 1 | 2 | 3 | 4 |
| How Much | | | | |

17. How much money does Sally save during week 2?

$ _____2_____

18. How much more money does Sally save in week 3 than in week 1?

$ _____2_____

19. Which book does Sally have enough money to buy—$20, $18, $15, $12?

$ _____12_____

20. How much money did Sally save in all?

$ _____14_____

STOP

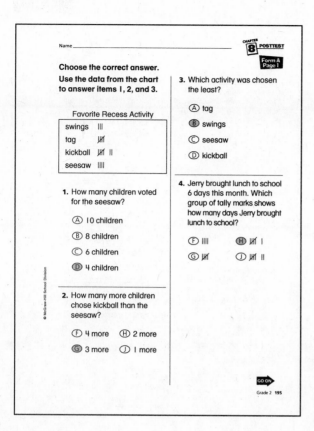

Choose the correct answer.
Use the data from the chart to answer items 1, 2, and 3.

Favorite Recess Activity

swings	III
tag	JHH
kickball	JHH II
seesaw	IIII

1. How many children voted for the seesaw?

- (A) 10 children
- (B) 8 children
- (C) 6 children
- (D) 4 children

2. How many more children chose kickball than the seesaw?

- (F) 4 more
- (H) 2 more
- (G) 3 more
- (J) 1 more

3. Which activity was chosen the least?

- (A) tag
- (B) swings
- (C) seesaw
- (D) kickball

4. Jerry brought lunch to school 6 days this month. Which group of tally marks shows how many days Jerry brought lunch to school?

- (F) IIII
- (H) JHH I
- (G) JHH
- (J) JHH II

GO ON

Grade 2 **195**

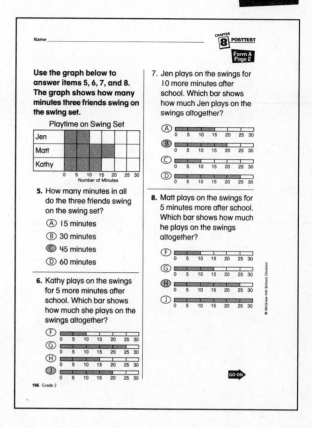

Use the graph below to answer items 5, 6, 7, and 8. The graph shows how many minutes three friends swing on the swing set.

Playtime on Swing Set

Jen	
Matt	
Kathy	

0 5 10 15 20 25 30
Number of Minutes

5. How many minutes in all do the three friends swing on the swing set?

- (A) 15 minutes
- (B) 30 minutes
- (C) 45 minutes
- (D) 60 minutes

6. Kathy plays on the swings for 5 more minutes after school. Which bar shows how much she plays on the swings altogether?

- (F) 0 5 10 15 20 25 30
- (G) 0 5 10 15 20 25 30
- (H) 0 5 10 15 20 25 30
- (J) 0 5 10 15 20 25 30

7. Jen plays on the swings for 10 more minutes after school. Which bar shows how much Jen plays on the swings altogether?

- (A) 0 5 10 15 20 25 30
- (B) 0 5 10 15 20 25 30
- (C) 0 5 10 15 20 25 30
- (D) 0 5 10 15 20 25 30

8. Matt plays on the swings for 5 minutes more after school. Which bar shows how much he plays on the swings altogether?

- (F) 0 5 10 15 20 25 30
- (G) 0 5 10 15 20 25 30
- (H) 0 5 10 15 20 25 30
- (J) 0 5 10 15 20 25 30

GO ON

196 Grade 2

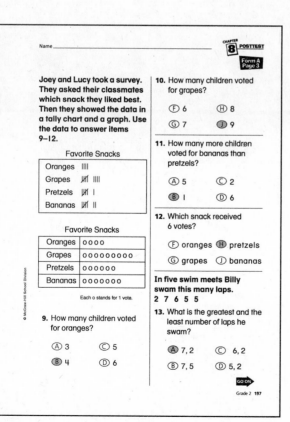

Joey and Lucy took a survey. They asked their classmates which snack they liked best. Then they showed the data in a tally chart and a graph. Use the data to answer items 9–12.

Favorite Snacks

Oranges	IIII
Grapes	JHH IIII
Pretzels	JHH I
Bananas	JHH II

Favorite Snacks

Oranges	o o o o
Grapes	o o o o o o o o o
Pretzels	o o o o o o
Bananas	o o o o o o o

Each o stands for 1 vote.

9. How many children voted for oranges?

- (A) 3
- (C) 5
- (B) 4
- (D) 6

10. How many children voted for grapes?

- (F) 6
- (H) 8
- (G) 7
- (J) 9

11. How many more children voted for bananas than pretzels?

- (A) 5
- (C) 2
- (B) 1
- (D) 6

12. Which snack received 6 votes?

- (F) oranges
- (H) pretzels
- (G) grapes
- (J) bananas

In five swim meets Billy swam this many laps.
2 7 6 5 5

13. What is the greatest and the least number of laps he swam?

- (A) 7, 2
- (C) 6, 2
- (B) 7, 5
- (D) 5, 2

GO ON

Grade 2 **197**

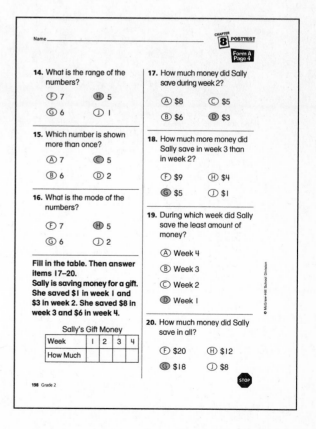

14. What is the range of the numbers?

- (F) 7
- (H) 5
- (G) 6
- (J) 1

15. Which number is shown more than once?

- (A) 7
- (C) 5
- (B) 6
- (D) 2

16. What is the mode of the numbers?

- (F) 7
- (H) 5
- (G) 6
- (J) 2

Fill in the table. Then answer items 17–20.
Sally is saving money for a gift. She saved $1 in week 1 and $3 in week 2. She saved $8 in week 3 and $6 in week 4.

Sally's Gift Money

Week	1	2	3	4
How Much				

17. How much money did Sally save during week 2?

- (A) $8
- (C) $5
- (B) $6
- (D) $3

18. How much more money did Sally save in week 3 than in week 2?

- (F) $9
- (H) $4
- (G) $5
- (J) $1

19. During which week did Sally save the least amount of money?

- (A) Week 4
- (B) Week 3
- (C) Week 2
- (D) Week 1

20. How much money did Sally save in all?

- (F) $20
- (H) $12
- (G) $18
- (J) $8

STOP

198 Grade 2

Page 1 (Grade 2, 199)

Name _____

Write the answer.
Use the data from the chart to answer items 1, 2, and 3.

Favorite Recess Activity

swings	III
tag	IIII
kickball	IIII II
seesaw	IIII

1. How many children voted for the seesaw?

____4____ children

2. How many more children chose kickball than the seesaw?

____3____ more children

3. Which activity was chosen the least?

_____swings_____

4. Jerry brought lunch to school 6 days this month. Draw tally marks to show how many days Jerry brought lunch to school.

_____IIII I_____

GO ON

Grade 2 **199**

Page 2 (Grade 2, 200)

Name _____

Use the graph below to answer items 5, 6, 7, and 8. The graph shows how many minutes three friends swing on the swing set.

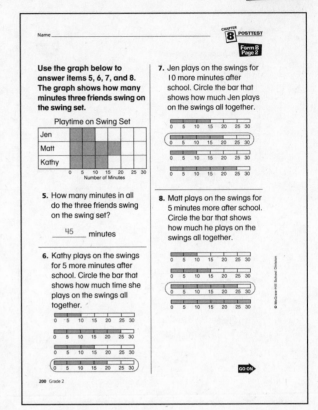

Playtime on Swing Set

Jen							
Matt							
Kathy							

Number of Minutes

5. How many minutes in all do the three friends swing on the swing set?

____45____ minutes

6. Kathy plays on the swings for 5 more minutes after school. Circle the bar that shows how much time she plays on the swings all together.

7. Jen plays on the swings for 10 more minutes after school. Circle the bar that shows how much Jen plays on the swings all together.

8. Matt plays on the swings for 5 minutes more after school. Circle the bar that shows how much he plays on the swings all together.

GO ON

200 Grade 2

Page 3 (Grade 2, 201)

Name _____

Joey and Lucy took a survey. They asked their classmates which snack they liked best. Then they showed the data in a tally chart and a graph. Use the data to answer items 9–12.

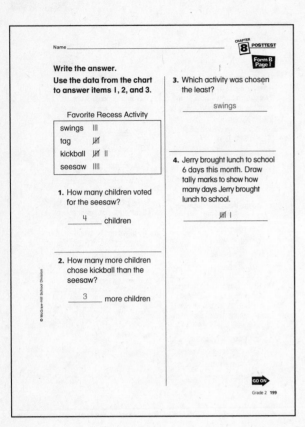

Favorite Snacks

Oranges	IIII
Grapes	IIII IIII
Pretzels	IIII I
Bananas	IIII II

Favorite Snacks

Oranges	o o o o
Grapes	o o o o o o o o o
Pretzels	o o o o o o
Bananas	o o o o o o o

Each o stands for 1 vote.

9. How many children voted for oranges?

____4____ children

10. How many children voted for grapes?

____9____ children

11. How many more children voted for bananas than pretzels?

____I____ more

12. Which snack received 6 votes?

_____pretzels_____

In five swim meets Billy swam this many laps.
2 7 6 5 5

13. What is the greatest and the least number of laps he swam?

Greatest number of laps: _7_

Least number of laps: _2_

GO ON

Grade 2 **201**

Page 4 (Grade 2, 202)

Name _____

14. What is the range of the numbers?

____5____

15. Which number is shown more than once?

____5____

16. What is the mode of the numbers?

____5____

Fill in the table. Then answer items 17–20.
Sally is saving money for a gift. She saved $1 in week 1 and $3 in week 2. She saved $8 in week 3 and $6 in week 4.

Sally's Gift Money

Week	1	2	3	4
How Much				

17. How much money did Sally save during week 2?

$ ____3____

18. How much more money did Sally save in week 3 than in week 2?

$ ____5____

19. During which week did Sally save the least amount of money?

_____Week I_____

20. How much money did Sally save in all?

$ ____18____

STOP

202 Grade 2

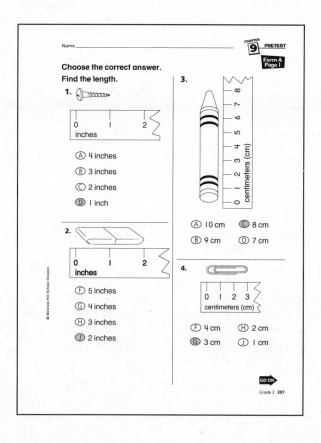

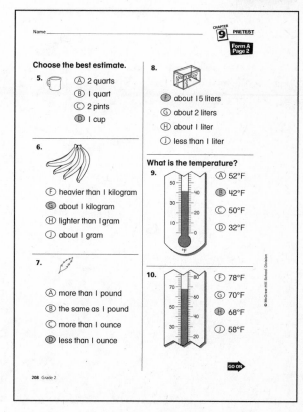

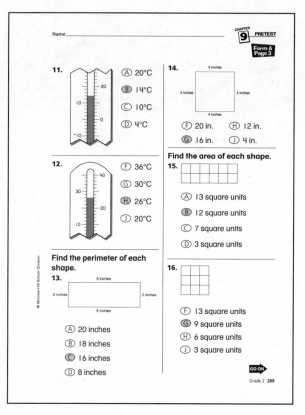

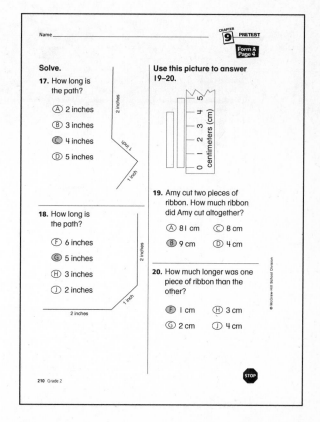

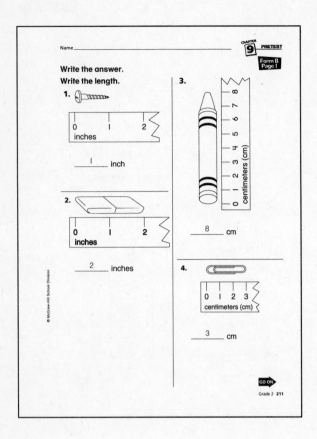

Name _____

CHAPTER **9** PRETEST
Form B
Page 1

Write the answer.
Write the length.

1.

0   1   2
inches

_____ 1 _____ inch

2.

0   1   2
inches

_____ 2 _____ inches

3.

centimeters (cm)

_____ 8 _____ cm

4.

0 1 2 3
centimeters (cm)

_____ 3 _____ cm

GO ON
Grade 2 **211**

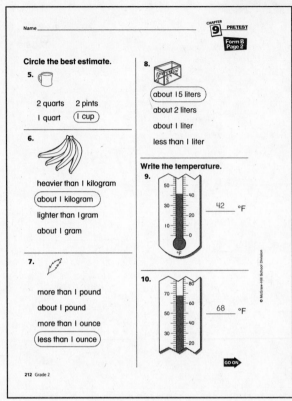

Name _____

CHAPTER **9** PRETEST
Form B
Page 2

Circle the best estimate.

5.

2 quarts   2 pints
1 quart   (I cup)

6.

heavier than 1 kilogram
(about 1 kilogram)
lighter than 1 gram
about 1 gram

7.

more than 1 pound
(about 1 pound)
more than 1 ounce
(less than 1 ounce)

8.

(about 15 liters)
about 2 liters
about 1 liter
less than 1 liter

Write the temperature.

9.

_____ 42 _____ °F

10.

_____ 68 _____ °F

GO ON

212 Grade 2

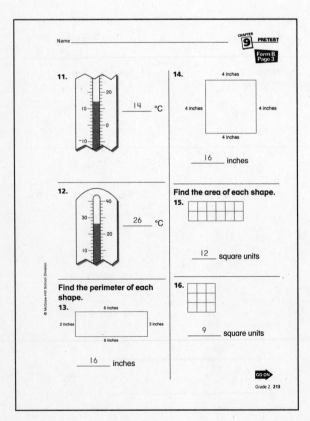

Name _____

CHAPTER **9** PRETEST
Form B
Page 3

11.

_____ 14 _____ °C

12.

_____ 26 _____ °C

Find the perimeter of each shape.

13.

6 inches
2 inches   2 inches
6 inches

_____ 16 _____ inches

14.

4 inches
4 inches   4 inches
4 inches

_____ 16 _____ inches

Find the area of each shape.

15.

_____ 12 _____ square units

16.

_____ 9 _____ square units

GO ON
Grade 2 **213**

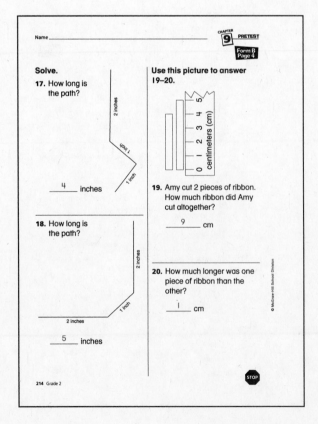

Name _____

CHAPTER **9** PRETEST
Form B
Page 4

Solve.

17. How long is
the path?

2 inches

1 inch

1 inch

_____ 4 _____ inches

18. How long is
the path?

2 inches

2 inches

1 inch

_____ 5 _____ inches

Use this picture to answer
19–20.

centimeters (cm)

19. Amy cut 2 pieces of ribbon.
How much ribbon did Amy
cut altogether?

_____ 9 _____ cm

20. How much longer was one
piece of ribbon than the
other?

_____ 1 _____ cm

STOP

214 Grade 2

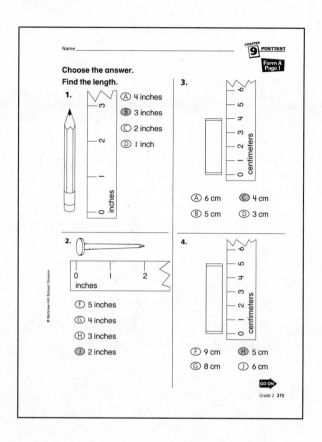

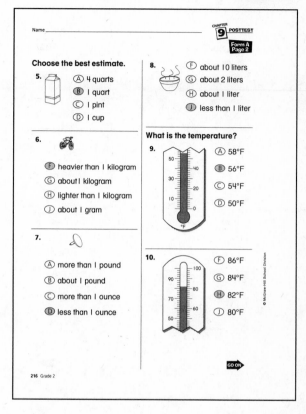

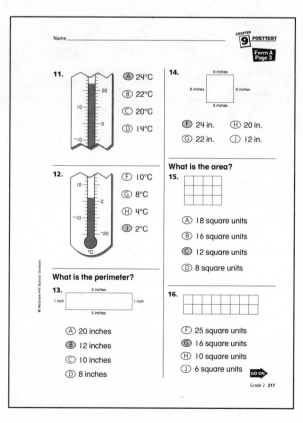

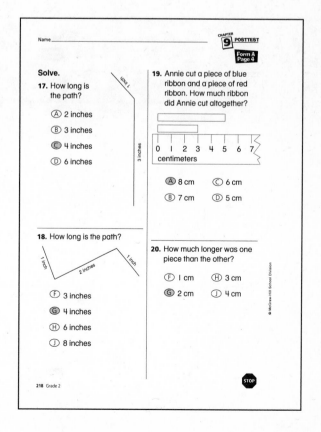

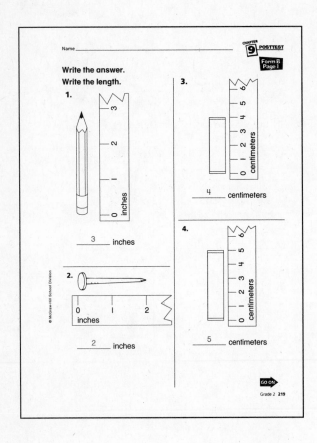

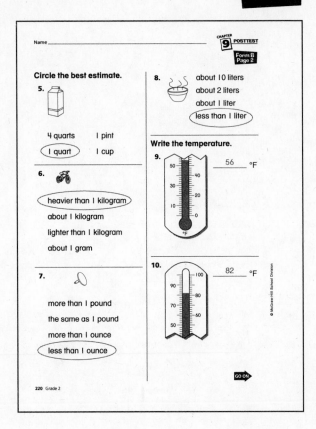

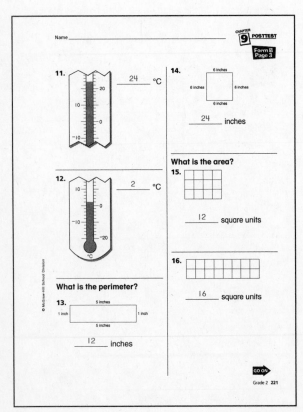

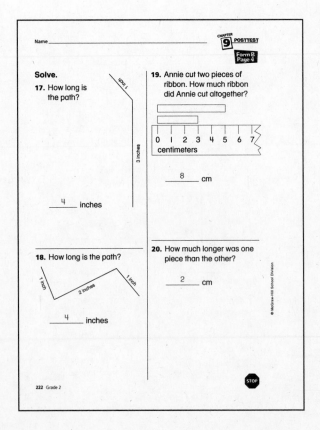

Page 1

Write the answer.
Write the length.

1. 3 inches

2. 2 inches

3. 4 centimeters

4. 5 centimeters

Page 2

Circle the best estimate.

5. (1 quart)

6. (heavier than 1 kilogram)

7. (less than 1 ounce)

8. (less than 1 liter)

Write the temperature.

9. 56 °F

10. 82 °F

Page 3

11. 24 °C

12. 2 °C

What is the perimeter?

13. 12 inches

14. 24 inches

What is the area?

15. 12 square units

16. 16 square units

Page 4

Solve.

17. How long is the path? 4 inches

18. How long is the path? 4 inches

19. Annie cut two pieces of ribbon. How much ribbon did Annie cut altogether? 8 cm

20. How much longer was one piece than the other? 2 cm

Page 1

Name _____

Choose the correct answer.

1. Name the solid figure.

Ⓐ cone   Ⓒ cylinder

Ⓑ cube   Ⓓ pyramid

2. What is this figure?

Ⓕ circle

Ⓖ rectangle

Ⓗ square

Ⓙ triangle

3. Which shapes are congruent?

Ⓐ ○ ○

Ⓑ △ △

Ⓒ ▢ ◇

Ⓓ ▭ ▭

4. How many faces does this solid figure have?

Ⓕ 8 faces

Ⓖ 5 faces

Ⓗ 6 faces

Ⓙ 4 faces

5. Which of these figures is a quadrilateral?

Ⓐ ○

Ⓑ ▢

Ⓒ △

Ⓓ ⬠

GO ON

Grade 2 **227**

Page 2

Name _____

6. What is a matching part for the figure?

Ⓕ

Ⓖ ○

Ⓗ

Ⓙ

7. How many edges does this solid figure have?

Ⓐ 16   Ⓒ 8

Ⓑ 12   Ⓓ 4

8. How many sides does this figure have?

Ⓕ 7   Ⓗ 6

Ⓖ 5   Ⓙ 4

9. Which shows a line of symmetry?

Ⓐ

Ⓑ

Ⓒ

Ⓓ

10. How many vertices does this solid figure have?

Ⓕ 10   Ⓗ 6

Ⓖ 12   Ⓙ 8

11. What is this figure?

Ⓐ triangle

Ⓑ trapezoid

Ⓒ parallelogram

Ⓓ pentagon

GO ON

228 Grade 2

Page 3

Name _____

12. Which shapes are congruent?

Ⓕ ▢ ▢

Ⓖ ▭ ▭

Ⓗ △ △

Ⓙ ○ ○

13. How many edges does this solid figure have?

Ⓐ 10 edges

Ⓑ 8 edges

Ⓒ 6 edges

Ⓓ 4 edges

14. How many angles does this figure have?

Ⓕ 6 angles   Ⓗ 5 angles

Ⓖ 4 angles   Ⓙ 3 angles

15. Name the solid figure.

Ⓐ cube   Ⓒ pyramid

Ⓑ cylinder   Ⓓ sphere

16. Which figure has 4 sides?

Ⓕ ▢

Ⓖ ○

Ⓗ △

Ⓙ ⬠

GO ON

Grade 2 **229**

Page 4

Name _____

Solve.

17. I have 3 sides and 3 angles. What am I?

Ⓐ circle

Ⓑ triangle

Ⓒ square

Ⓓ rectangle

18. I have 5 sides and 5 angles. What am I?

Ⓕ rectangle

Ⓖ hexagon

Ⓗ pentagon

Ⓙ trapezoid

19. How many of these triangles does it take to make this figure?

Ⓐ 4 triangles

Ⓑ 3 triangles

Ⓒ 2 triangles

Ⓓ 1 triangle

20. How many of these squares does it take to make this figure?

Ⓕ 4 squares

Ⓖ 3 squares

Ⓗ 2 squares

Ⓙ 1 square

STOP

230 Grade 2

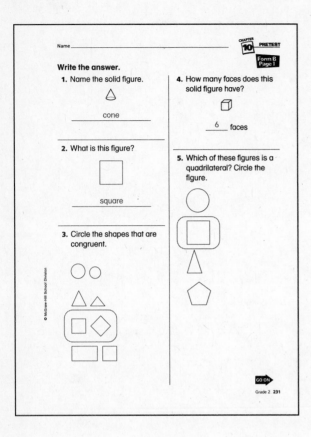

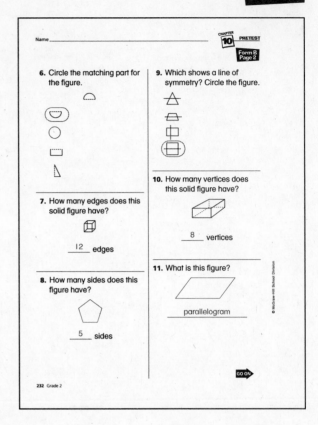

Write the answer.

1. Name the solid figure.

cone

2. What is this figure?

square

3. Circle the shapes that are congruent.

4. How many faces does this solid figure have?

6 faces

5. Which of these figures is a quadrilateral? Circle the figure.

GO ON

Grade 2 **231**

6. Circle the matching part for the figure.

7. How many edges does this solid figure have?

12 edges

8. How many sides does this figure have?

5 sides

9. Which shows a line of symmetry? Circle the figure.

10. How many vertices does this solid figure have?

8 vertices

11. What is this figure?

parallelogram

GO ON

232 Grade 2

12. Circle the shapes that are congruent.

13. How many edges does this solid figure have?

8 edges

14. How many angles does this figure have?

4 angles

15. Name the solid figure.

cylinder

16. Which figure has 4 sides: a circle, a square, a triangle, or a pentagon?

square

GO ON

Grade 2 **233**

Solve.

17. I have 3 sides and 3 angles. What am I?

triangle

18. I have 5 sides and 5 angles. What am I?

pentagon

19. How many of these triangles does it take to make this figure?

2 triangles

20. How many of these squares does it take to make this figure?

4 squares

STOP

234 Grade 2

© McGraw-Hill School Division

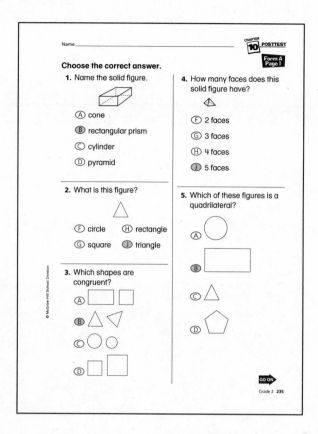

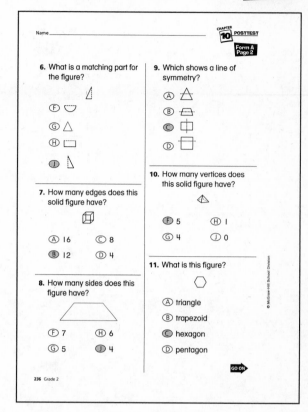

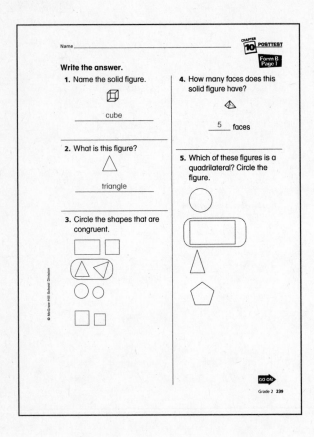

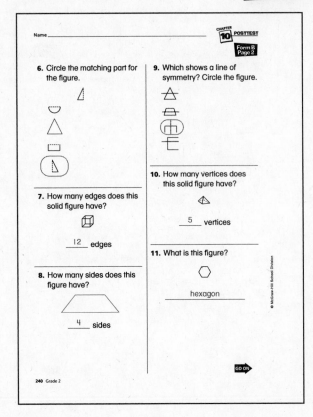

Page 1

Write the answer.

1. Name the solid figure. — cube

2. What is this figure? — triangle

3. Circle the shapes that are congruent.

4. How many faces does this solid figure have? — 5 faces

5. Which of these figures is a quadrilateral? Circle the figure.

Page 2

6. Circle the matching part for the figure.

7. How many edges does this solid figure have? — 12 edges

8. How many sides does this figure have? — 4 sides

9. Which shows a line of symmetry? Circle the figure.

10. How many vertices does this solid figure have? — 5 vertices

11. What is this figure? — hexagon

Page 3

12. Circle the shapes that are congruent.

13. How many edges does this solid figure have? — 12 edges

14. How many angles does this figure have? — 3 angles

15. Name the solid figure. — sphere

16. What figure has 3 sides? — triangle

Page 4

Solve.

17. I have 6 sides and 6 angles. What plane figure am I? — hexagon

18. I have 4 sides and 4 angles. What plane figure am I? — rectangle

19. How many of these triangles does it take to make this figure? — 6 triangles

20. How many of these squares does it take to make this figure? — 4 squares

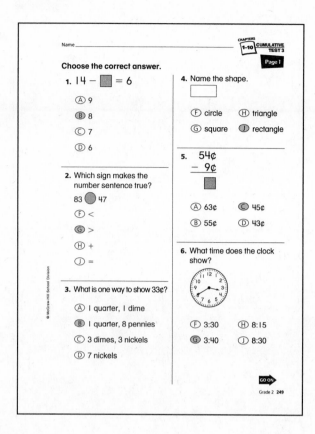

Choose the correct answer.

1. $14 - \blacksquare = 6$

Ⓐ 9
Ⓑ 8
Ⓒ 7
Ⓓ 6

2. Which sign makes the number sentence true?

83 ⬤ 47

Ⓕ <
Ⓖ >
Ⓗ +
Ⓙ =

3. What is one way to show 33¢?

Ⓐ 1 quarter, 1 dime
Ⓑ 1 quarter, 8 pennies
Ⓒ 3 dimes, 3 nickels
Ⓓ 7 nickels

4. Name the shape.

Ⓕ circle   Ⓗ triangle
Ⓖ square   Ⓙ rectangle

5.
$$\begin{array}{r} 54¢ \\ -\ 9¢ \\ \hline \blacksquare \end{array}$$

Ⓐ 63¢   Ⓒ 45¢
Ⓑ 55¢   Ⓓ 43¢

6. What time does the clock show?

Ⓕ 3:30   Ⓗ 8:15
Ⓖ 3:40   Ⓙ 8:30

GO ON

Grade 2 **249**

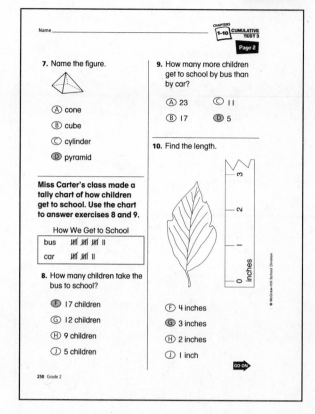

7. Name the figure.

Ⓐ cone
Ⓑ cube
Ⓒ cylinder
Ⓓ pyramid

Miss Carter's class made a tally chart of how children get to school. Use the chart to answer exercises 8 and 9.

How We Get to School	
bus	卌 卌 卌 II
car	卌 卌 II

8. How many children take the bus to school?

Ⓕ 17 children
Ⓖ 12 children
Ⓗ 9 children
Ⓙ 5 children

9. How many more children get to school by bus than by car?

Ⓐ 23   Ⓒ 11
Ⓑ 17   Ⓓ 5

10. Find the length.

Ⓕ 4 inches
Ⓖ 3 inches
Ⓗ 2 inches
Ⓙ 1 inch

GO ON

250 Grade 2

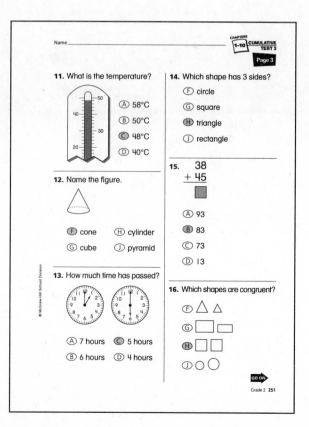

11. What is the temperature?

Ⓐ 58°C
Ⓑ 50°C
Ⓒ 48°C
Ⓓ 40°C

12. Name the figure.

Ⓕ cone   Ⓗ cylinder
Ⓖ cube   Ⓙ pyramid

13. How much time has passed?

Ⓐ 7 hours   Ⓒ 5 hours
Ⓑ 6 hours   Ⓓ 4 hours

14. Which shape has 3 sides?

Ⓕ circle
Ⓖ square
Ⓗ triangle
Ⓙ rectangle

15.
$$\begin{array}{r} 38 \\ +\ 45 \\ \hline \blacksquare \end{array}$$

Ⓐ 93
Ⓑ 83
Ⓒ 73
Ⓓ 13

16. Which shapes are congruent?

Ⓕ △ △
Ⓖ ▭ ▭
Ⓗ ☐ ☐
Ⓙ ◯ ◯

GO ON

Grade 2 **251**

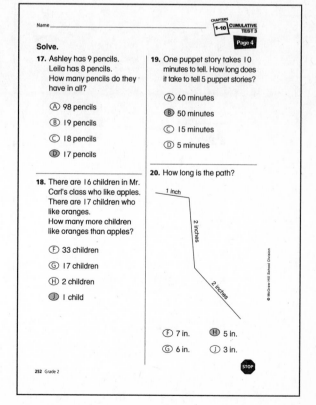

Solve.

17. Ashley has 9 pencils. Leila has 8 pencils. How many pencils do they have in all?

Ⓐ 98 pencils
Ⓑ 19 pencils
Ⓒ 18 pencils
Ⓓ 17 pencils

18. There are 16 children in Mr. Carl's class who like apples. There are 17 children who like oranges. How many more children like oranges than apples?

Ⓕ 33 children
Ⓖ 17 children
Ⓗ 2 children
Ⓙ 1 child

19. One puppet story takes 10 minutes to tell. How long does it take to tell 5 puppet stories?

Ⓐ 60 minutes
Ⓑ 50 minutes
Ⓒ 15 minutes
Ⓓ 5 minutes

20. How long is the path?

1 inch
2 inches
2 inches

Ⓕ 7 in.   Ⓗ 5 in.
Ⓖ 6 in.   Ⓙ 3 in.

STOP

252 Grade 2

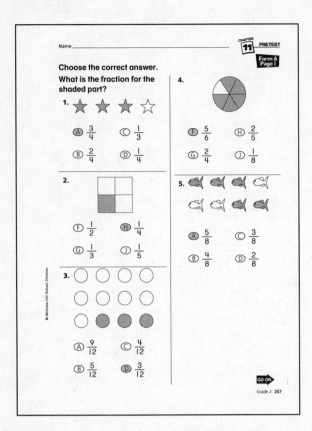

Choose the correct answer.
What is the fraction for the shaded part?

1. ★ ★ ★ ☆

Ⓐ $\frac{3}{4}$ Ⓒ $\frac{1}{3}$

Ⓑ $\frac{2}{4}$ Ⓓ $\frac{1}{4}$

2.

Ⓕ $\frac{1}{2}$ Ⓗ $\frac{1}{4}$

Ⓖ $\frac{1}{3}$ Ⓙ $\frac{1}{5}$

3.

Ⓐ $\frac{9}{12}$ Ⓒ $\frac{4}{12}$

Ⓑ $\frac{5}{12}$ Ⓓ $\frac{3}{12}$

4.

Ⓕ $\frac{5}{6}$ Ⓗ $\frac{2}{5}$

Ⓖ $\frac{2}{4}$ Ⓙ $\frac{1}{8}$

5.

Ⓐ $\frac{5}{8}$ Ⓒ $\frac{3}{8}$

Ⓑ $\frac{4}{8}$ Ⓓ $\frac{2}{8}$

GO ON
Grade 2 **257**

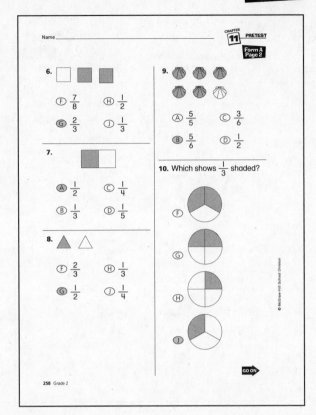

6.

Ⓕ $\frac{7}{8}$ Ⓗ $\frac{1}{2}$

Ⓖ $\frac{2}{3}$ Ⓙ $\frac{1}{3}$

7.

Ⓐ $\frac{1}{2}$ Ⓒ $\frac{1}{4}$

Ⓑ $\frac{1}{3}$ Ⓓ $\frac{1}{5}$

8.

Ⓕ $\frac{2}{3}$ Ⓗ $\frac{1}{3}$

Ⓖ $\frac{1}{2}$ Ⓙ $\frac{1}{4}$

9.

Ⓐ $\frac{5}{5}$ Ⓒ $\frac{3}{6}$

Ⓑ $\frac{5}{6}$ Ⓓ $\frac{1}{2}$

10. Which shows $\frac{1}{3}$ shaded?

Ⓕ

Ⓖ

Ⓗ

Ⓙ

GO ON
258 Grade 2

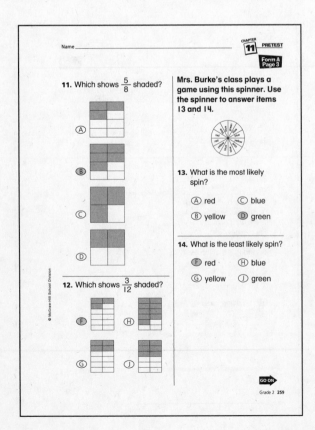

11. Which shows $\frac{5}{8}$ shaded?

Ⓐ

Ⓑ

Ⓒ

Ⓓ

12. Which shows $\frac{3}{12}$ shaded?

Ⓕ   Ⓗ

Ⓖ   Ⓙ

Mrs. Burke's class plays a game using this spinner. Use the spinner to answer items 13 and 14.

13. What is the most likely spin?

Ⓐ red Ⓒ blue

Ⓑ yellow Ⓓ green

14. What is the least likely spin?

Ⓕ red Ⓗ blue

Ⓖ yellow Ⓙ green

GO ON
Grade 2 **259**

Use the picture for items 15–16.

15. Which shape is the most likely to be picked?

Ⓐ triangle Ⓒ square

Ⓑ circle Ⓓ rectangle

16. Which shape is the least likely to be picked?

Ⓕ triangle Ⓗ square

Ⓖ circle Ⓙ rectangle

Solve.

17. Mark folds a piece of paper into 4 equal parts. He colors 3 of the parts. What fraction of the paper does he color?

Ⓐ $\frac{3}{4}$ Ⓒ $\frac{1}{3}$

Ⓑ $\frac{2}{3}$ Ⓓ $\frac{1}{4}$

18. Amy's mural has 6 sections. She colors 1 section purple. What fraction of the mural is purple?

Ⓕ $\frac{4}{6}$ Ⓗ $\frac{1}{4}$

Ⓖ $\frac{3}{6}$ Ⓙ $\frac{1}{6}$

19. Zach has 8 shells in a basket. There are 5 pink shells and 3 gray ones. What fraction of the shells are pink?

Ⓐ $\frac{6}{8}$ Ⓒ $\frac{3}{8}$

Ⓑ $\frac{5}{8}$ Ⓓ $\frac{3}{5}$

20. Erika has 6 grapes in a cup. There are 5 red grapes and 1 green one. What fraction of Erika's grapes are red?

Ⓕ $\frac{7}{8}$ Ⓗ $\frac{1}{5}$

Ⓖ $\frac{5}{6}$ Ⓙ $\frac{1}{6}$

STOP
260 Grade 2

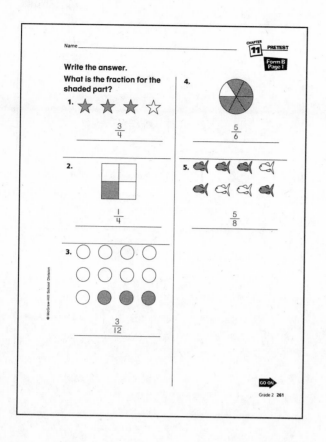

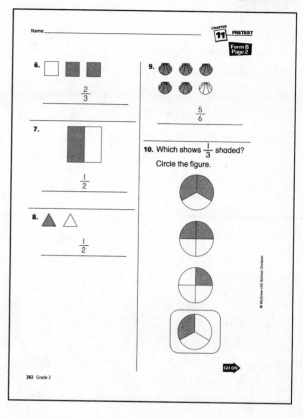

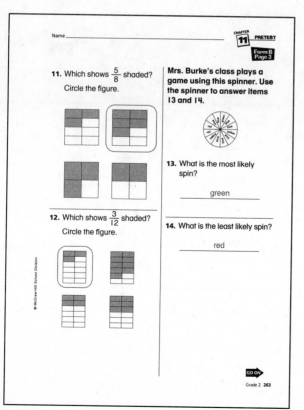

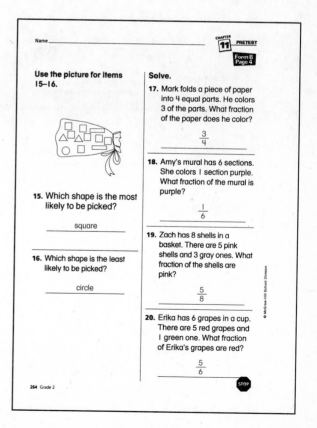

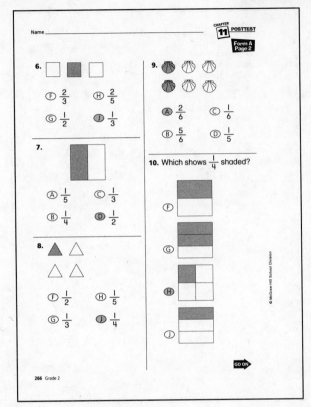

Name_____

Choose the correct answer.
What is the fraction for the shaded area?

1.
Ⓐ $\frac{3}{4}$ Ⓒ $\frac{1}{4}$
Ⓑ $\frac{2}{4}$ Ⓓ $\frac{1}{6}$

2.
Ⓕ $\frac{2}{3}$ Ⓗ $\frac{1}{3}$
Ⓖ $\frac{2}{5}$ Ⓙ $\frac{1}{4}$

3.
Ⓐ $\frac{9}{12}$ Ⓒ $\frac{5}{12}$
Ⓑ $\frac{7}{12}$ Ⓓ $\frac{1}{12}$

4.
Ⓕ $\frac{3}{6}$ Ⓗ $\frac{1}{3}$
Ⓖ $\frac{1}{5}$ Ⓙ $\frac{1}{6}$

5.
Ⓐ $\frac{5}{8}$ Ⓒ $\frac{1}{2}$
Ⓑ $\frac{3}{5}$ Ⓓ $\frac{3}{8}$

GO ON

Grade 2 **265**

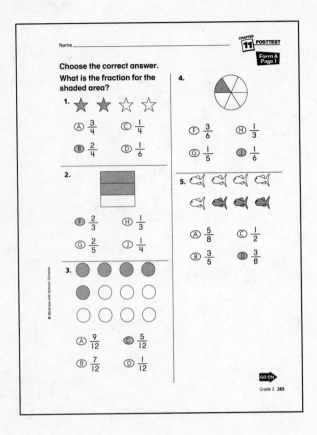

Name_____

6.
Ⓕ $\frac{2}{3}$ Ⓗ $\frac{2}{5}$
Ⓖ $\frac{1}{2}$ Ⓙ $\frac{1}{3}$

7.
Ⓐ $\frac{1}{5}$ Ⓒ $\frac{1}{3}$
Ⓑ $\frac{1}{4}$ Ⓓ $\frac{1}{2}$

8.
Ⓕ $\frac{1}{2}$ Ⓗ $\frac{1}{5}$
Ⓖ $\frac{1}{3}$ Ⓙ $\frac{1}{4}$

9.
Ⓐ $\frac{2}{6}$ Ⓒ $\frac{1}{6}$
Ⓑ $\frac{5}{6}$ Ⓓ $\frac{1}{5}$

10. Which shows $\frac{1}{4}$ shaded?
Ⓕ
Ⓖ
Ⓗ
Ⓙ

GO ON

266 Grade 2

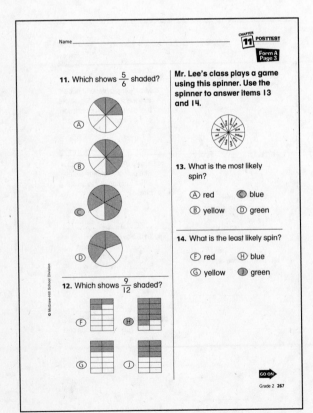

Name_____

11. Which shows $\frac{5}{6}$ shaded?
Ⓐ
Ⓑ
Ⓒ
Ⓓ

12. Which shows $\frac{9}{12}$ shaded?
Ⓕ Ⓗ
Ⓖ Ⓙ

Mr. Lee's class plays a game using this spinner. Use the spinner to answer items 13 and 14.

13. What is the most likely spin?
Ⓐ red Ⓒ blue
Ⓑ yellow Ⓓ green

14. What is the least likely spin?
Ⓕ red Ⓗ blue
Ⓖ yellow Ⓙ green

GO ON

Grade 2 **267**

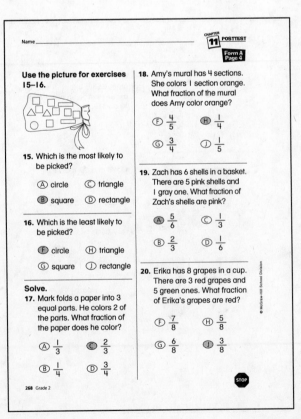

Name_____

Use the picture for exercises 15–16.

15. Which is the most likely to be picked?
Ⓐ circle Ⓒ triangle
Ⓑ square Ⓓ rectangle

16. Which is the least likely to be picked?
Ⓕ circle Ⓗ triangle
Ⓖ square Ⓙ rectangle

Solve.
17. Mark folds a paper into 3 equal parts. He colors 2 of the parts. What fraction of the paper does he color?
Ⓐ $\frac{1}{3}$ Ⓒ $\frac{2}{3}$
Ⓑ $\frac{1}{4}$ Ⓓ $\frac{3}{4}$

18. Amy's mural has 4 sections. She colors 1 section orange. What fraction of the mural does Amy color orange?
Ⓕ $\frac{4}{5}$ Ⓗ $\frac{1}{4}$
Ⓖ $\frac{3}{4}$ Ⓙ $\frac{1}{5}$

19. Zach has 6 shells in a basket. There are 5 pink shells and 1 gray one. What fraction of Zach's shells are pink?
Ⓐ $\frac{5}{6}$ Ⓒ $\frac{1}{3}$
Ⓑ $\frac{2}{3}$ Ⓓ $\frac{1}{6}$

20. Erika has 8 grapes in a cup. There are 3 red grapes and 5 green ones. What fraction of Erika's grapes are red?
Ⓕ $\frac{7}{8}$ Ⓗ $\frac{5}{8}$
Ⓖ $\frac{6}{8}$ Ⓙ $\frac{3}{8}$

STOP

268 Grade 2

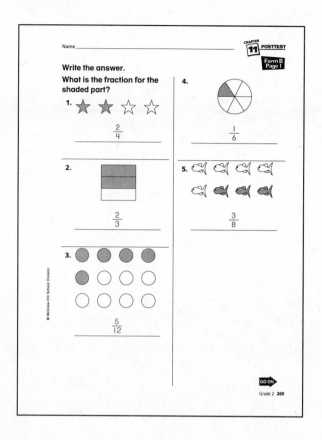

Name _____

Write the answer.

What is the fraction for the shaded part?

1. ★ ★ ☆ ☆

$\frac{2}{4}$

4.

$\frac{1}{6}$

2.

$\frac{2}{3}$

5.

$\frac{3}{8}$

3.

$\frac{5}{12}$

GO ON

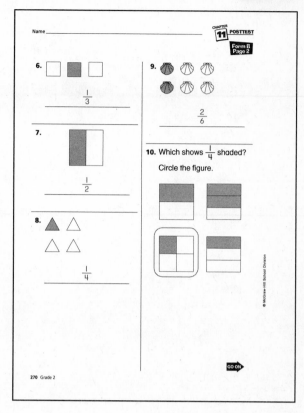

Name _____

6.

$\frac{1}{3}$

7.

$\frac{1}{2}$

8.

$\frac{1}{4}$

9.

$\frac{2}{6}$

10. Which shows $\frac{1}{4}$ shaded?

Circle the figure.

GO ON

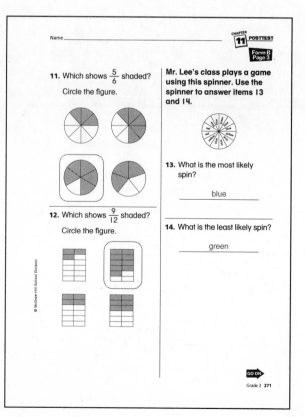

Name _____

11. Which shows $\frac{5}{6}$ shaded?

Circle the figure.

12. Which shows $\frac{9}{12}$ shaded?

Circle the figure.

Mr. Lee's class plays a game using this spinner. Use the spinner to answer items 13 and 14.

13. What is the most likely spin?

blue

14. What is the least likely spin?

green

GO ON

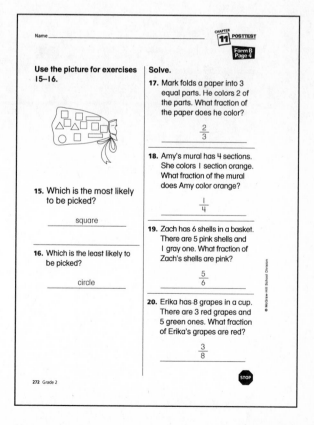

Name _____

Use the picture for exercises 15–16.

15. Which is the most likely to be picked?

square

16. Which is the least likely to be picked?

circle

Solve.

17. Mark folds a paper into 3 equal parts. He colors 2 of the parts. What fraction of the paper does he color?

$\frac{2}{3}$

18. Amy's mural has 4 sections. She colors 1 section orange. What fraction of the mural does Amy color orange?

$\frac{1}{4}$

19. Zach has 6 shells in a basket. There are 5 pink shells and 1 gray one. What fraction of Zach's shells are pink?

$\frac{5}{6}$

20. Erika has 8 grapes in a cup. There are 3 red grapes and 5 green ones. What fraction of Erika's grapes are red?

$\frac{3}{8}$

STOP

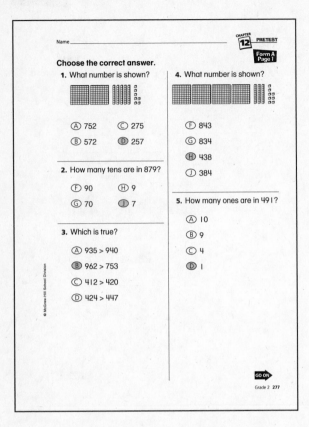

Name_____

Choose the correct answer.

1. What number is shown?

Ⓐ 752 Ⓒ 275
Ⓑ 572 Ⓓ 257

2. How many tens are in 879?

Ⓕ 90 Ⓗ 9
Ⓖ 70 Ⓙ 7

3. Which is true?

Ⓐ 935 > 940
Ⓑ 962 > 753
Ⓒ 412 > 420
Ⓓ 424 > 447

4. What number is shown?

Ⓕ 843
Ⓖ 834
Ⓗ 438
Ⓙ 384

5. How many ones are in 491?

Ⓐ 10
Ⓑ 9
Ⓒ 4
Ⓓ 1

GO ON

Grade 2 **277**

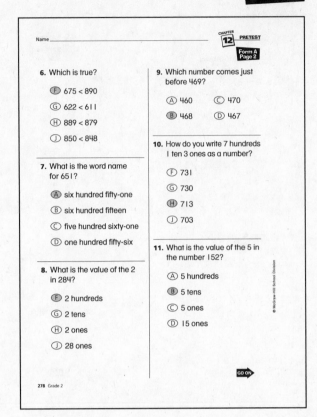

Name_____

6. Which is true?

Ⓕ 675 < 890
Ⓖ 622 < 611
Ⓗ 889 < 879
Ⓙ 850 < 848

7. What is the word name for 651?

Ⓐ six hundred fifty-one
Ⓑ six hundred fifteen
Ⓒ five hundred sixty-one
Ⓓ one hundred fifty-six

8. What is the value of the 2 in 284?

Ⓕ 2 hundreds
Ⓖ 2 tens
Ⓗ 2 ones
Ⓙ 28 ones

9. Which number comes just before 469?

Ⓐ 460 Ⓒ 470
Ⓑ 468 Ⓓ 467

10. How do you write 7 hundreds 1 ten 3 ones as a number?

Ⓕ 731
Ⓖ 730
Ⓗ 713
Ⓙ 703

11. What is the value of the 5 in the number 152?

Ⓐ 5 hundreds
Ⓑ 5 tens
Ⓒ 5 ones
Ⓓ 15 ones

GO ON

278 Grade 2

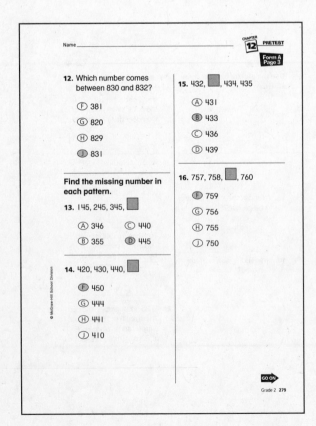

Name_____

12. Which number comes between 830 and 832?

Ⓕ 381
Ⓖ 820
Ⓗ 829
Ⓙ 831

Find the missing number in each pattern.

13. 145, 245, 345, ▨

Ⓐ 346 Ⓒ 440
Ⓑ 355 Ⓓ 445

14. 420, 430, 440, ▨

Ⓕ 450
Ⓖ 444
Ⓗ 441
Ⓙ 410

15. 432, ▨, 434, 435

Ⓐ 431
Ⓑ 433
Ⓒ 436
Ⓓ 439

16. 757, 758, ▨, 760

Ⓕ 759
Ⓖ 756
Ⓗ 755
Ⓙ 750

GO ON

Grade 2 **279**

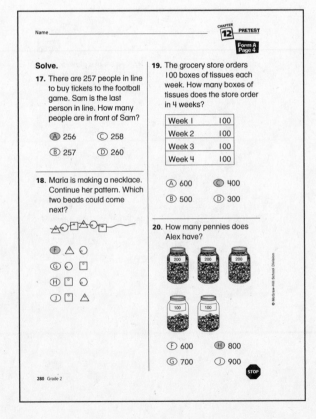

Name_____

Solve.

17. There are 257 people in line to buy tickets to the football game. Sam is the last person in line. How many people are in front of Sam?

Ⓐ 256 Ⓒ 258
Ⓑ 257 Ⓓ 260

18. Maria is making a necklace. Continue her pattern. Which two beads could come next?

Ⓕ △ ◯
Ⓖ ◯ ▢
Ⓗ ▢ ◯
Ⓙ ▢ △

19. The grocery store orders 100 boxes of tissues each week. How many boxes of tissues does the store order in 4 weeks?

Week 1	100
Week 2	100
Week 3	100
Week 4	100

Ⓐ 600 Ⓒ 400
Ⓑ 500 Ⓓ 300

20. How many pennies does Alex have?

Ⓕ 600 Ⓗ 800
Ⓖ 700 Ⓙ 900

STOP

280 Grade 2

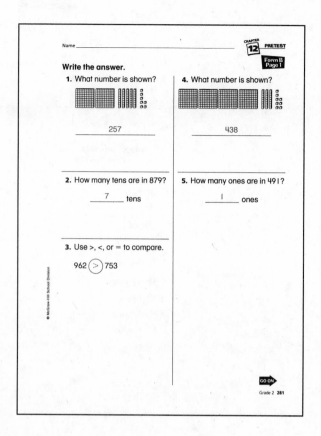

Name _____

Write the answer.

1. What number is shown?

_____257_____

2. How many tens are in 879?

____7____ tens

3. Use >, <, or = to compare.

962 (>) 753

4. What number is shown?

_____438_____

5. How many ones are in 491?

____1____ ones

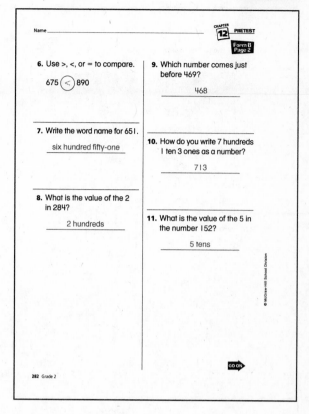

Name _____

6. Use >, <, or = to compare.

675 (<) 890

7. Write the word name for 651.

six hundred fifty-one

8. What is the value of the 2 in 284?

2 hundreds

9. Which number comes just before 469?

_____468_____

10. How do you write 7 hundreds 1 ten 3 ones as a number?

_____713_____

11. What is the value of the 5 in the number 152?

5 tens

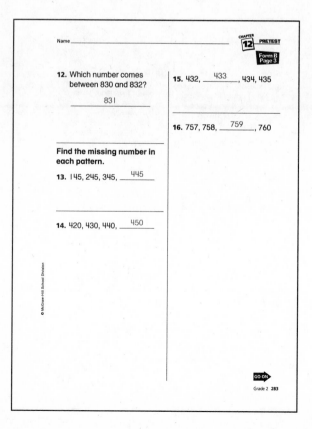

Name _____

12. Which number comes between 830 and 832?

_____831_____

Find the missing number in each pattern.

13. 145, 245, 345, ___445___

14. 420, 430, 440, ___450___

15. 432, ___433___, 434, 435

16. 757, 758, ___759___, 760

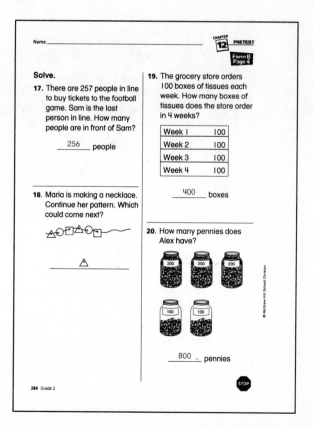

Name _____

Solve.

17. There are 257 people in line to buy tickets to the football game. Sam is the last person in line. How many people are in front of Sam?

____256____ people

18. Maria is making a necklace. Continue her pattern. Which could come next?

△

19. The grocery store orders 100 boxes of tissues each week. How many boxes of tissues does the store order in 4 weeks?

Week 1	100
Week 2	100
Week 3	100
Week 4	100

____400____ boxes

20. How many pennies does Alex have?

____800____ pennies

Name _____

Choose the correct answer.

1. What number is shown?

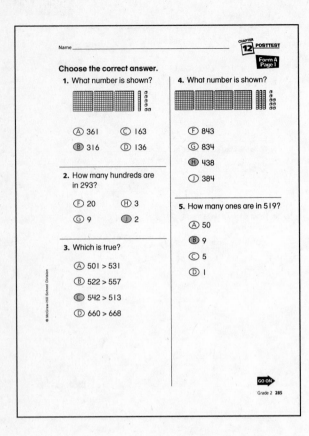

Ⓐ 361   Ⓒ 163

Ⓑ 316   Ⓓ 136

2. How many hundreds are in 293?

Ⓕ 20   Ⓗ 3

Ⓖ 9   Ⓙ 2

3. Which is true?

Ⓐ 501 > 531

Ⓑ 522 > 557

Ⓒ 542 > 513

Ⓓ 660 > 668

4. What number is shown?

Ⓕ 843

Ⓖ 834

Ⓗ 438

Ⓙ 384

5. How many ones are in 519?

Ⓐ 50

Ⓑ 9

Ⓒ 5

Ⓓ 1

Name _____

6. Which is true?

Ⓕ 710 < 701

Ⓖ 762 < 785

Ⓗ 843 < 813

Ⓙ 886 < 854

7. What is the word name for 745?

Ⓐ seven hundred fifty-four

Ⓑ seven hundred forty-five

Ⓒ four hundred fifty-seven

Ⓓ five hundred forty-seven

8. What is the value of the 7 in 371?

Ⓕ 7 hundreds

Ⓖ 7 tens

Ⓗ 7 ones

Ⓙ 37 ones

9. Which number comes just after 333?

Ⓐ 233   Ⓒ 334

Ⓑ 332   Ⓓ 343

10. How do you write 4 hundreds 1 ten 6 ones as a number?

Ⓕ 461

Ⓖ 460

Ⓗ 416

Ⓙ 406

11. What is the value of the 6 in the number 618?

Ⓐ 6 hundreds

Ⓑ 6 tens

Ⓒ 6 ones

Ⓓ 61 ones

Name _____

12. Which number comes between 634 and 636?

Ⓕ 345

Ⓖ 635

Ⓗ 639

Ⓙ 643

Find the missing number in each pattern.

13. 235, 335, 435, ▢

Ⓐ 436   Ⓒ 535

Ⓑ 445   Ⓓ 545

14. 510, 520, 530, ▢

Ⓕ 580

Ⓖ 540

Ⓗ 535

Ⓙ 525

15. 234, ▢, 236, 237

Ⓐ 239

Ⓑ 338

Ⓒ 235

Ⓓ 233

16. 577, 578, ▢, 580

Ⓕ 581

Ⓖ 579

Ⓗ 576

Ⓙ 570

Name _____

Solve.

17. There are 324 people in line to buy tickets to the football game. How many people are in front of the last person in line?

Ⓐ 350   Ⓒ 324

Ⓑ 325   Ⓓ 323

18. Maria is making a necklace. Continue her pattern. Which two beads could come next?

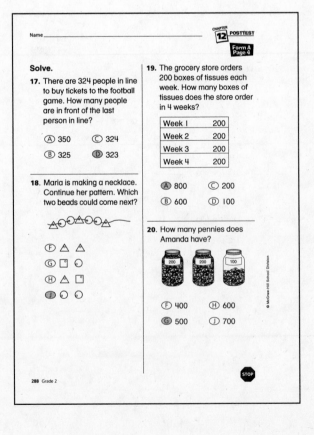

Ⓕ △ △

Ⓖ ▢ ○

Ⓗ △ ▢

Ⓙ ○ ○

19. The grocery store orders 200 boxes of tissues each week. How many boxes of tissues does the store order in 4 weeks?

Week 1	200
Week 2	200
Week 3	200
Week 4	200

Ⓐ 800   Ⓒ 200

Ⓑ 600   Ⓓ 100

20. How many pennies does Amanda have?

Ⓕ 400   Ⓗ 600

Ⓖ 500   Ⓙ 700

Page 1

Write the answer

1. What number is shown?

316

2. How many hundreds are in 293?

_____2_____ hundreds

3. Use >, <, or = to compare.

542 (>) 513

4. What number is shown?

438

5. How many ones are in 519?

_____9_____ ones

Page 2

6. Use >, <, or = to compare.

762 (<) 785

7. What is the word name for 745?

seven hundred forty-five

8. What is the value of the 7 in 371?

7 tens

9. Which number comes just after 333?

334

10. How do you write 4 hundreds 1 ten 6 ones as a number?

416

11. What is the value of the 6 in the number 618?

6 hundreds

Page 3

12. Which number comes between 634 and 636?

635

Find the missing number in each pattern.

13. 235, 335, 435, _____535_____

14. 510, 520, 530, _____540_____

15. 234, _____235_____, 236, 237

16. 577, 578, _____579_____, 580

Page 4

Solve.

17. There are 324 people in line to buy tickets to the football game. How many people are in front of the last person in line?

_____323_____ people

18. Maria is making a necklace. Continue her pattern. Draw the bead that could come next.

_____◯_____

19. The grocery store orders 200 boxes of tissues each week. How many boxes of tissues does the store order in 4 weeks?

Week 1	200
Week 2	200
Week 3	200
Week 4	200

_____800_____ boxes

20. How many pennies does Amanda have?

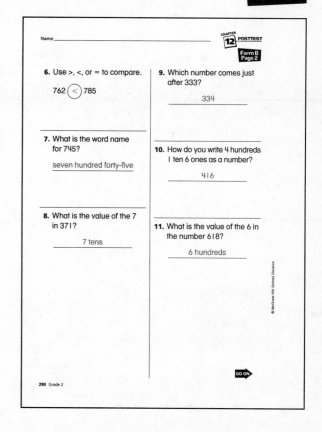

_____500_____ pennies

Page 1

Name _____

Choose the correct answer.

1.
$$400 + 300$$

Ⓐ 800   Ⓒ 600
Ⓑ 700   Ⓓ 100

2.
$$326 + 243$$

Ⓕ 669
Ⓖ 579
Ⓗ 569
Ⓙ 529

3.
$$648 + 137$$

Ⓐ 785   Ⓒ 771
Ⓑ 775   Ⓓ 512

4.
$$275 + 63$$

Ⓕ 348
Ⓖ 338
Ⓗ 248
Ⓙ 238

5.
$$535 + 386$$

Ⓐ 931   Ⓒ 831
Ⓑ 921   Ⓓ 821

6.
$$724 + 192$$

Ⓕ 926   Ⓗ 876
Ⓖ 916   Ⓙ 816

GO ON

© McGraw-Hill School Division

Page 2

Name _____

7.
$$600 - 300$$

Ⓐ 500   Ⓒ 300
Ⓑ 400   Ⓓ 200

8.
$$457 - 234$$

Ⓕ 283
Ⓖ 223
Ⓗ 124
Ⓙ 123

9.
$$816 - 205$$

Ⓐ 621   Ⓒ 521
Ⓑ 611   Ⓓ 511

10.
$$738 - 46$$

Ⓕ 582
Ⓖ 592
Ⓗ 682
Ⓙ 692

11.
$$642 - 137$$

Ⓐ 579   Ⓒ 506
Ⓑ 519   Ⓓ 505

12.
$$324 - 256$$

Ⓕ 580   Ⓗ 68
Ⓖ 132   Ⓙ 58

GO ON

© McGraw-Hill School Division

Page 3

Name _____

13.
$$\$9.37 - 6.54$$

Ⓐ $15.91
Ⓑ $3.23
Ⓒ $2.84
Ⓓ $2.83

14.
$$\$7.25 - 1.17$$

Ⓕ $8.42
Ⓖ $6.18
Ⓗ $6.08
Ⓙ $6.07

15.
$$\$5.00 + 2.86$$

Ⓐ $8.86
Ⓑ $7.86
Ⓒ $3.14
Ⓓ $2.14

16.
$$\$7.81 + 1.59$$

Ⓕ $9.50
Ⓖ $9.40
Ⓗ $8.40
Ⓙ $6.40

GO ON

© McGraw-Hill School Division

Page 4

Name _____

Solve.

17. This graph shows how many minutes three friends walked in the Walkathon.

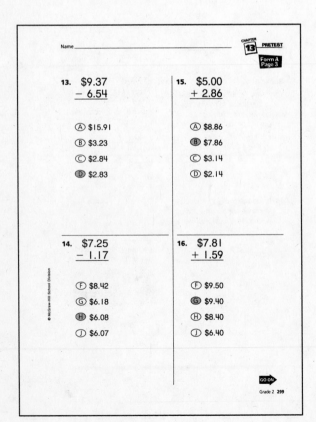

Jae walked for 5 more minutes. Which bar shows how much time Jae walked altogether?

18. Brad's class collects 294 cans of dog food. Theo's class collects 127 cans of dog food for dogs at the animal shelter. How many cans do they collect in all?

Ⓕ 421 cans   Ⓗ 321 cans
Ⓖ 412 cans   Ⓙ 312 cans

19. Kathy has $7.50. She spends $6.68 on a present for her mom. How much change will she have left?

Ⓐ $0.58   Ⓒ $0.82
Ⓑ $0.62   Ⓓ $0.88

20. Andy's scout troop has 354 phone books. If they hand out 272 phone books, how many will they have left?

Ⓕ 524 phone books
Ⓖ 182 phone books
Ⓗ 82 phone books
Ⓙ 62 phone books

STOP

© McGraw-Hill School Division

Page 1

Write the answer.

1. 400
   + 300
   700

2. 326
   + 243
   569

3. 648
   + 137
   785

4. 275
   + 63
   338

5. 535
   + 386
   921

6. 724
   + 192
   916

GO ON

Grade 2 **301**

Page 2

7. 600
   − 300
   300

8. 457
   − 234
   223

9. 816
   − 205
   611

10. 738
   − 46
   692

11. 642
   − 137
   505

12. 324
   − 256
   68

GO ON

302 Grade 2

Page 3

13. $9.37
   − 6.54
   $2.83

14. $7.25
   − 1.17
   $6.08

15. $5.00
   + 2.86
   $7.86

16. $7.81
   + 1.59
   $9.40

GO ON

Grade 2 **303**

Page 4

Solve.

17. This graph shows how many minutes three friends walked in the Walkathon.

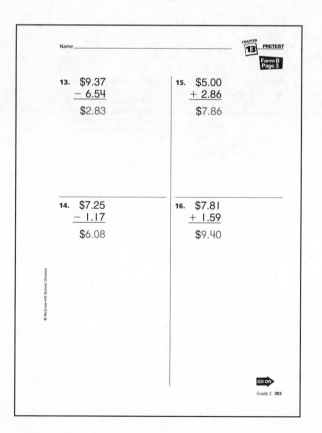

WALKATHON

Number of Minutes

Jae walked for 5 more minutes. Circle the bar that shows how much time Jae walked altogether.

18. Brad's class collects 294 cans of dog food. Theo's class collects 127 cans of dog food for dogs at the animal shelter. How many cans do they collect in all?

   421 cans

19. Kathy has $7.50. She spends $6.68 on a present for her mom. How much change will she have left?

   $ 0.82

20. Andy's scout troop has 354 phone books. If they hand out 272 phone books, how many will they have left?

   82 phone books

STOP

304 Grade 2

© McGraw-Hill School Division

Grade 2 **391**

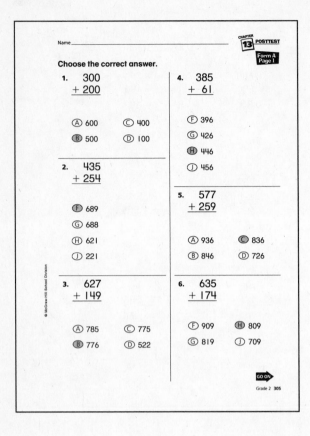

Choose the correct answer.

1. 300
   + 200

   Ⓐ 600   Ⓒ 400
   Ⓑ 500   Ⓓ 100

2. 435
   + 254

   Ⓕ 689
   Ⓖ 688
   Ⓗ 621
   Ⓙ 221

3. 627
   + 149

   Ⓐ 785   Ⓒ 775
   Ⓑ 776   Ⓓ 522

4. 385
   + 61

   Ⓕ 396
   Ⓖ 426
   Ⓗ 446
   Ⓙ 456

5. 577
   + 259

   Ⓐ 936   Ⓒ 836
   Ⓑ 846   Ⓓ 726

6. 635
   + 174

   Ⓕ 909   Ⓗ 809
   Ⓖ 819   Ⓙ 709

GO ON

7. 700
   − 300

   Ⓐ 500   Ⓒ 300
   Ⓑ 400   Ⓓ 200

8. 347
   − 124

   Ⓕ 283
   Ⓖ 223
   Ⓗ 124
   Ⓙ 123

9. 926
   − 314

   Ⓐ 640   Ⓒ 612
   Ⓑ 632   Ⓓ 512

10. 626
    − 57

    Ⓕ 683
    Ⓖ 603
    Ⓗ 569
    Ⓙ 553

11. 451
    − 246

    Ⓐ 605   Ⓒ 214
    Ⓑ 215   Ⓓ 205

12. 437
    − 288

    Ⓕ 651   Ⓗ 149
    Ⓖ 251   Ⓙ 141

GO ON

13. $8.29
    − 6.47

    Ⓐ $14.76
    Ⓑ $3.23
    Ⓒ $2.22
    Ⓓ $1.82

14. $5.26
    − 2.18

    Ⓕ $7.42
    Ⓖ $3.32
    Ⓗ $3.08
    Ⓙ $3.02

15. $4.00
    + 2.59

    Ⓐ $6.39
    Ⓑ $6.59
    Ⓒ $7.59
    Ⓓ $7.09

16. $4.72
    + 3.68

    Ⓕ $9.40
    Ⓖ $8.50
    Ⓗ $8.40
    Ⓙ $7.40

GO ON

Solve.

17. This graph shows how many minutes three friends walked in the Walkathon.

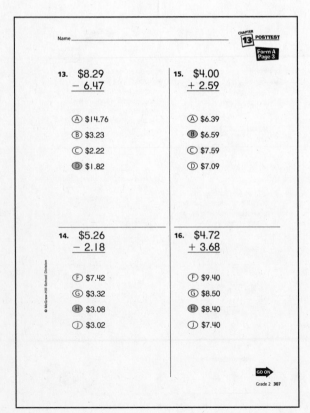

WALKATHON

Number of Minutes

Sara walked for 10 more minutes. Which bar shows how much time Sara walked altogether?

Ⓐ
Ⓑ
Ⓒ
Ⓓ

18. Theo's class collects 283 cans of dog food for the dogs at the animal shelter. Brad's class collects 325 cans of dog food. How many cans do they collect in all?

    Ⓕ 609 cans   Ⓗ 508 cans
    Ⓖ 608 cans   Ⓙ 42 cans

19. Jina has $8.50. She spends $7.15 on a birthday present for her dad. How much change will she have left?

    Ⓐ $0.85   Ⓒ $1.05
    Ⓑ $0.95   Ⓓ $1.35

20. Andy's scout troop has 286 phone books. If they hand out 167 phone books, how many will they have left?

    Ⓕ 453 phone books
    Ⓖ 451 phone books
    Ⓗ 121 phone books
    Ⓙ 119 phone books

STOP

Name _____

CHAPTER **13** POSTTEST
Form B
Page 1

Write the answer.

1. 300
  + 200
  500

4. 385
  + 61
  446

2. 435
  + 254
  689

5. 577
  + 259
  836

3. 627
  + 149
  776

6. 635
  + 174
  809

© McGraw-Hill School Division

GO ON

Grade 2 **309**

Name _____

CHAPTER **13** POSTTEST
Form B
Page 2

7. 700
  − 300
  400

10. 626
  − 57
  569

8. 347
  − 124
  223

11. 451
  − 246
  205

9. 926
  − 314
  612

12. 437
  − 288
  149

© McGraw-Hill School Division

GO ON

310 Grade 2

Name _____

CHAPTER **13** POSTTEST
Form B
Page 3

13. $8.29
  − 6.47
  $1.82

15. $4.00
  + 2.59
  $6.59

14. $5.26
  − 2.18
  $3.08

16. $4.72
  + 3.68
  $8.40

© McGraw-Hill School Division

GO ON

Grade 2 **311**

Name _____

CHAPTER **13** POSTTEST
Form B
Page 4

Solve.

17. This graph shows how many minutes three friends walked in the Walkathon.

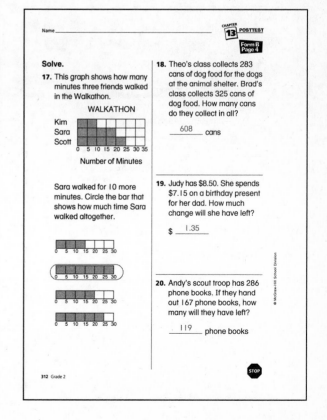

WALKATHON

Kim
Sara
Scott

0 5 10 15 20 25 30 35

Number of Minutes

Sara walked for 10 more minutes. Circle the bar that shows how much time Sara walked altogether.

18. Theo's class collects 283 cans of dog food for the dogs at the animal shelter. Brad's class collects 325 cans of dog food. How many cans do they collect in all?

_____608_____ cans

19. Judy has $8.50. She spends $7.15 on a birthday present for her dad. How much change will she have left?

$ ____1.35____

20. Andy's scout troop has 286 phone books. If they hand out 167 phone books, how many will they have left?

____119____ phone books

© McGraw-Hill School Division

STOP

312 Grade 2

© McGraw-Hill School Division

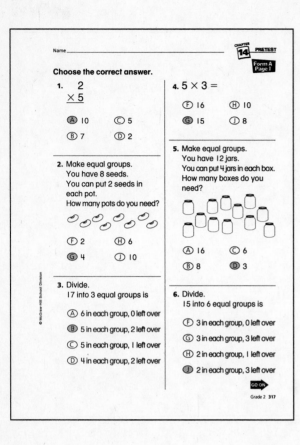

Choose the correct answer.

1.
$$\begin{array}{r} 2 \\ \times\, 5 \end{array}$$

Ⓐ 10 Ⓒ 5
Ⓑ 7 Ⓓ 2

2. Make equal groups.
You have 8 seeds.
You can put 2 seeds in each pot.
How many pots do you need?

Ⓕ 2 Ⓗ 6
Ⓖ 4 Ⓙ 10

3. Divide.
17 into 3 equal groups is

Ⓐ 6 in each group, 0 left over
Ⓑ 5 in each group, 2 left over
Ⓒ 5 in each group, 1 left over
Ⓓ 4 in each group, 2 left over

4. $5 \times 3 =$

Ⓕ 16 Ⓗ 10
Ⓖ 15 Ⓙ 8

5. Make equal groups.
You have 12 jars.
You can put 4 jars in each box.
How many boxes do you need?

Ⓐ 16 Ⓒ 6
Ⓑ 8 Ⓓ 3

6. Divide.
15 into 6 equal groups is

Ⓕ 3 in each group, 0 left over
Ⓖ 3 in each group, 3 left over
Ⓗ 2 in each group, 1 left over
Ⓙ 2 in each group, 3 left over

GO ON

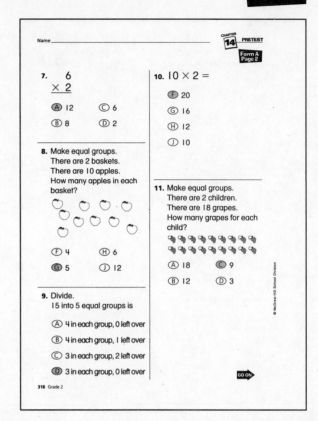

7.
$$\begin{array}{r} 6 \\ \times\, 2 \end{array}$$

Ⓐ 12 Ⓒ 6
Ⓑ 8 Ⓓ 2

8. Make equal groups.
There are 2 baskets.
There are 10 apples.
How many apples in each basket?

Ⓕ 4 Ⓗ 6
Ⓖ 5 Ⓙ 12

9. Divide.
15 into 5 equal groups is

Ⓐ 4 in each group, 0 left over
Ⓑ 4 in each group, 1 left over
Ⓒ 3 in each group, 2 left over
Ⓓ 3 in each group, 0 left over

10. $10 \times 2 =$

Ⓕ 20
Ⓖ 16
Ⓗ 12
Ⓙ 10

11. Make equal groups.
There are 2 children.
There are 18 grapes.
How many grapes for each child?

Ⓐ 18 Ⓒ 9
Ⓑ 12 Ⓓ 3

GO ON

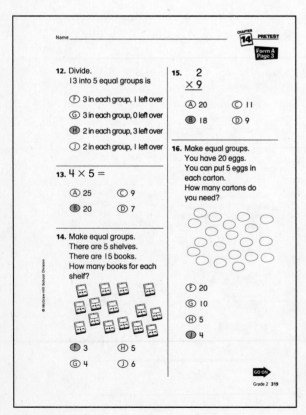

12. Divide.
13 into 5 equal groups is

Ⓕ 3 in each group, 1 left over
Ⓖ 3 in each group, 0 left over
Ⓗ 2 in each group, 3 left over
Ⓙ 2 in each group, 1 left over

13. $4 \times 5 =$

Ⓐ 25 Ⓒ 9
Ⓑ 20 Ⓓ 7

14. Make equal groups.
There are 5 shelves.
There are 15 books.
How many books for each shelf?

Ⓕ 3 Ⓗ 5
Ⓖ 4 Ⓙ 6

15.
$$\begin{array}{r} 2 \\ \times\, 9 \end{array}$$

Ⓐ 20 Ⓒ 11
Ⓑ 18 Ⓓ 9

16. Make equal groups.
You have 20 eggs.
You can put 5 eggs in each carton.
How many cartons do you need?

Ⓕ 20
Ⓖ 10
Ⓗ 5
Ⓙ 4

GO ON

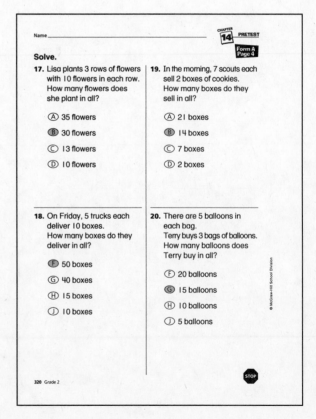

Solve.

17. Lisa plants 3 rows of flowers with 10 flowers in each row. How many flowers does she plant in all?

Ⓐ 35 flowers
Ⓑ 30 flowers
Ⓒ 13 flowers
Ⓓ 10 flowers

18. On Friday, 5 trucks each deliver 10 boxes. How many boxes do they deliver in all?

Ⓕ 50 boxes
Ⓖ 40 boxes
Ⓗ 15 boxes
Ⓙ 10 boxes

19. In the morning, 7 scouts each sell 2 boxes of cookies. How many boxes do they sell in all?

Ⓐ 21 boxes
Ⓑ 14 boxes
Ⓒ 7 boxes
Ⓓ 2 boxes

20. There are 5 balloons in each bag. Terry buys 3 bags of balloons. How many balloons does Terry buy in all?

Ⓕ 20 balloons
Ⓖ 15 balloons
Ⓗ 10 balloons
Ⓙ 5 balloons

STOP

Page 1

Name _____

Write the answer.

1.
$$\begin{array}{r} 2 \\ \times 5 \\ \hline 10 \end{array}$$

4. $4 \times 3 = \underline{12}$

5. Make equal groups.
You have 12 jars.
You can put 4 jars in each box.
How many boxes do you need?

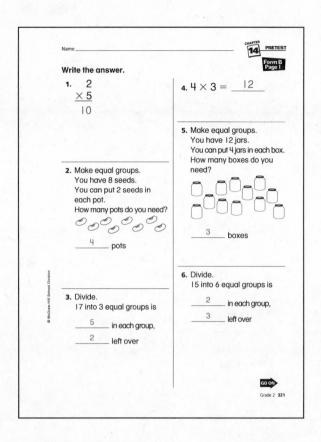

_3_ boxes

2. Make equal groups.
You have 8 seeds.
You can put 2 seeds in each pot.
How many pots do you need?

_4_ pots

6. Divide.
15 into 6 equal groups is

_2_ in each group,

_3_ left over

3. Divide.
17 into 3 equal groups is

_5_ in each group,

_2_ left over

GO ON

Page 2

Name _____

7.
$$\begin{array}{r} 6 \\ \times 2 \\ \hline 12 \end{array}$$

10. $10 \times 2 = \underline{20}$

8. Make equal groups.
There are 2 baskets.
There are 10 apples.
How many apples in each basket?

_5_ apples

11. Make equal groups.
There are 2 children.
There are 18 grapes.
How many grapes for each child?

_9_ grapes

9. Divide.
12 into 4 equal groups is

_3_ in each group,

_0_ left over

GO ON

Page 3

Name _____

12. Divide.
13 into 5 equal groups is

_2_ in each group,

_3_ left over

15.
$$\begin{array}{r} 2 \\ \times 9 \\ \hline 18 \end{array}$$

13. $4 \times 5 = \underline{20}$

16. Make equal groups.
You have 18 eggs.
You can put 6 eggs in each carton.
How many cartons do you need?

_3_ cartons

14. Make equal groups.
There are 5 shelves.
There are 15 books.
How many books for each shelf?

_3_ books

GO ON

Page 4

Name _____

Solve.

17. Lisa plants 3 rows of flowers with 6 flowers in each row.
How many flowers does she plant in all?

_18_ flowers

19. In the morning, 7 scouts each sell 4 boxes of cookies.
How many boxes do they sell in all?

_28_ boxes

18. On Friday, 5 trucks each deliver 10 boxes.
How many boxes do they deliver in all?

_50_ boxes

20. There are 5 balloons in each bag.
Terry buys 3 bags of balloons.
How many balloons does Terry buy in all?

_15_ balloons

STOP

Name _____

Choose the correct answer.

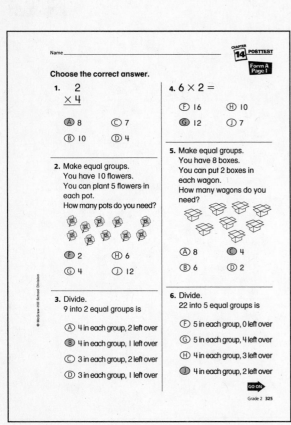

1.   2
   $\times 4$

Ⓐ 8   Ⓒ 7
Ⓑ 10   Ⓓ 4

2. Make equal groups.
You have 10 flowers.
You can plant 5 flowers in
each pot.
How many pots do you need?

Ⓕ 2   Ⓗ 6
Ⓖ 4   Ⓙ 12

3. Divide.
9 into 2 equal groups is

Ⓐ 4 in each group, 2 left over
Ⓑ 4 in each group, 1 left over
Ⓒ 3 in each group, 2 left over
Ⓓ 3 in each group, 1 left over

4. $6 \times 2 =$

Ⓕ 16   Ⓗ 10
Ⓖ 12   Ⓙ 7

5. Make equal groups.
You have 8 boxes.
You can put 2 boxes in
each wagon.
How many wagons do you
need?

Ⓐ 8   Ⓒ 4
Ⓑ 6   Ⓓ 2

6. Divide.
22 into 5 equal groups is

Ⓕ 5 in each group, 0 left over
Ⓖ 5 in each group, 4 left over
Ⓗ 4 in each group, 3 left over
Ⓙ 4 in each group, 2 left over

GO ON

Name _____

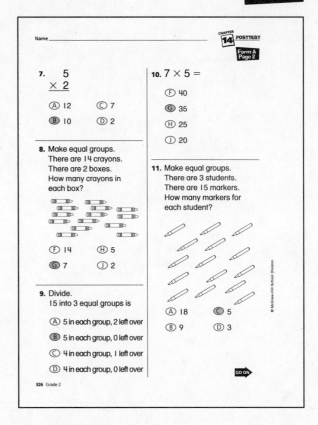

7.   5
   $\times 2$

Ⓐ 12   Ⓒ 7
Ⓑ 10   Ⓓ 2

8. Make equal groups.
There are 14 crayons.
There are 2 boxes.
How many crayons in
each box?

Ⓕ 14   Ⓗ 5
Ⓖ 7   Ⓙ 2

9. Divide.
15 into 3 equal groups is

Ⓐ 5 in each group, 2 left over
Ⓑ 5 in each group, 0 left over
Ⓒ 4 in each group, 1 left over
Ⓓ 4 in each group, 0 left over

10. $7 \times 5 =$

Ⓕ 40
Ⓖ 35
Ⓗ 25
Ⓙ 20

11. Make equal groups.
There are 3 students.
There are 15 markers.
How many markers for
each student?

Ⓐ 18   Ⓒ 5
Ⓑ 9   Ⓓ 3

GO ON

Name _____

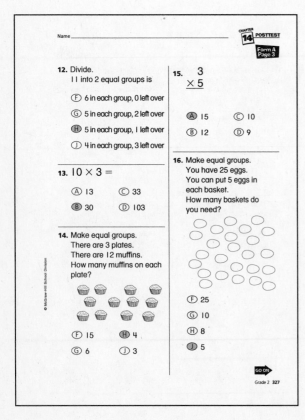

12. Divide.
11 into 2 equal groups is

Ⓕ 6 in each group, 0 left over
Ⓖ 5 in each group, 2 left over
Ⓗ 5 in each group, 1 left over
Ⓙ 4 in each group, 3 left over

13. $10 \times 3 =$

Ⓐ 13   Ⓒ 33
Ⓑ 30   Ⓓ 103

14. Make equal groups.
There are 3 plates.
There are 12 muffins.
How many muffins on each
plate?

Ⓕ 15   Ⓗ 4
Ⓖ 6   Ⓙ 3

15.   3
   $\times 5$

Ⓐ 15   Ⓒ 10
Ⓑ 12   Ⓓ 9

16. Make equal groups.
You have 25 eggs.
You can put 5 eggs in
each basket.
How many baskets do
you need?

Ⓕ 25
Ⓖ 10
Ⓗ 8
Ⓙ 5

GO ON

Name _____

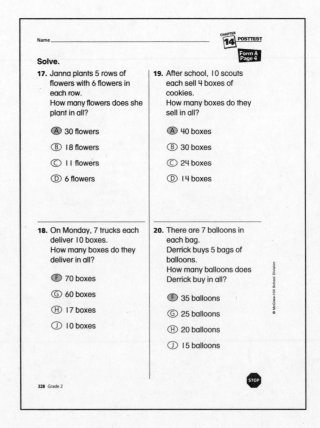

Solve.

17. Janna plants 5 rows of
flowers with 6 flowers in
each row.
How many flowers does she
plant in all?

Ⓐ 30 flowers
Ⓑ 18 flowers
Ⓒ 11 flowers
Ⓓ 6 flowers

18. On Monday, 7 trucks each
deliver 10 boxes.
How many boxes do they
deliver in all?

Ⓕ 70 boxes
Ⓖ 60 boxes
Ⓗ 17 boxes
Ⓙ 10 boxes

19. After school, 10 scouts
each sell 4 boxes of
cookies.
How many boxes do they
sell in all?

Ⓐ 40 boxes
Ⓑ 30 boxes
Ⓒ 24 boxes
Ⓓ 14 boxes

20. There are 7 balloons in
each bag.
Derrick buys 5 bags of
balloons.
How many balloons does
Derrick buy in all?

Ⓕ 35 balloons
Ⓖ 25 balloons
Ⓗ 20 balloons
Ⓙ 15 balloons

STOP

Page 1

Name _____

Write the answer.

1. $\begin{array}{r} 2 \\ \times\,4 \\ \hline 8 \end{array}$

4. $6 \times 2 =$ ___12___

2. Make equal groups.
You have 9 flowers.
You can plant 3 flowers in each pot.
How many pots do you need?

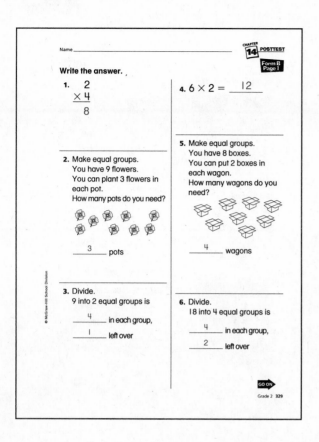

___3___ pots

5. Make equal groups.
You have 8 boxes.
You can put 2 boxes in each wagon.
How many wagons do you need?

___4___ wagons

3. Divide.
9 into 2 equal groups is

___4___ in each group,

___1___ left over

6. Divide.
18 into 4 equal groups is

___4___ in each group,

___2___ left over

GO ON

Grade 2 **329**

Page 2

Name _____

7. $\begin{array}{r} 5 \\ \times\,2 \\ \hline 10 \end{array}$

10. $7 \times 5 =$ ___35___

8. Make equal groups.
There are 14 crayons.
There are 2 boxes.
How many crayons in each box?

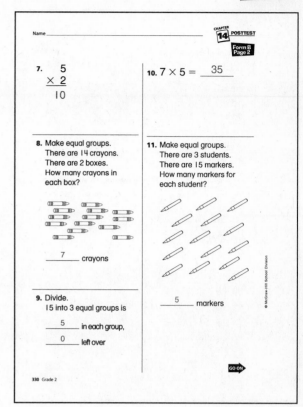

___7___ crayons

11. Make equal groups.
There are 3 students.
There are 15 markers.
How many markers for each student?

___5___ markers

9. Divide.
15 into 3 equal groups is

___5___ in each group,

___0___ left over

GO ON

330 Grade 2

Page 3

Name _____

12. Divide.
11 into 2 equal groups is

___5___ in each group,

___1___ left over

15. $\begin{array}{r} 3 \\ \times\,5 \\ \hline 15 \end{array}$

13. $10 \times 3 =$ ___30___

16. Make equal groups.
You have 24 eggs.
You can put 6 eggs in each basket.
How many baskets do you need?

___4___ baskets

14. Make equal groups.
There are 3 plates.
There are 12 muffins.
How many muffins on each plate?

___4___ muffins

GO ON

Grade 2 **331**

Page 4

Name _____

Solve.

17. Janna plants 5 rows of flowers with 6 flowers in each row.
How many flowers does she plant in all?

___30___ flowers

19. After school, 10 scouts each sell 4 boxes of cookies.
How many boxes do they sell in all?

___40___ boxes

18. On Monday, 7 trucks each deliver 10 boxes.
How many boxes do they deliver in all?

___70___ boxes

20. There are 7 balloons in each bag.
Derrick buys 5 bags of balloons.
How many balloons does Derrick buy in all?

___35___ balloons

STOP

332 Grade 2

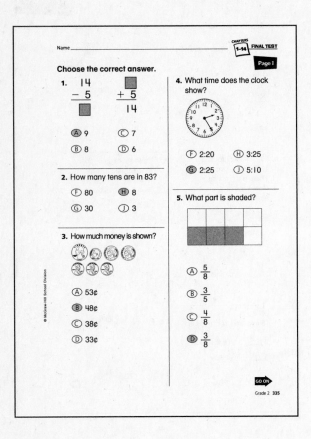

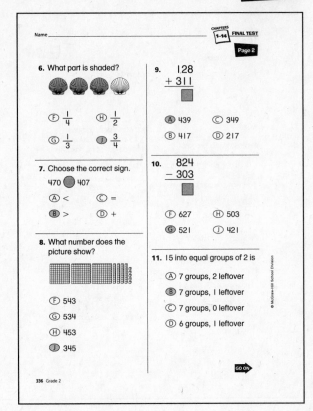

Page 1

Name _____

Choose the correct answer.

1.

$$14 - 5 = \square$$

$$\square + 5 = 14$$

- (A) 9
- (B) 8
- (C) 7
- (D) 6

2. How many tens are in 83?

- (F) 80
- (G) 30
- (H) 8
- (J) 3

3. How much money is shown?

- (A) 53¢
- (B) 48¢
- (C) 38¢
- (D) 33¢

4. What time does the clock show?

- (F) 2:20
- (G) 2:25
- (H) 3:25
- (J) 5:10

5. What part is shaded?

- (A) $\frac{5}{8}$
- (B) $\frac{3}{5}$
- (C) $\frac{4}{8}$
- (D) $\frac{3}{8}$

GO ON

Grade 2 **335**

Page 2

Name _____

6. What part is shaded?

- (F) $\frac{1}{4}$
- (G) $\frac{1}{3}$
- (H) $\frac{1}{2}$
- (J) $\frac{3}{4}$

7. Choose the correct sign.

470 ◯ 407

- (A) <
- (B) >
- (C) =
- (D) +

8. What number does the picture show?

- (F) 543
- (G) 534
- (H) 453
- (J) 345

9.

$$128 + 311 = \square$$

- (A) 439
- (B) 417
- (C) 349
- (D) 217

10.

$$824 - 303 = \square$$

- (F) 627
- (G) 521
- (H) 503
- (J) 421

11. 15 into equal groups of 2 is

- (A) 7 groups, 2 leftover
- (B) 7 groups, 1 leftover
- (C) 7 groups, 0 leftover
- (D) 6 groups, 1 leftover

GO ON

336 Grade 2

Page 3

Name _____

12.

$$468 - \square = 253$$

- (F) 222
- (G) 215
- (H) 121
- (J) 111

13. Make equal groups.
You have 15 boxes.
You can put 5 boxes in each wagon.
How many wagons do you need?

- (A) 15
- (B) 5
- (C) 3
- (D) 2

14. $5 \times 4 = \square$

- (F) 25
- (G) 20
- (H) 9
- (J) 1

15. Which digit is in the tens place?

326

- (A) 6
- (B) 4
- (C) 3
- (D) 2

16. What is the temperature?

- (F) 74°F
- (G) 72°F
- (H) 70°F
- (J) 68°F

GO ON

Grade 2 **337**

Page 4

Name _____

Solve.

Anna's class collected pet food for the animal shelter. Use the pictograph to answer exercise 17.

Pet Food Pictograph

Week 1	☐☐☐☐
Week 2	☐☐☐☐☐☐
Week 3	☐☐☐☐☐☐☐
Week 4	☐☐

☐ = 2 cans

17. How many more cans were collected in week 2 than in week 1?

- (A) 8 cans
- (B) 6 cans
- (C) 4 cans
- (D) 1 can

18. I have 4 sides and 4 vertices. What plane figure am I?

- (F) circle
- (G) triangle
- (H) rectangle
- (J) pentagon

19. There are 318 people in line to buy tickets for a concert. How many people are in front of the last person?

- (A) 320
- (B) 318
- (C) 317
- (D) 310

20. Andrew buys 4 packs of markers.
There are 5 markers in each pack.
How many markers does he buy in all?

- (F) 25 markers
- (G) 20 markers
- (H) 9 markers
- (J) 5 markers

STOP

338 Grade 2